INTRODUCTION TO
THE BASIC COMPUTER

PRENTICE-HALL SERIES IN ELECTRONIC TECHNOLOGY

DR. IRVING L. KOSOW, EDITOR

CHARLES M. THOMSON, JOSEPH J. GERSHON, AND JOSEPH A. LABOK,
CONSULTING EDITORS

PRENTICE-HALL INTERNATIONAL, INC., London
PRENTICE-HALL OF AUSTRALIA, PTY. LTD., Sydney
PRENTICE-HALL OF CANADA, LTD., Toronto
PRENTICE-HALL OF INDIA PRIVATE LTD., New Delhi
PRENTICE-HALL OF JAPAN, INC., Tokyo

DONALD EADIE

Senior Development Engineer
Honeywell, Inc., St. Petersburg, Florida

INTRODUCTION TO
THE BASIC COMPUTER

PRENTICE-HALL, INC.
Englewood Cliffs, New Jersey

To my family—
Ruth, Susan, and Carol

PREFACE

This book is intended to serve as an introductory text on the fundamentals of digital computers. The early chapters develop the basic theory required for study of digital devices generally and digital processors in particular. The text progresses from basic theory (the first five chapters) to a description of logic-circuit elements. Emphasis has been placed throughout on semiconductor integrated circuits, as having the logic most likely to prevail; the treatment here concentrates on applications and not intensively on semiconductor theory.

Later chapters describe how a computer performs arithmetic operations, how a modern memory operates, how a program controls the computer, and how the computer adapts itself to the many peripheral devices (typewriters, tape equipment, displays, etc.) employed with modern systems. A chapter is included on typical peripheral devices, and a final chapter on the relationship of analog, digital, and hybrid systems. The treatment is *hardware oriented*—that is, equipment function rather than operational usage is emphasized.

This book originated in class notes prepared for a highly successful in-company course taught previously at Honeywell, Inc. at St. Petersburg, Florida.

There has been extensive demand for these notes. The course was intended for technicians and engineers who required orientation in the digital field.

The present text should be sufficient to satisfy the needs of a 40-hour course at the junior college, technical school, or undergraduate level. It should also find use as a reference book for engineers and others working with computers who wish to review basic digital systems. The subjects of programming, computer usage, and specialized technologies are not stressed in this work. It should serve, however, as an excellent starting point from which the student can proceed to study of these specialized subjects. Review problems appear at the end of each chapter.

Much credit, of course, goes to those people at Honeywell, Inc., St. Petersburg who were extremely helpful in assisting me to put this material into readable form. Special thanks go to Edward L. Daniels for use of material originally generated by him on integrated circuits. Vance Carter and the typists of his department (Sandy Wakely, Jeanne McGee, and Norma Smith) prepared the bulk of the typescript. My thanks also to Ron Overstreet, F. X. Pesuth, C. I. Brown, and A. W. Sullivan, without whose encouragement this project would not have continued. I am very grateful to William Phalen for editing the original in-company edition and to Mrs. Millie J. Andrews for drawing most of the figures. My wife, Ruth, also helped immeasurably by personally typing five chapters of the manuscript and numerous letters. Harry Sussman's counsel was most helpful, as were the comments of others who used the original notes.

Outside of the Honeywell Aero-Florida Division, I should like to thank the following people for securing either pictures or for granting permission to use other material: Mr. Ralph Auf der Heide of Kennedy, Inc.; Mr. Martin D. Kerber of the Kleinschmidt Division of SEM Corporation; Mr. Philip D. Shipp of Librascope Division, General Precision, Inc.; Mr. Regis R. McKenna of the Microelectronics Division of Philco-Ford Corporation; Mr. Al Fisch of Texas Instruments, Inc.; Mr. William Taylor, Computer Control Division, Honeywell, Inc.; and Mr. M. Dittman, EDP Division, Honeywell, Inc. Also, my appreciation for the help of Mr. J. M. Lufkin of the corporate offices of Honeywell, Inc. who guided me in matters of company policy.

I wish to express my deep appreciation to the Editor of this series, Dr. Irving L. Kosow, for his in-depth review of the manuscript and for many helpful suggestions. Dr. Ivan Flores kindly permitted me to adapt the Glossary from his text, *Computer Design* (Prentice-Hall, 1960). My sincere thanks also to Mr. Bert N. Zelman and his associates at Prentice-Hall for their smooth handling of the production details for this volume.

Donald Eadie

CONTENTS

INTRODUCTION TO
THE BASIC COMPUTER

INTRODUCTION 1

This chapter serves as a general introduction to the field of digital devices, with particular emphasis on those devices called *computers,* or more properly *data processors*. The name data processor is more inclusive because modern machines in this general classification not only compute in the usual sense but also perform other functions with the data which flow to and from them. For example, data processors may gather data from various incoming sources, sort it, rearrange it, and then print it. None of these operations involves the arithmetic operations normally associated with a computing device but the term computer is often applied anyway.

Therefore, for our purpose a computer is really a data processor. Even such data processing operations as rearranging data may require simple arithmetic such as addition. This explains why a certain amount of imprecision has entered our language and why confusion exists between the terms *computer* and *data processor*. The two terms are so loosely used at present that often one has to inquire further to determine exactly what is meant.

The term *digital techniques* has been generally applied to the technology required to develop devices that operate with *coded* control and use data in coded forms.

Digital data processors are among the most highly developed devices that make use of digital techniques. A careful study of these devices should lead the reader through most of the fundamentals of digital techniques. Therefore, a study of digital data processors and computers is a systematic method of learning the basic elements that define any digital system, large or small.

Digital techniques have been applied to many systems, including data processors of all types, data transmission devices, and instrumentation. Over the past 20 years, the application of digital techniques has literally transformed the methods of solving many problems of instrumentation and the transmission of information.

A typical application of digital method is in an elementary communication system. Samuel B. Morse's invention of the telegraph introduced a type of digital transmission. We can even go back to the use of semaphore (flag signals) or Indian smoke signals as earlier applications of digital techniques.

All the above communication methods transmitted data in code. The message was first converted to a code, the code was transmitted from a sending point to a receiving point, and the message then decoded. The basic difference between these early systems and those of today lies in the type of code employed. The early systems used combinations of long and short electrical impulses, flag positions, or puffs of smoke as the transmission code. Today we use codes which represent numbers, and the combinations of these numbers represent the data or message. Of course, contemporary transmissions are at much greater speeds and over tremendously increased distances.

A modern communications network which transmits data in digital coded form is an example of a digital system. Such a system can often be broken down into the basic blocks shown in Fig. 1-1.

The *input digital converter* converts the input signal (normally an electrical waveform varying in amplitude with time) into a code which is often in the *serial* form of coded numbers, one following another in time. The numbers are processed and put in a form suitable for the terminal output and then transmitted by radio or land line as a number code from terminal 1 to terminal 2. At terminal 2, in the *output converter,* the numbers are reconverted to a time-varying waveform which ideally is a duplicate of the original waveform fed into the terminal 1 processor.

There are many advantages in such a system. For instance, it is easier to transmit a number code over noisy circuits or atmospheric paths than to transmit a time-varying waveform. Also, many messages may be transmitted over the same link or circuit. The terminal equipment contains circuitry which separates the individual messages, converts the digital code to a second code for transmission, reconverts the second code back to digital code, and provides routing to the proper destinations.

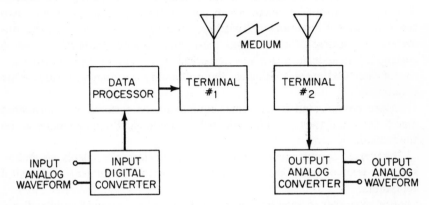

FIG. 1-1   Basic communication network.

Definitions are developed in the following paragraphs as a starting point for discussions of the fundamentals of digital techniques, systems, and computers.

Digital techniques is a broad term. In the example already given, it refers to the process of *converting* analog data (to be defined) to digital numerical form, *processing* the numbers, and reconverting them to analog form again. Digital techniques refers to the *processing of coded data* only. The code employed can be one of several, some of which are discussed subsequently.

A more formal definition is: *digital techniques* are the techniques of applying integers to the quantities that occur in a system and the process of instrumenting such systems with devices that base their operations on the manipulation of integers. (numbers) whole number system

Although we used a conversion process to illustrate the use of digital techniques, the above example may be somewhat confusing to the reader. Digital techniques, as such, are applied only to the portion of the (communications) system in which the data are in the form of an *integer code*. Before the conversion to integer form or at the output end of the process after reconversion to analog form, the data are not presumably in the form of integers. At these points they are analog data. Only intermediate between these end points is the system a digital one and are digital techniques applicable. Such a system, which is partially analog and partially digital, is often referred to as a *hybrid* system.

DIGITAL DEVICES AND ANALOG DEVICES

A simple *digital device* may be an elementary electrical circuit, mechanical element, or hydraulic element which adds, substracts, multiplies, etc., two coded numerical quantities or switches, controls and even stores these numerical quantities. The fact that these manipulated quantities are in a *coded* form and have a *discrete* numerical value (often represented by a row of ones and zeroes) enhances the probability that they are truly digital in nature.

More complicated instruments, equipment, or systems are considered digital devices if they are built primarily of the basic digital elements to be studied here.

Examples of extremely complex digital devices are telephone dialing systems, teletype networks, digital data-reduction equipment and digital computers.

For example, to specify a problem in *digital* form, one would indicate a second-floor height in terms of the number of steps of a staircase. Height above the lower floor can be expressed as an integral number of steps. In analog form, the second-floor height might be 18.657 ft.

With analog devices, quantities are not uniquely identifiable as having discrete levels but are continuously variable in a practical sense. Analog devices may represent quantities, e.g., by their physical attributes, such as translational or rotational position, current or voltage level, or electrical resistance. The speedometer on your automobile is an example of an analog device; it measures velocity in a continuous manner.

Computers may be constructed either of analog or digital devices. The basic distinction between an analog and a digital computer lies in how the variables are represented. A computer whose variables take on *any* value in an approximately *continuous* fashion is usually an analog computer. Potentiometers, summing electrical networks, servos, resolvers, etc., are characteristic hardware components of analog machines. The devices cited all handle numerical quantities as *measurable* quantities, often voltage or current levels.

A digital computer, on the other hand, represents numbers in the form of a *code* having *discrete* and *finite* values. There are numerous ways to code numbers, as will be described in the following chapters. These coded numbers are processed much as mechanical hand calculators are or as one performs longhand arithmetic—except, of course, that the process is mechanized.

EARLY HISTORY (1642 TO 1900)

While the object of this text is to discuss the techniques of digital devices, a brief history of digital computing devices is in order.

The earliest device that qualifies as a digital computer is the *abacus* (sometimes called a *soroban*). A calculation aid invented about 600 B.C., the abacus permits the users to represent numbers by the position of beads on a rack. Simple addition and subtraction can be carried out rapidly and efficiently by positioning the beads appropriately. The abacus is still widely used in the Orient and its users can calculate at amazing speeds.

The first mechanical adding machine was invented by Blaise Pascal, a French customs official, in 1642. Baron Gottfried Wilhelm von Leibniz of Germany in 1671 invented the first calculator for multiplication. It is still undergoing improvement. Keyboard machines originated in the United States in the 1880's, and, of course, continue to this day.

Business machines and calculators made their appearance in Europe and America toward the end of the nineteenth century. They are the products of such present industrial giants as International Business Machines Corporation, the Remington Rand Division of Sperry Rand Corporation, the Monroe Calculating Division of Litton Industries, The National Cash Register Company, etc.

The father of the modern digital computer is considered to be Charles Babbage, a nineteenth century professor at Cambridge University, who proposed a differential engine to the British Admiralty. He was given funds in 1823 to develop such a device but did not succeed. In 1833, on his own, he started development of an analytical engine and worked on it until 1842. Neither of these devices were successful, mainly because of the hardware limitations of the period. However, his efforts established a number of principles which have been shown to be fundamental to the design of any digital computer.

Later, in 1853, a successful analytical engine appeared in Sweden. In 1858, one was produced in the United States.

THE MODERN COMPUTER

The development of relays, vacuum tubes, and transistors hastened the construction of modern computer hardware. Harvard University, in conjunction with International Business Machines Corporation and Bell Telephone Laboratories, Inc., between 1940 and 1942 developed a series of relay computers. Although highly reliable, they were quickly superseded by the much higher-speed and more efficient electronic computers.

The first all-vacuum-tube computer (ENIAC) was designed by the University of Pennsylvania (Moore School of Engineering) and installed at Aberdeen Proving Ground, Maryland, in 1946. It eventually contained about thirty thousand vacuum tubes and was designed to compute ballistic tables. ENIAC did a yeoman job in cleaning up the backlog of computational work that had piled up in World War II. The limited number of people and adding machines that could be mobilized for the job were soon outclassed by this computer.

The circuit which made the ENIAC possible was the Eccles–Jordan flip-flop. Originally patented in 1919, it was not extensively used until the late 1930's and then only in the radar and television type of devices.

Although ENIAC was all electronic, the internal organization was not optimum for performing general-purpose scientific computations. Consequently, its design was not copied in later machines to any great extent. ENIAC was modified several times before finally being retired from service in the late 1950's.

A host of large-scale-tube type of computers followed ENIAC, including EDVAC, SEAC, Whirlwind, UNIVAC I, ORDVAC, and the IBM 604.

All-transistor computers began making their appearance in the mid-1950's. Probably military applications encouraged their development because of the obvious need to conserve weight, power, and volume in mobile equipment. Commercial installations are not often under these restrictions. In the military field, the Autonetics Verdan transistor computer appeared in 1954, followed by Transac and others.

Late in the 1950's, commercial transistor machines appeared such as the Honeywell 400 and 800 and the IBM 704. Airborne computers employing drum memories continued their development with the introduction of the Librascope LD 23 and ASN-24 and the Honeywell Mark I and Mark II, to name a few. The 1960's saw the introduction of both integrated circuits and core memories to the military field with the A. C. Spark Plug Magic, the Autonetics Monica series, the General Electric A212, and the Honeywell Alert.

With integrated circuit production catching up with demand, it is quite clear that commercial computers will soon be predominantly integrated circuit in construction. The IBM 360 series, the RCA Spectra 70 series, and the Honeywell 2200 series are all committed to integrated-circuit designs in one form or another and are examples of the trend in commercial machines which began in 1967.

ANALOG COMPUTERS

Although the ENIAC and other early machines pointed the way to digital data processors, the immediate development after World War II featured analog computers.

Analog machines received their impetus from V. Bush's mechanical differential analyzer, several copies of which were built between 1930 and 1942. These machines based their operation on the Kelvin integrater, a mechanical device invented much earlier (1876), but not applied in complex computer operations because the necessary mechanical amplifiers were not also available. The electronic technology developments occurring in World War II made it possible for electronic versions of the differential analyzer to be produced. These machines produced in quantity proved to be most useful for the study of complex systems which could be represented in the form of differential equations. Problems in servomechanisms, aircraft control systems, complete aircraft dynamic simulations, etc., could all be solved to accuracies within the 1 per cent range quite readily.

The machines mentioned were truly analog machines, with the variable quantities represented by voltage levels. The usual way in which the differential analyzer is arranged is to have many separate components available so they can be linked together in such a manner as to represent the system under study or, more precisely, so a mathematical equation of the system can be simulated by these components by the way they are connected together. Typical components include:

1. Summing operational amplifiers
2. Summing integrators
3. Precision potentiometers
4. Analog multipliers
5. Function generators
6. Resolvers

The signal connections of all these components are brought to a centralized plug-board panel where the operator can interconnect them in the desired manner to simulate (i.e., represent the analog of) the problem he is attempting to solve. To solve a second problem he must reconnect the components to a second configuration. This slow reconnection process was eased by using plug-boards that were removable from the machine, so that another plug-board, previously wired, could be inserted to continue that particular problem.

The electronic differential analyzer (EDA) was most useful, as stated before, in solving those problems that could be stated in the form of differential equations. Although differential equations are most important in scientific thought and engineering, not all scientific problems requiring solution are of this form. For this reason, and also because of accuracy limitations, other types of computers received added attention. These new computers of interest belonged generally to the digital family.

Before dismissing the EDA completely though, one more development should be mentioned. This is the digital form of the EDA, or the digital differential analyzer (DDA). Floyd Steel of Northrop Aircraft, Inc., proposed a method by which integration could be accomplished digitally. Integration is one of the fundamental processes accomplished on the EDA. Steel's contribution was to show how integration and similar processes could be mechanized digitally and how the *timesharing* capabilities of digital machines could be harnessed to do a job equivalent to that of the analog EDA, but cheaper, simpler, and with much higher accuracy. The interconnections of the digital integrators and other components in the original DDA designs were similar to the interconnections in the EDA machines. Later DDA versions made use of programming—a method of control exploited to the fullest in digital machines. Starting in 1950, Northrop built these machines and gave them the interesting name, MADDIDA (mad-Ida).

The remaining chapters of this text will concern themselves primarily with those techniques required to implement general-purpose digital computers or data processors. This concludes the introduction to analog machines. However, Chapter 15 reopens the subject and deals briefly with the elements of analog and hybrid systems. Also, Chapter 12 discusses analog–digital and digital–analog converters. These particular devices bridge the gap between analog and digital families of data processing equipment and instrumentation.

SUMMARY

Chapter 1 introduced the reader to some of the terms used in the general field of digital techniques. The discussion continued with a comparison of digital versus analog devices, followed by a review of the development of machine computation before, during, and after World War II. The chapter concluded by outlining analog and hybrid computer developments that paralleled those of early digital processors.

REVIEW QUESTIONS AND PROBLEMS

1-1. What is meant by the term *digital techniques?*

1-2. Give an example of the application of digital techniques.

1-3. Which of the following would you consider an analog device? Why?
    a. Meat scale.   c. Surveyor's transit.
    b. Stop watch.   d. Automobile speedometer.

1-4. Are any of the following digital devices? Why?
    a. Slide rule.   c. Traffic counter.
    b. Cash register.   d. Racetrack totalizer.

1-5. What is meant by *a coded number?* *No. such as 0 or 1 used to represent a quantity*

1-6. What is the advantage of the conversion of analog information (data) to digital form before transmission over long distances? *More data over same circuit noise no problem*

1-7. What is the basic difference between an analog and a digital device?

1-8. What is each of the following? What is its significance?
    a. Abacus. *DIGITAL COMP.*
    b. Analytical engine. *COMP. (DIG.) N.G.*
    c. Eccles–Jordan circuit. *FLIP-FLOP CIRCUIT*

1-9. Identify the following: *MACHINE 1642*
    a. Blaise Pascal. *ADD*   d. Leibniz. *CALC. 1671*
    b. Charles Babbage.   e. Floyd Steel. *DIG. FORM OF EDA AND*
    c. ENIAC. *ANALYTICAL*   *DDA*

1ST COMP TUBE TYPE— *MACHINE 1823*

EDA = ELECTRONIC DIFFERENTIAL ANALYZER
DDA = DIGITAL

1-7 analog used a variable quantity such as a voltage or a ¼
Digital used coded numbers.
(Discrete values)

Cale + comp diff —

BASIC
CONCEPTS

2

Because much of the basic digital language originated with large-scale digital computers, a description of a general-purpose computer will introduce many terms now widely used.

In reality, a digital computer performs the *same* basic operations as a common desk calculator; it adds, subtracts, divides, and multiplies. However, it performs these operations at a speed perhaps a million times greater than the desk calculator. It is also possible to *command* the machine to perform a sequence of calculations *without* human intervention. This planned sequence is called the *program*. A program must be carefully planned and all programming errors eliminated before the data processor will execute the calculations correctly.

ELEMENTARY OPERATIONS

To perform a sequence of mathematical calculation under the control of a program, the large-scale computer must have some features not normally

a part of a desk calculator. One of these is the *memory*. The data (numbers) used in the calculations must be stored in the memory until the program says they are to be used. Also, the program, in the form of *machine instructions* (sometimes called "commands"), must be stored in the memory if automatic sequential operation is to be obtained. A machine instruction is a code which commands the computer to calculate or transfer data according to the program. The memory organization differs with individual EDP (electronic data processing) machines. *Data* and *instruction* words may be stored in a common memory or in two separate memories, one allocated to data and the other to machine instructions. The computer itself is so arranged that it will examine the machine instructions one at a time in order and execute the specified calculation or transfer of data. The machine instructions generally call-out (1) an *address* in the *memory section* where the data are located, (2) what calculation is desired, and (3) where to put the results of a calculation.

BASIC COMPUTER ORGANIZATION

A block diagram of basic computer organization is illustrated in Fig. 2-1. The *arithmetic unit* performs *all calculations*. It is subject to control by the machine instructions. Data are moved to and from the memory by

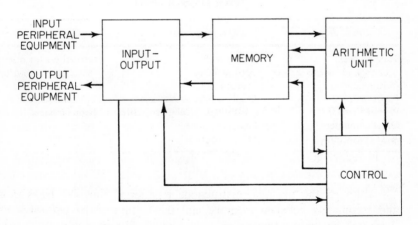

FIG. 2-1   Basic organization of a general purpose computer (central processor).

command of the machine instructions. The memory is therefore the storage place for data and also for machine instructions. Each cell where a data number is stored in the memory is identified and given a location number, called an *address*. This permits the machine instruction to call for the data by asking for the contents of cell number *XXX,* etc. It also permits the data to be *stored* at a particular cell, identified by an individual address number *XXX* .... Cells are usually numbered in sequence beginning at 000 ... and proceeding up to the maximum cells provided. Data and machine instructions, when stored in the memory together, are *coded* so the machine recognizes one from the other. They may also be stored separately in the memory with the computer having a prior knowledge of where the machine instructions and data are stored.

The unit marked *control* (Fig. 2-1) in the computer (1) accepts the machine instructions in sequence; (2) decodes them; (3) causes the transfer of data into the *arithmetic unit;* (4) commands the arithmetic operation; and (5) transfers the computed data out to the desired memory cell. It is in reality the "commander" of the computer since it also (6) controls the *input–output* unit.

The input–output unit provides access between the computer and the outside world. It allows the connection of tape recorders, paper-tape punches, paper-tape readers, digital typewriters, printers, keyboards, or other devices to the computer. Typical devices are listed in Table 2-1 and are identified as input, output, or bidirectional (input and output).

TABLE 2-1
Typical peripheral devices

Input devices	Output devices	Bidirectional devices
Tape readers:	Tape punches	Flexowriters (or other
paper and magnetic tape	Card punches	automatic typewriters)
Card readers	Printers	Teletype equipment
Keyboards	Displays (alphanumeric):	Communication modems
Page readers	cathode-ray tube projection	Magnetic tapes
Other computers	Other computers	
A/D converters	D/A converters	

Although the machine instructions mentioned thus far transfer data and commands between memory and the arithmetic or control section, there will be many other types of instruction in any computer repertory. These include instructions which transfer data from register to register in the machine, instructions which shift the word to the left or right in a given register, instructions which modify other instructions, instructions which control input–output including the peripheral equipment, instructions which mask data, and instructions which perform tests—to name a few. The decisions on what types of instructions are to be included in an instruction repertory require close cooperation and study among the programmer, the designer, and even the eventual user of the machine.

LOW-SPEED WORLD AND HIGH-SPEED COMPUTER

The outside world is primarily a decimal (base 10) and alphabet world. The computer, however, may operate internally with a different number system, such as *binary* (base 2) or *binary-coded* decimal (to be described later). The input–output section must translate information that is in the outside-world code into the machine code. It also provides a *speed-shifting* function. The human world is very slow compared with the computer; hence, the data transfer *rate* must often be shifted to a speed compatible with that used in the computer (from a few digits per second to a million digits per second, e.g.). The reverse process is also provided by the input–output, i.e., shifting from the higher computer internal speed to a slower speed for communication with the devices of the outside world.

A somewhat different problem handled by the input–output is to provide communication between different computers, each with different internal speeds and different internal word formats. In addition, communication may be required with analog devices which must be integrated into the system. For this last communication *interface,* special devices called *analog-to-digital* (A/D) *converters* or *digital-to-analog* (D/A) *converters* are often a part of the input–output section. Again, the *control* section keeps the input–output section operating in the proper space–time relationships with the remainder of the computer.

Data transferred in or out of the computer by the input–output section is generally to and from the memory, but this routing may vary with specific designs of the system.

An *auxiliary* memory (or *external* memory) is often connected with the computer by the input–output. In the case of large problems, data (and machine instructions) can be transferred from a relatively slow speed, large capacity external memory into the relatively high speed internal memory discussed previously. This transfer is often accomplished in large blocks, consisting of many datum words and machine-instruction words per block.

A *display panel* may be controlled by the input–output. Where it is desired to see numerical results displayed (e.g., a racetrack totalizer or a navigation display for aircraft or submarine), large numerical display panels are often employed to serve the needs for real-time† display.

† The computer operates fast enough to solve problems and display the solution almost simultaneous with the actual time of occurrence. This is called *real-time* operation. A *non-real-time* computer performs the calculations and input–output transfer together at faster or slower speeds than actual time.

All of the above computer units or sections are built up from logic circuits which use tubes, transistors, magnetic cores, and integrated circuits. Circuit methods will be covered in later sections.

Another way to describe computer organization is shown in Fig. 2-2.

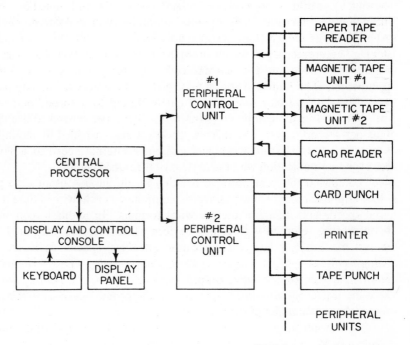

FIG. 2-2 A sample computer.

In this case, the data processor contains the internal memory, the arithmetic unit, and control section in one unit. A second unit called the *peripheral control* unit actually is the input–output section. It provides control and interface to the numerous peripheral units.

Because of its importance to the operator, the control console is defined as a separate block. This particular unit absorbs some of the functions of both *peripherals* (display and keyboard) and the input–output shown in Fig. 2-2.

SERIAL AND PARALLEL COMPUTERS

Perhaps the best way to describe a computer is in terms of data transfer and arithmetic operation.

Basically, data can be transferred in two ways: (1) either one digit at a time in sequence or (2) the entire number at one time with all digits in parallel on separate lines. If 10 digits are in the number, 10 separate sets of lines must be provided for parallel operation.

Arithmetic operations, such as the addition $A + B$, can also be performed by using one digit at a time or by simultaneously adding A and B at one instant in time with all digits in parallel. Basically, a computer which performs transfer operations and arithmetic operations one digit at a time is a *serial* computer, while a computer that operates on all digits simultaneously is a *parallel* computer. However, many modern computers cannot be classified this way because one section is likely to be *parallel* and another, *serial*.

The advantage of serial operation is that hardware and components are conserved but at the expense of the greatest speed of operation possible. Conversely, parallel operation is faster but at the expense of additional hardware. The choice between parallel or serial operation is left to the designer, who must weigh the requirements of the specifications.

BINARY-CODE WORD ORGANIZATION

The *binary code* is the most commonly used code within the computer. In this code all numbers are represented by "1's" (ones) and "0's" (zeros). It is easier for electronic devices to recognize and operate reliably on a *two-state* signal [e.g., ground (or 0 volts) and +10 volts] than on the

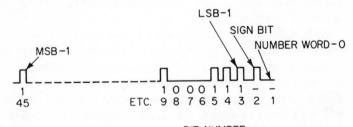

FIG. 2-3   Binary number word.

10-level signal required for a decimal number. A number stored in the memory cell may appear as shown in Fig. 2-3. Note the sign of the number (positive or negative) indicated by a 1 or 0. Computer numbers usually contain from 10 to 45 binary digits called *bits*. The position of the bit from right to left indicates its numerical weight.

A "one" bit may be represented as a positive or negative level, whereas a "zero" bit may be represented by ground. As shown in Figs. 2-3 and 2-4, a one (1) bit can be defined as the existence of a pulse in a particular time slot and a zero (0) bit as the absence of a pulse in a particular time slot.

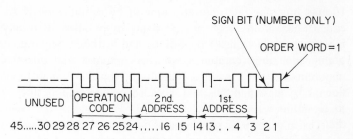

FIG. 2-4   Binary two-address order word.

Nevertheless, the bit position in the word next to the farthest right (the sign bit) is the lowest-order or least-significant bit (LSB). The bit farthest to the left is the most-significant bit (MSB). Depending on the design, the number words in a *serial* machine are sequentially moved about in series, with either the MSB or LSB first.

A word transferred serially requires as many *bit times* to move it past a stationary point in the circuit as there are bits in the number. A 40-bit word, e.g., would require 40-bit times. If the bit time is 1 μsec, it would require 40 μsec to transfer the entire word.

A parallel move of the same word (all bits move at once) will require only one-bit time, or 1 μsec. The definition itself illustrates why a parallel machine is faster.

Both data and machine instructions are coded in binary-digit form and may be stored in the same manner in a memory. The term used for number data or machine instruction is *word*. The machine will recognize a machine instruction either by its position in the memory or by a *marker bit,* which in turn may be either in a bit position in the memory or in a bit position not used in a number. An example is given in Fig. 2-4.

The example of the machine instruction given in Fig. 2-4 is atypical, oversimplified, and shown only as a sample. To the untrained eye, machine instructions and numbers may look very much alike but there is some characteristic (whether it be location in memory, a special identifying bit, or whatever) which enables the computer to recognize one from the other and interpret each in its own way.

A machine instruction is designed so that portions of the word are arranged to accomplish separate tasks. For example, a word may be broken into three portions. The first bit, if a 1, identifies it as a machine instruction and causes the word to be routed to the control section where it is de-coded on command. A data word would have a 0 in the bit position. The next bit is blank in a machine instruction. The next 10 bits are called the *first address*. The first address is a number code which identifies the cell in the memory from which it is desired to acquire a data word. The next 10 bits are called the *second* address. This portion of the word is the coded address where the result of the computation is to be placed after it is performed. The last four bits are the code for the computation and are often called the *operation code*. This instruction is called a two-address instruction. Some machines use one-, two-, three-, or four-address instructions. Again, the number of instructions in the repertory, how they are to be modified, and the internal control scheme of the computer together dictate the type and organization of the instruction word.

Although Fig. 2-4 shows a number word being coded as a binary number, this is not always the case. Data may be inserted in the memory where groups of bits represent either a *decimal* digit, an *octal* digit, or an *alpha* character. An operator must be familiar with all coding methods because some of the more complex computers can act in more than one mode. They can operate on data whether it is coded in pure binary, in decimal groups, or in octal groups. The complex computer must be instructed by its command repertory on how to interpret a data word. In the examples given in the text we shall assume that the data words are all of the binary type, but this is an artificial restriction designed to simplify discussion of the pure binary computer organization.

USES OF DIGITAL COMPUTERS

Digital computers are employed in a wide variety of applications and only a brief summary of uses is given here. Figure 2-5 illustrates a large-scale processor.

Scientific Calculations

Computers are used to perform scientific calculations of all types and all magnitudes of difficulty. Extensive operative routines have been developed for these purposes. This class of applications furnished the impetus for the original development of computers.

Business Calculations

Most business calculations can be performed on a computer, ranging from preparation of payrolls and paychecks to the prediction of production

FIG. 2-5 A large-scale processor, the H2200 data processor (courtesy Honeywell Inc.).

schedules. These applications were the next logical development after scientific calculators. It was found that science-oriented machines were not ideal for business-data processing. This discovery led to the development of specialized business-oriented machines.

Control

Machine tools and processes are programmed by digital computers to perform control functions. The skilled machine or process operator may be displaced to some extent by the skilled programmer. It is conceivable that complete plants will be controlled by a computer in the near future.

Military Applications

All types of military problems find their way to the computer. The more complex problems involve the solution of war-game problems or the planning of logistic support. Better known applications include the use of mobile computers to solve fire-control, bombing, or navigation problems. These computers include those that perform control functions only as well as those that perform control and operate extensive real-time displays, provide data to and from communication channels, and perform other services.

Communication

Because of the communication explosion forecast for the 1970's, data-processing computers are being developed to route voice, teletype, and digital information world-wide automatically.

Foreign-Language Translation

Although language translation is one of the most challenging of problems, computers are now being developed for this purpose. This usage could grow, dependent upon the development of larger memories, more efficient sorting techniques, and a better fundamental understanding of language syntax and structures. Idiomatic differences between two languages discouraged earlier approaches of cataloging corresponding phrases for the two languages. Although limited success has been reported, eventually smoothly worded translations are anticipated—though conceded to be not as easy to achieve as once thought.

Space Applications

The wide publicity given to the space programs have focused attention on the role of the computer in these programs. Through 1966, the major role was in ground-control calculation of vehicle trajectories, in calculation of other parameters such as maneuvering fuel, remaining oxygen, etc., and in operation of displays. These computers have been ground-based or ship-based machines. The *Gemini* flights saw the application of the first spaceborne digital computer. This application will grow. *Apollo* and the later craft will require the use of spaceborne computers. These data processors will assist in navigation, controlling the attitude of the vehicle, supervising communications, monitoring the condition of vehicular lift-support systems, computing the best paths to follow for fuel conservation, monitoring the astronauts' physical condition, operating the sensory equipment, etc. Digital computers may soon be placed in unmanned satellites to assist automatically in data-reduction processes—even before the data is transmitted to earthbound ground stations.

Aircraft Applications

Special analog computers (not the EDA type), until the late 1960's, dominated the aircraft scene, both commercial and military. The advent of the C 5A aircraft and the Pan American Inertial Navigation system extended the use of specialized digital computers aboard aircraft. In the military field, digital computers appeared in the C 141 cargo aircraft and even earlier on specialized classified applications. It is anticipated that digital-computer use will widely expand in the 1970's with airborne computers performing fire control, navigation, tactical command and control, antisubmarine warfare systems, monitoring, and other tasks, many of which cannot be revealed because of security classification.

A major use of the airborne data processor lies in monitoring the

FIG. 2-6 The Alert Airborne military processor (courtesy Honeywell Inc.).

sensors located on a new aircraft that is being tested. This use leads to another similar application, that of performing a continuous check-out of all systems aboard an aircraft. Any failure or malfunction, even though the equipment is not being used actively, is relayed to the flight crew, which then switches to standby equipment or uses alternate systems. Figure 2-6 shows a military airborne computer.

FUTURE TRENDS

The early computers were ground-based, nonmobile, and intended for scientific-data processing. They were eventually followed by business data processing types. These machines were also used by the large government agencies for processing census data, income tax returns, and a multitude of other paper work. The current trend is toward faster processing, larger memories, more reliable performance, more choice in peripheral equipment, etc.

The larger machines of the middle 1960's operate at a rate of 500,000 commands/sec and have internal memories of 32,000 to 128,000 words of perhaps 48 bits each, with 8 to 32 external magnetic-tape drives and perhaps a dozen or so other peripheral devices. Quite often these machines do several programs at once. Some are organized on a character rather than a word basis to remove the restrictions associated with a fixed word length.† Examples of these large machines include the Honeywell H 200 and H 800 series, the General Electric 625, the IBM 1401 and 7090, and the Control Data 6000; there are, of course, many more.

Smaller and less complex machines are used in control applications. These machines have smaller memories of 2000 to 16,000 words, word lengths in the 16- to 24-bit category, and perhaps one to five peripherals. Examples in this class include the SDS 930, DDP 116, and PDP 8. A high-speed control computer introduced in 1967 is the DDP 516 illustrated in Fig. 2-7.

The mobile computers are more likely to have a special-purpose design, but there are exceptions to this also. The Burroughs D 84, the UNIVAC 1830, the IBM 4 PI, and the Honeywell Alert are examples of essentially general-purpose computers. These computers are typically compact, rugged, of low power and low weight, and meet many military environ-

---

† *Word-organized machines* have a fixed word length; the word will be composed of a specific number of characters. *Character-organized machines* can vary the number of characters per word to suit the computation; hence, they have greater flexibility when it comes to data storage in the memory or data processing. No attempt has been made to differentiate the machines discussed here as to whether they are character- or word-organized.

FIG. 2-7 A control computer (courtesy Computer Control Division, Honeywell Inc.).

mental specifications. Because of the stringent design qualifications necessary to achieve all these objectives, these are usually high-priced machines in comparison with other commercial quality machines.

Recent trends include:

1. The sharing of a computer between several users all on line, with each user having a separate private control point. Project MAC at the Massachusetts Institute of Technology, among others, pioneered this time-sharing approach.
2. The establishment of computer utilities as a logical extension of time-sharing. Users will be billed for computer service in the same manner as for other utilities such as electricity and telephone service.

At the time of this writing, there are no computers to successfully design computers automatically but there have been some experimental trends in that direction. Engineers are examining their traditional methods of design to see if these can be replaced by computer-aided designing. Many drudgery assignments may be eliminated in this profession if this trend continues. The same applies to the fields of law, medicine, insurance, banking, and many other professions and businesses.

With the proliferation of computer applications, the problems of program writing have expanded. If there is a major trend to report at the time of this writing, it is in the field of computer programming. The computer design (*hardware*) task has been reasonably well solved, but the programming task (called *software*) continues to grow with no end in sight.

New and more sophisticated programs are needed. Users buying new machines to replace those formerly owned encounter a large translation problem in converting old programs to new machines. Assemblers and *compilers* are making it easier to write software but the problem of converting a program tape prepared for one machine for use on a second machine of different manufacture is one that needs increasing attention.

SUMMARY

In this chapter, many terms relating to the data-processing field were introduced. These terms included *program, memory, machine instruction, arithmetic unit, address,* and *input–output.* The basic computer block diagram was presented as well as a sample computer in which the basic organization defined earlier was modified. A *serial* computer and a *parallel* computer were compared. Basic computer word organizations were introduced with examples of how *instruction* words and *number* words differ. The chapter concluded with an outline of uses for digital computers and some predictions of future trends.

REVIEW QUESTIONS AND PROBLEMS

2-1. Draw a block diagram of a digital computer, and describe the functions of each block.

2-2. The input–output section has at least two functions; describe them in detail.

2-3. What is meant by the following terms?
   - a. Program.
   - b. Machine instruction.
   - c. Auxiliary memory.
   - d. Peripheral device.
   - e. Serial computer.
   - f. Address.

2-4. What is the organization of a machine instruction?

2-5. What is the organization of a number word?

2-6. Define a serial computer, and describe the advantages of such a design. What are its relative disadvantages?

2-7. What are the advantages in employing a binary code in the design of a digital machine?

2-8. How does a machine recognize an *instruction* from a *number* (data word)?

2-9. What is meant by *real-time?*

2-10. In the section *Uses of Digital Computers* several general fields of applications were listed. Can you name at least four others? Can you describe in a general way how the computer is employed?

NUMBER SYSTEMS, ARITHMETIC, AND CODES 3

This chapter begins the detailed study of those elements which are fundamental to an understanding of computer operation. First, basic modern number systems are explored. The number systems of the orient and the ancient world have no interest to us here because their structure does not follow the form of a mathematic progression (see Eq. 3-3). Because of its basic simplicity and wide use, the binary code system will be studied. However, other number systems can also be coded quite easily. Teletype systems, e.g., code alphanumeric symbols and control signals by successions of "marks" and "spaces." A mark is a positive intermachine current flow, whereas a space is zero current. The sequence of the mark and spaces along with a known starting or synchronizing indicator is the system code. Sometimes this code appears as hole patterns on paper tape, hole patterns on cards, or magnetic spot patterns on magnetic tape. Devices of this type will be studied in Chapter 13.

Binary arithmetic receives attention in this chapter because it is often employed in computer systems. Its simplicity and special advantages for the computer field will become evident as we proceed.

This chapter concludes with a discussion of some other codes one encounters in the digital field. Other codes are also discussed in Chapter 12.

NUMBER SYSTEMS

Since digital systems use numbers, it is necessary to review certain elements of number systems. First consider a typical decimal number 987.32. What is represented by the shorthand notation 987.32? In reality we have represented the following:

$$(9 \times 100) + (8 \times 10) + (7 \times 1) + (3 \times 0.1) + (2 \times 0.01) \qquad (3\text{-}1)$$

or

$$(9 \times 10^2) + (8 \times 10^1) + (7 \times 10^0) + (3 \times 10^{-1}) + (2 \times 10^{-2}) \qquad (3\text{-}2)$$

The numbers, 9, 8, 7, 3, and 2 are called *coefficients*. The number 10 is the *base* (or *radix*) of the decimal number system. The *exponent* term, of course, indicates what *power* of the radix is involved.

Any number system, therefore, can be represented by the following general equation:

$$\alpha_n x^n + \alpha_{n-1} x^{n-1} + \cdots + \alpha_0 x^0 + \alpha_{-1} x^{-1} + \alpha_{-2} x^{-2} + \cdots + \alpha_{-m} x^{-m} \qquad (3\text{-}3)$$

For the decimal system,

the coefficient α may be any number from 9 to 0 (1 less than the base)
the base x is 10
the exponent n may be any number that designates the power of 10 required to express the number

For a binary system,

the coefficient $\alpha = 1, 0$ (1 less than the base)
the exponent n = highest exponent required
the base $x = 2$

Example 3-1: Express the decimal number 28 in binary form.

Solution: $(1 \times 2^4) + (1 \times 2^3) + (1 \times 2^2) + (0 \times 2^1) + (0 \times 2^0) = 28$

or expressing coefficients,

11100 binary = 28 decimal

A notation often used is $11100_{(2)}$ for binary and $28_{(10)}$ for decimal.

An octal number system would have

the coefficient α = 1, 2, 3, 4, 5, 6, 7, 0   (1 less than the base)
the exponent n = the highest exponent required
the base x = 8

For instance,

$$(4 \times 8^3) + (5 \times 8^2) + (2 \times 8^1) + (1 \times 8) = 4521_{(8)} = 2385_{(10)}$$

The corresponding decimal, octal, and binary numbers from 0 to 24 are given in Table 3-1.

TABLE 3-1

Decimal, octal, and binary numbers

Decimal	Octal	Binary	Decimal	Octal	Binary
0	0	00000	13	15	01101
1	1	00001	14	16	01110
2	2	00010	15	17	01111
3	3	00011	16	20	10000
4	4	00100	17	21	10001
5	5	00101	18	22	10010
6	6	00110	19	23	10011
7	7	00111	20	24	10100
8	10	01000	21	25	10101
9	11	01001	22	26	10110
10	12	01010	23	27	10111
11	13	01011	24	30	11000
12	14	01100			

BINARY ARITHMETIC

Addition in the binary system is quite simple with the use of the following rules:

$$0 + 0 = 0$$
$$0 + 1 = 1$$
$$1 + 0 = 1$$
$$1 + 1 = 0 \text{ plus a } carry \text{ of 1 to next higher column}$$
$$1 + 1 + 1 = 1 \text{ plus a } carry \text{ of 1 to next higher column}$$

Example 3-2: Add the following numbers in both decimal and binary form:

	Binary	*Corresponding Decimal*
	01101	13
	01010	+10
Solution:	$10111_{(2)}$	$23_{(10)}$

NOTE: In adding the fourth column of the binary example, a carry is generated.

The rules for subtraction are

$$0 - 0 = 0$$
$$1 - 0 = 1$$
$$1 - 1 = 0$$
$$0 - 1 = 1 \text{ with a } borrow \text{ of 1 from the next higher column}$$

Example 3-3: Subtract the following numbers in both decimal and binary form:

	Binary	*Corresponding Decimal*
	01110	14
	−01011	−11
Solution:	+00011	+3

Example 3-3 requires two *borrows*.

NOTE: In the following Example 3-4, it is necessary to borrow for both the third and fourth columns.

Example 3-4: Subtract the following numbers in decimal and binary form:

	Binary	*Corresponding Decimal*
	11010	26
	−01100	−12
Solution:	$01110_{(2)}$	$14_{(10)}$

Multiplication in the binary system also follows the same general rules as decimal multiplication. However, learning the binary multiplication table is a trivial task because

$$1 \times 1 = 1$$
$$1 \times 0 = 0$$
$$0 \times 0 = 0$$
$$0 \times 1 = 0$$

It is that simple! You now know the multiplication table for elementary binary multiplication.

Example 3-5: Multiply the following numbers in decimal and binary form:

<pre>
        Binary   Decimal
        01101   13
      × 01001   × 9
        01101   117₍₁₀₎ (check)
        00000
       001101 add
       00000
      0001101 add
      01101
     01110101 add
     00000
    001110101₍₂₎ Final answer
</pre>

Note that, whenever there is a 1 in the multiplier, the multiplicand is added to the previous sum but is displaced one place to the left. Whenever 0 is in the multiplier, a string of zero's is added instead. The addition is performed after each partial sum to illustrate one manner in which an elementary digital computer actually performs the steps of multiplication.

In actual practice, whenever a 0 appears in the multiplier, *no addition is required,* only a *left shift.* As a result, Example 3-5 may be reduced to

<pre>
          01101
        × 01001
          01101
        01101SS   (S = left shift)
        01110101₍₂₎
</pre>

A computer would also follow this procedure in performing multiplication.

The division process is performed in a manner similar to decimal division. The rules for division are

$$0 \div 1 = 0$$
$$1 \div 1 = 1$$

Example 3-6: Divide the following numbers in decimal and binary form:

<pre>
            Binary   Decimal
          0111 (quotient)   7 (check)
   0111⟌0110111 (dividend)   7⟌55
          00111   49
          001101   6 (remainder)
          000111
          001101
          000111
          000110 (remainder)
</pre>

NOTE: When the divisor of Example 3-6 is subtracted in the first step from the four most left-hand digits, the result would be negative. Therefore, a 0 is entered in the quotient, and the divisor is shifted one place *right*. Now a valid subtraction can take place, and a 1 is entered in the next position of the quotient. The divisor is shifted one more place to the right, and a third subtraction is attempted, etc.

NUMERICAL CONVERSIONS

To convert a decimal number, e.g., $125_{(10)}$, to binary form, continuously divide by 2, until zero is reached, and *list* the remainders R as the binary number

$$125 \div 2 = 62 + 1\ R$$
$$62 \div 2 = 31 + 0\ R$$
$$31 \div 2 = 15 + 1\ R$$
$$15 \div 2 = 7 + 1\ R$$
$$7 \div 2 = 3 + 1\ R$$
$$3 \div 2 = 1 + 1\ R$$
$$1 \div 2 = 0 + 1\ R$$

Decimal 125 is 1111101 in binary notation.

(NOTE: The remainders are listed in the *reverse* order of the above division process.)

In converting a binary number to a decimal number, the process is reasonably obvious; one merely *adds the decimal weight* of each binary digit, as in the following:

11011101.101 binary is equal to

$$
\begin{aligned}
1 \times 2^7 &= 128 \\
1 \times 2^6 &= 64 \\
0 \times 2^5 &= 0 \\
1 \times 2^4 &= 16 \\
1 \times 2^3 &= 8 \\
1 \times 2^2 &= 4 \\
0 \times 2^1 &= 0 \\
1 \times 2^0 &= 1 \\
1 \times 2^{-1} &= 0.5 \\
0 \times 2^{-2} &= 0 \\
1 \times 2^{-3} &= \underline{0.125} \\
&\quad\ 221.625 \text{ decimal}
\end{aligned}
$$

Note carefully how the digits to the right of the binary point are handled to give the fractional portion of the answer.

The following conversion rules may be of some assistance:

To convert a whole decimal number to one of smaller radix,

1. Divide the number by the (new radix) continuously, noting the remainders, until the quotient is zero.
2. Arrange the remainders with the first as the least significant digit (LSD) and the last as the most significant digit (MSD).

To convert a fractional decimal number to a smaller fractional radix,

1. Multiply by the new radix continuously, noting the overflow, until the product is zero.
2. Arrange the overflow with the first as the MSD and the last as the LSD.
3. The process can be stopped when the desired accuracy is achieved if the product does not go to zero.

Example 3-7: Convert $469_{(10)}$ to $?_{(4)}$.

Solution:

$$469 \div 4 = 117 + 1\,R$$
$$117 \div 4 = 29 + 1\,R$$
$$29 \div 4 = 7 + 1\,R$$
$$7 \div 4 = 1 + 3\,R$$
$$1 \div 4 = 0 + 1\,R$$

Equals: $13111_{(4)}$

Example 3-8: Convert $0.523_{(10)}$ to $?_{(8)}$.

Solution:

$$8 \times 0.523 = 4.184$$
$$8 \times 0.184 = 1.472$$
$$8 \times 0.472 = 3.096$$
$$8 \times 0.096 = 0.768$$

[handwritten: 3.776, 6.208, 0.776]

The equivalent fraction in base 8 is therefore

$$0.4130\ldots_{(8)}$$

[handwritten: $0.4136\ldots_{(8)}$]

COMPLEMENTS

The true complement of a number is obtained by subtracting each digit of the number from the radix minus 1 and then adding a 1 to the least significant digit. The true complement of a decimal number is known as the *ten's* complement. The true complement of a binary number is the *two's* complement.

Examples of true complements are:

(a) For decimal 57, the complement is

$$100 - 1 \text{ (or 99)} - 57 + 1 = 43$$

The true complement may also be found directly by subtracting

$$100 - 57 = 43$$

(b) For the true complement of binary 110111, change all the 1's to 0's and 0's to 1's, and *add* a 1 to the LSD.

$$001000 + 000001 = 001001$$

which is the true complement of 110111.

In equation form, the ten's complement is

$$\ldots 9999 - S + 1 = 1 \times 10^n - S = \bar{S}_{10} \tag{3-4}$$

where n is the word length in digits, S is the number whose complement is to be found, and $\bar{S}_{10}$ is the true complement of a decimal number.

The equation for a number which is the nine's complement is

$$\ldots 9999 - S = 1 \times 10^n - S - 1 = \bar{S}_9$$

where n and S are defined as before and $\bar{S}_9$ is obviously the nine's complement. The nine's complement of the decimal system is an example of a radix-minus-1 complement.

The radix-minus-1 complement is not really of great use with the decimal system, since the computation of the nine's or ten's complement is equally difficult. For the binary system, however, where the radix-minus-1 complement (or *one's* complement, as it is often called) is obtained merely by reversal of "1's" and "0's," the process simplifies both subtraction and division. A 1 is added to the LSD only if the two's complement is desired; hence, the one's complement is usually one step less complicated to obtain. A simple hardware approach, however, permits the two's complement of a binary number to be generated if the system is serial.

The principle use of a complement number is to perform either subtraction or division by the process of addition. To perform a subtraction the subtrahend is put in its complement form, and the minuend and the complement subtrahend are added. The result of this addition turns out to be the difference of the two numbers; i.e., a subtraction results.

The reason for performing subtraction by this method is that a computer never needs to be taught to subtract since subtraction may be performed by addition. Thus, the computer can add, subtract, multiply, and divide by the simple process of addition, only. This is often desirable since complementation, especially the one's complement, is generally easily performed in a computer and usually saves hardware. Example 3-8 illustrates complementation with a ten's complement.

Example 3-8: Subtract 57 from 89 using complementary decimal addition.

Solution:

	Decimal number	*To find the true*
	normal subtraction	*complement*

	89 (minuend)	100
	−57 (subtrahend)	−57
	32	43 (complement of 57)

To perform
a subtraction

89
+43 (complement of 57)
1 32 (ignore the 1)

The answer is the same as that established by normal subtraction.

Example 3-9 illustrates complementation with a nine's complement.

Example 3-9: Subtract 57 from 89 using the nine's complement.

Solution:

99
−57
42 (nine's complement of 57)

To perform the subtraction with the nine's complement,

89
42 (nine's complement of 57)
1 31
carry 1 └→1
32

This process also gives the original result.

Example 3-10 illustrates binary complementation (radix minus 1), or one's complement.

Example 3-10: Subtract decimal number 10 from 16 in binary using the one's complement.

Solution:

(minuend)	16	10000	
(subtrahend)	−10	−01010	(for complement, reverse 1's and 0's)

Proceeding in the same manner as in the decimal examples above,

10000
10101 (complement)
add   1 00101
carry 1 └────→1
00110 (answer = decimal 6)

The basic difference between the two's and the one's complement is where and how the 1 is added. In the two's complement, the 1 is added directly to the result *after* the 1's are changed to 0's and the 0's to 1's. In the one's complement, the 1 is added by allowing the carry 1 to be added to the LSD. This is known as *end-around carry*. The last two examples illustrate end-around carry.

SIGNED ADDITION

So far, it has been assumed that the subtrahend was the smaller number so that, whenever a subtraction was called for, the results would be positive. But suppose the number to be subtracted (subtrahend) was larger than the minuend or that both numbers to be added were negative. Could the complement approach still be used to advantage? Yes, computations involving signed numbers may be handled by complement arithmetic.

In any example of signed binary arithmetic, negative numbers are represented by their complements. In solving the problem, however, it

TABLE 3-2

Signed addition examples

Add					Rule
$A + B$	A	*	00110111	55	No complementing. The
	B		00101110	+46	output is *not* comple-
		0	01100101	101	mented. The sign of the sum is positive.
$A + (-B)$	A	*	00110111	55	The sum is *not* recomple-
$A < B$ $A > B$	B		11010010 (complement)	−46	mented if the carry is 1, and only one comple-
		1	00001001	+9	ment has been required. The sign of the sum is positive.
$(-A) + B$	A	*	11001001 (complement)	−55	The sum is recomple-
$A > B$	B		00101110	+46	mented if the carry is 0
		0	11110111	−9	and only one comple-
			00001001 (recomplement)		ment has been required. The sign is negative.
$(-A) + (-B)$	A	*	11001001 (complement)	−55	The sum is recomple-
$A > B$	B		11010010 (complement)	−46	mented if the carry is 1
		1	10011011	−101	and two complements
			01100101 (recomplement)		are required. The sign is negative.

* Overflow column.

must be remembered that the complement has been employed. The addition is performed in the normal manner, but it must be noted whether or not a carry occurs beyond the left-hand side (MSD). The carry (or lack of carry) plus the knowledge of which of the two original numbers appeared in complement form determines the *sign* of the result and also whether a *recomplementation* of the result is necessary. Table 3-2 demonstrates the process and gives the rules for signed addition. Any hardware designed for arithmetic operations on signed numbers must have the ability to detect the proper sign and recomplement a number if the rules indicate it should be done. The hardware approach to the arithmetic chart takes this problem into account in Chapter 9.

BINARY-CODED DECIMAL (BCD) AND EXCESS-THREE CODE (X_s3 CODE)

As as been pointed out, the world outside the computer is a decimal world, while that within the computer is often a binary world. The conversion of a decimal number to binary form and vice versa is not usually a direct process, but an intermediate step is necessary.

The intermediate step normally is to convert a decimal number to a *coded* binary form, the digits 0 to 9 being represented by binary codes 0000 through 1001 (decimal 0 through 9). An example of a three-decimal digit number 937 in *binary-coded decimal* (BCD) form is 1001 0011 0111. The BCD is then converted to binary form.

In the reverse direction, a *binary* number is first converted to BCD and then to decimal.

An example of a decimal to binary conversion would be a keyboard input to a computer whose internal language is binary. The keyboard generates a BCD code, which, in the input–output section (or within the computer by a program), is converted to the binary form used in computer computations.

To display or print the output data, the above process is reversed. In this case, binary data is converted to BCD form, which in turn operates a decimal device such as a digital decimal display or a decimal print wheel.

The detailed explanation of these conversions is reserved for later chapters.

The BCD code is an example of what is called a *weighted code*. A "1" in the extreme left-hand digit position has a weight of 8, a "1" in the next proceeding positions from left to right have weights of 4, 2, and 1, respectively. One obtains the value of the number represented by adding up the weight of the "1's." Examples of two such codes are given in Table 3-3.

TABLE 3-3

Representative number codes

Decimal number	BCD		X_s3		X_s3 complement	
0		0000		0011		1100
1		0001		0100		1011
2		0010		0101		1010
3		0011		0110		1001
4		0100		0111		1000
5		0101		1000		0111
6		0110		1001		0110
7		0111		1010		0101
8		1000		1011		0100
9		1001		1100		0011
10	0001	0000	0100	0011	1011	1100
11	0001	0001	0100	0100	1011	1011
12	0001	0010	0100	0101	1011	1010
13	0001	0011	0100	0110	1011	1001
14	0001	0100	0100	0111	1011	1000
15	0001	0101	0100	1000	1011	0111
16	0001	0110	0100	1001	1011	0110
17	0001	0111	0100	1010	1011	0101
18	0001	1000	0100	1011	1011	0100
19	0001	1001	0100	1100	1011	0011
20	0010	0000	0101	0011	1010	1100
etc.						

Note that, in the BCD code used for representing 0 to 9, four binary bits are required. The total numbers that could be represented by four bits is 16; hence, six 4-bit combinations are not used. These are sometimes called *forbidden* numbers; however, they may be used for error checking.

Although the BCD code is very useful for input–output operations, it has limited use in arithmetic operations. For this reason, a modified BCD is often used in computers whose calculation mode is decimal. This modified code is called *excess-three code* (X_s3 code) and is obtained from the BCD code by merely adding a binary three (011) to each BCD number.

In the X_s3 code, decimal-arithmetic operation can be performed, and the carry is managed as in normal decimal arithmetic. In addition to this, the X_s3 code number complement (the nine's complement) can be formed by replacing 0's with 1's and 1's with 0's. Examples of the BCD code, the X_s3 code, and the X_s3 code's complements are given in Table 3-3.

Examples of addition and subtraction in X_s3 code follow:

To add, when the sum is 9 or less,   *Subtract 3 from Sum*

Decimal	X_s3
+5	1000
+3	0110
+8	1110

−0011 (subtract 3)

1011 = 8 in X_s3 code

NOTE: 5 and 3 in X_s3 code:

$$+5 = 0101 + 0011 = 1000$$
$$+3 = 0011 + 0011 = 0110$$

To add, when the sum is in excess of 9,   *add 3 as seen below*

Decimal	X_s3
+9	1100
+7	1010
+16	1 0110 (note the 1 carry)

To get the final results in X_s3 code, add 3 to both digit codes, as follows:

0001	0110
0011	0011
0100	1001

The result is 16 in X_s3 code (0100, 1001).

Subtraction can be shown easily by the following example. Suppose the result of $9 - 7$ is desired:

Decimal	X_s3
9	1100
−7	0101 (complement of 7 in X_s3)
2	1 0001

└──→1 (end-around carry)   *Note the add*

0010

0011 (add 3)

0101 = 2 in X_s3 code

The X_s3 code is only one example of codes that may be used to represent decimal numbers and perform decimal arithmetic.

AN ELEMENTARY ERROR-DETECTING CODE

Other codes, such as biquinary, have their special attributes and have been used in some systems. One important factor favoring the use of these codes is their ability to pinpoint an error such as that of a 1 and a 0 becoming accidentally interchanged. This error-sensing feature normally requires the addition of more bits to the code. In the biquinary code, a misplaced bit (a better term is *interchanged*) shows up as an *extra* 1 or 0. All coded numbers in the biquinary code contain five 0's and two 1's; hence, an extra 1 or 0 automatically indicates an error.

An example of a biquinary code is shown in the tabulation.

Decimal	Biquinary						
	5	0	4	3	2	1	0
0	0	1	0	0	0	0	1
1	0	1	0	0	0	1	0
2	0	1	0	0	1	0	0
3	0	1	0	1	0	0	0
4	0	1	1	0	0	0	0
5	1	0	0	0	0	0	1
6	1	0	0	0	0	1	0
7	1	0	0	0	1	0	0
8	1	0	0	1	0	0	0
9	1	0	1	0	0	0	0

This particular code, another example of a weighted code, might be used to transmit data from one machine to another. It is easy to check for errors, since a total of more than two 1's occurring or two 1's occurring in the wrong grouping can be detected with a small amount of checking circuitry. Other error-detecting codes are possible and have been developed to a high degree of sophistication; some of them, such as those attributed to R. W. Hamming, will actually *correct* errors when designed to do so. In general, error-detecting and error-correcting codes contain *more* bits than a simple code such as BCD. The student will note this by comparing the BCD code with the biquinary code.

More modern communication codes for transmitting data will be discussed in Chapter 12, along with other methods of protecting the validity of data such as the addition of a parity bit.

GRAY CODE

Gray code has proven useful in the implementation of mechanical coding devices. In a mechanical encoder, electrical contacts ride on the surface of coded disks. Unless the design is very precise and the tolerances tightly controlled, a possibility exists that the contact at some time may straddle two coded areas. With a binary code, many binary bits may change at a transition point (e.g., between 7 and 8, four bits change—0111 to 1000); hence, an error read in one bit could mean a large change in the coded value.

To prevent such an occurrence, the Gray code has been proposed and is often used in mechanical coding devices. In this code, only one bit changes between successive numbers. It is *not* a weighted code and, as a result, conversion back to a binary code or another code is usually necessary. The Gray conversion to and from binary is not difficult; hence, it is very popular.

A list of corresponding binary numbers and Gray-code numbers is given by Table 3-4.

TABLE 3-4

Examples of binary and Gray codes*

	Binary	*Gray*
1	0001	0001
2	0010	0011
3	0011	0010
4	0100	0110
5	0101	0111
6	0110	0101
7	0111	0100
8	1000	1100
9	1001	1101
10	1010	1111
11	1011	1110
12	1100	1010
etc.	etc.	etc.

* NOTE: Only one digit changes between successive numbers of the Gray code.

The rule for changing from binary code to Gray code is as follows. Start at the MSD end and compare each bit with the preceding one. (To start with, compare the first digit with 0.) If they are alike put a 0 in the Gray-code position; if they are unlike put a 1 in the Gray-code position. The following example illustrates this procedure:

```
        MSD                        LSD
Binary: 0 1 0 1 1 0 1 1 1 0 1
Gray:   1 1 1 0 1 1 0 0 1 1
```

To go from Gray code to binary code, again start at the MSD end. For the first bit repeat in binary the same bit that is in the Gray code. Following this, whenever the Gray bit is a 1, make the binary word bit different from the *preceding bit (in the binary word)*; whenever the Gray bit is a 0, repeat the preceding binary bit in the binary word. The following example illustrates the method:

MSD   LSD

Gray: 1   1   1   0   0   1   1   0   1   0   1

Binary: 1   0   1   1   1   0   1   1   0   0   1

RELATIONSHIP BETWEEN BINARY-CODED OCTAL AND BINARY CODES

In the same manner as decimal numbers are coded in 1's and 0's to form the BCD form, octal numbers can be coded into *binary-coded octal* (BCO) form. In this case, only three bits are required to represent a number.

An interesting and useful relationship exists between binary and BCO. If a pure binary number is grouped by threes beginning at the binary point, the resulting group can be interpreted as BCO and the number read in octal. Similarly, an octal number can be coded into BCO and this code combined in sequence to give the same quantity in binary form. This characteristic of binary and octal numbers is easy to check by examples. It makes possible an easy transformation back and forth between binary and octal numbers. This facility is also useful for computers and explains why some displays are in octal rather than decimal form. The hardware requirements are much simpler in going from binary to octal than from binary to decimal form. The reverse octal to binary transfers are also less complex than decimal to binary transfers.

An example of the relationship between octal, BCO, and binary is illustrated below:

Octal Number: $3421_{(8)}$

BCO: 011   100   010   001

Binary Number: 011100010001

SUMMARY

This chapter attempted to show the relationship between various number systems. The binary system was examined because of its usefulness in the digital computer. With the adoption of a binary arithmetic, an understanding of binary computation is, of course, necessary. The situation becomes somewhat more complicated when both positive and negative numbers must be handled; hence, a discussion of *signed* numbers followed.

The chapter concluded with a brief discussion of some of the more elementary codes, both weighted and unweighted. The BCD, X_s3, biquinary, and Gray codes were introduced. More complicated codes, such as ASC II, will be discussed in later chapters.

REVIEW QUESTIONS AND PROBLEMS

3-1. Add, and check by converting to decimal:

$$110111$$
$$+ \underline{011011}$$

3-2. Subtract:

$$110111$$
$$- \underline{011011}$$

3-3. Convert 011011 to its one's complement and add to 110111. The results should be the same as the answer to Problem 3-2.

3-4. Multiply:

$$110111$$
$$\times \underline{011011}$$

3-5. Divide 1101110 by 111. Carry the result at least two places to the right of the binary point.

3-6. Convert $372_{(10)}$ to $?_{(4)}$.

3-7. Convert $3,425_{(6)}$ to $?_{(10)}$.

3-8. Find the octal number corresponding to 110101010001110010.

3-9. Convert to binary $342761_{(8)}$.

3-10. What is $274_{(10)}$ in BCD code?

3-11. Convert decimal numbers 9 and 8 to X_s3 code. Add, and show the results in X_s3 code. What are the rules of addition in this code?

3-12. Write the first 20 digits of the following number systems, inventing symbols if necessary:
  a. Base 4.
  b. Base 7.
  c. Base 12.

3-13. Find the true complement of each of the following numbers:
  a. 110011.
  b. $7234_{(8)}$.
  c. $3231_{(4)}$.

3-14. Convert to X_s3 code, and add:

$$17$$
$$+ \underline{34}$$

3-15. Add: 1011.11; 0.101; 11.001; −101.00.

3-16. Multiply: 11011×11.01. $= 1 0 1 0 1 1 1 . 1 1 = 87.75$

3-17. Multiply: $231_{(8)} \times 7.17_{(8)}$. $= 2122.69$

3-18. Convert $0.932_{(10)}$ to $?_{(3)}$ (carry to 4 places only). $= 0.492$

3-19. What is the primary advantage of performing subtraction by the complement method in a digital computer? *computer doesn't*

3-20. Divide: 10101.11 by 110.1. $= 11.0101$ *have to sub.*

3-21. Convert 1010111011 (binary) to $?$ (Gray code). *(add instead)*

3-22. Convert 1110110100 (Gray) to $?$ (binary code). *.ub)*

3-23. What is the error in the following biquinary codes? What numbers could these codes represent if it is assumed there are only errors in the 1's?
  a. 1100100.
  b. 1011000.
  c. 0100011.

3.19 the computer can solve both sub. + div. by the process of add.

3-17 231
7.17
———
20 57
23 1
2057
———
2122 4 7

SWITCHING-CIRCUIT THEORY AND RELATED SUBJECTS

4

Digital systems may be characterized as small, medium-size, or gigantic switching systems. The study of switching is fundamental and necessary if one is to understand how specific functions are accomplished in a computer or any digital system electronic device. This chapter and Chapter 5 deal with elementary switching-circuit theory, introducing two of the methods employed to simplify complicated switching networks. Some of the common digital logic devices for performing elementary switching operations (including AND and OR gates) are introduced; NAND and NOR gates are introduced in Chapter 5.

THE GENERAL SWITCHING PROBLEM

The designer of a switching network is usually faced with the problem of providing switching between a set of inputs $A, B, \ldots, Z$ and a set of outputs 1, 2, 3, . . . , *n* (see Fig. 4-1). The order and exact nature of the switch closures vary with the application. Another set of inputs (I, II, III, . . . , *a*) are the *control lines,* i.e., the lines that control the sequence of the switch relays and cause them to open and close in a predetermined manner.

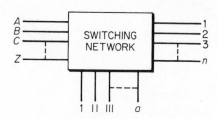

FIG. 4-1   General switching network.

The design problem involves switching the relays in a desired sequence to close the lines between *A, B*, . . . , *Z* and 1, 2, 3, . . . , *n* in a desired and predicted pattern. This problem is easily solved for simple configurations but gets more difficult as the complexity of the switching requirements increases. Some of the more elementary aspects of this problem will be studied in this chapter.

ALGEBRA FOR RELAY CONTACTS

Relay contacts are either open or closed. Determining the optimum number of contacts required for a given sequence may be accomplished intuitively in simple networks. As more complex networks are involved, a method for the removal of unnecessary relays and their contacts will help decrease the network and control-circuit complexity. Boolean algebra (to be introduced later) is a useful tool for determining the minimum number of contacts required.

THE "AND" CIRCUIT

Consider the elementary case of three contacts connected in a series. Assume that the load does not receive power unless all the relay contacts are closed. There are eight possibilities of how these relays could be wired so that a circuit closure is achieved. Two examples are illustrated in Fig. 4-2. The load circuit shown in Fig. 4-2a is completed if *A* and *B* are unenergized and *C* is energized. The load circuit shown in Fig. 4-2b is completed if *A* and *B* are energized and *C* is not energized.

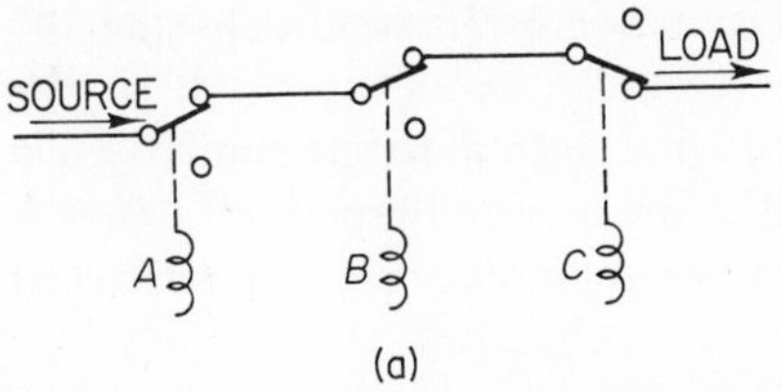

FIG. 4-2a   Example 1. 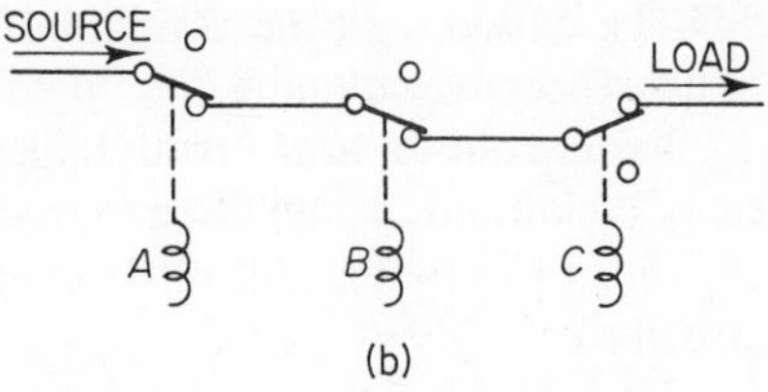   **FIG. 4-2b**   Example 2.

It has been found useful to represent the position of the relay contacts by a form of algebra (for the moment called here "switching-circuit algebra" but, as the student will see eventually, it is really Boolean algebra notation). In this representation, the circuit of Fig. 4-2a in the closed or *true* position is expressed by the equation

$$y_1 = \overline{A} \cdot \overline{B} \cdot C$$

where $\overline{A}$ (not A) represents an open contact on relay A (or not A); $\overline{B}$ (not B) represents an open contact on relay B (or not B); and C represents a closed contact on relay C.

The closed condition shown in the second example, Fig. 4-2b, has the equation

$$y_2 = A \cdot B \cdot \overline{C}$$

Another way of representing the two conditions of the closed contacts in the figure is by means of a *truth table*. A truth table is an orderly listing of all possible (eight) positions of the (three) relays with a notation as to whether the circuit is to be closed (*true*) with a particular relay contact combination.

In the accompanying tabulation (and symbolically), an energized relay is represented by a "1," and an unenergized relay is represented by a "0."

Relay conditions			*Example* *Fig. 4-2a*	*Example* *Fig. 4-2b*
A	B	C	y_1	y_2
0	0	0	0	0
0	0	1	1	0
0	1	0	0	0
0	1	1	0	0
1	0	0	0	0
1	0	1	0	0
1	1	0	0	1
1	1	1	0	0

The closed, or true, condition of y_1 and y_2 are represented by the "1" in the respective columns.

Example 4-2a in the truth table and Figure 4-2b illustrate similarly that relay conditions A and B energized and C unenergized represent a closed, or *true*, (1) circuit. All other combinations represent open, or *false*, (0) circuits.

The elementary circuits discussed here are AND circuits, since *A and B and C* must be in a prescribed position for the circuit connection to be complete.

THE "OR" CIRCUIT

A second elementary condition for these relay contacts can be easily specified. Note that, in Fig. 4-3, the three relays are in parallel, and the contact closure of any one of the three relays completes the circuit between source and load.

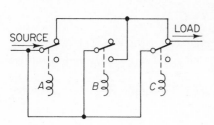

The circuit algebraic expression representing the contacts shown in Fig. 4-3 is

FIG. 4-3 OR circuit.

$$y_3 = \overline{A} + B + \overline{C}$$

where $+$ = OR.

The accompanying truth table is for the elementary OR circuit illustrated in Fig. 4-3.

Relay contacts			
A	*B*	*C*	y_3
0	0	0	1
0	0	1	1
0	1	0	1
0	1	1	1
1	0	0	1
1	0	1	0
1	1	0	1
1	1	1	1

Observe that the load circuit is completed in seven out of eight possible relay contact configurations. The student should study the OR truth table to make sure that he understands its formation.

COMBINATION "AND" AND "OR" CIRCUITS

The more common case of relaying involves circuits that are not simply AND or OR circuits but combinations of both. A more complex circuit is illustrated in Fig. 4-4.

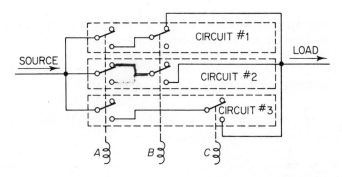

FIG. 4-4   Complex circuit.

[NOTE: This circuit may be broken down into components, as follows:

True condition for circuit 1 is: $y_1 = A \cdot \bar{B}$
True condition for circuit 2 is: $y_2 = \bar{A} \cdot B$
True condition for circuit 3 is: $y_3 = A \cdot C$

Circuits 1 and 2 can be combined as an OR circuit which will have the equation

$$y_1 + y_2 = A \cdot \bar{B} + \bar{A} \cdot B = A\bar{B} + \bar{A}B$$

where $+$ = OR.]

Except in rare cases for emphasis, the dot ($\cdot$) will be dropped henceforth between terms of the AND expressions. From now on $A \cdot \bar{B}$ will be $A\bar{B}$ and read *A and B*.

This combined circuit is then ORed (i.e., the OR operation is performed) with circuit 3 to give a final circuit equation of

$$y = y_1 + y_2 + y_3 = A\bar{B} + \bar{A}B + AC$$

The truth table for this equation may be arranged as shown here.

$\bar{A}$	$\bar{B}$	$\bar{C}$	A	B	C	$A\bar{B}$	$\bar{A}B$	AC	$A\bar{B} + \bar{A}B + AC$
1	1	1	0	0	0	0	0	0	0
1	1	0	0	0	1	0	0	0	0
1	0	1	0	1	0	0	1	0	1
1	0	0	0	1	1	0	1	0	1
0	1	1	1	0	0	1	0	0	1
0	1	0	1	0	1	1	0	1	1
0	0	1	1	1	0	0	0	0	0
0	0	0	1	1	1	0	0	1	1

The student should make sure he understands the derivation of this table and test himself by developing similar ones.

GENERAL INFORMATION ON COMPUTER GATES

The technique of expressing relay switching by algebraic expressions may be extended to other types of switching circuits. Relays are seldom used to switch signals in modern computers because of their relatively slow switching speed. A more common type of switching is accomplished by applying a voltage to each input line of an AND circuit (generally called

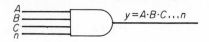

FIG. 4-5 AND gate symbol.

an AND *gate*). This voltage is represented by a "1." (For example, positive 10 volts might be represented by "1," while zero volts, or ground, would be represented by "0." If all inputs of the AND gate are "1," the gate is said to be *turned-on* and transmission of data through the gate will occur. The symbol for an AND gate is shown in Fig. 4-5.

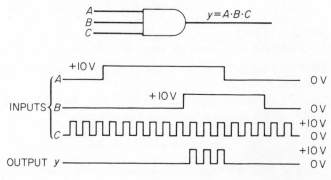

FIG. 4-6 AND gate signals and output.

In an AND gate, an output occurs only during the time $A, B, C, \ldots, n$ are *all* at the "1" level. For instance, if it is assumed that the "1" inputs are a positive level (+10 volts), the output for the AND gate is as shown in Fig. 4-6. The logic and voltage truth tables for an AND gate are given here. Observe the similarity between this AND table and that obtained with relay switching.

Logic truth table				Voltage truth table			
A	*B*	*C*	*y*	*A,* volts	*B,* volts	*C,* volts	*y,* volts
0	0	0	0	0	0	0	0
0	0	1	0	0	0	10	0
0	1	0	0	0	10	0	0
0	1	1	0	0	10	10	0
1	0	0	0	10	0	0	0
1	0	1	0	10	0	10	0
1	1	0	0	10	10	0	0
1	1	1	1	10	10	10	10

(handwritten: $y = ABC$)

(handwritten: 10 Volts = "1", 0 volts = "0")

The OR condition is represented in a similar manner. In this case, any one of the inputs at a "1" level will produce a "1" level at the output. The OR gate is represented in Fig. 4-7.

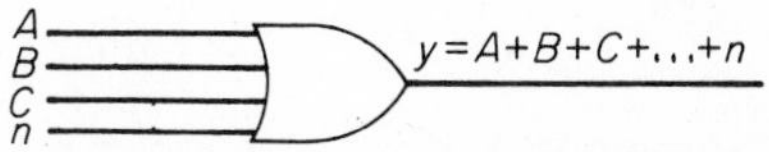

$$y = A + B + C + \ldots + n$$

FIG. 4-7   OR gate symbol.

(NOTE: Any 10-volt signal at the inputs A, B, and C is represented in the output waveform y, as shown in Fig. 4-8.)

The truth table and a representative output are given in the tables shown here.

$$y = A + B + C$$

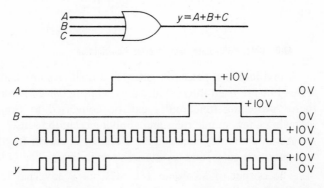

FIG. 4-8   OR gate signals.

Logic truth table			
A	*B*	*C*	*y*
0	0	0	0
0	0	1	1
0	1	0	1
0	1	1	1
1	0	0	1
1	0	1	1
1	1	0	1
1	1	1	1

Voltage truth table			
A, volts	*B,* volts	*C,* volts	*y,* volts
0	0	0	0
0	0	10	10
0	10	0	10
0	10	10	10
10	0	0	10
10	0	10	10
10	10	0	10
10	10	10	10

$y = A + B + C$

$10 \text{ volts} = \text{"1"}$

$0 \text{ volts} = \text{"0"}$

An *inversion,* or *complement,* of an input signal (often called a *variable*) is obtained by a device called an *inverter.* For instance, if the input to an *inverter* is +10 volts, the output will be 0 volts; or, if the input to the inverter is 0 volts, the output will be +10 volts. Thus A can be made into $\overline{A}$ or $\overline{A}$ can be made into A by the use of the inverter.

The symbol and truth table for an inverter is shown in Fig. 4-9.

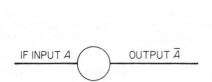

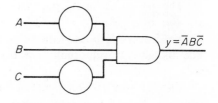

FIG. 4-9 Inverter symbol.

FIG. 4-10 Gating example: AND gate and inverter combination.

(*Question:* What would the "1" output be for the AND gate in Fig. 4-10? Why?)

"AND" Gate, "OR" Gate, and Inverter Combination

Individual AND gates, OR gates, and inverters are seldom used by themselves but are used in combinations. *Gating combinations* (we have called these "switching functions") can be converted to Boolean equations by following a few simple rules and applying common sense.

As an example, consider the Boolean equation for the combination of AND gates, OR gates, and inverters shown in Fig. 4-11.

The output of AND gate 1 is AB but is inverted to $\overline{AB}$ before being applied, as an input to OR gate 4. The output of AND gate 3 is $EF,$ and this

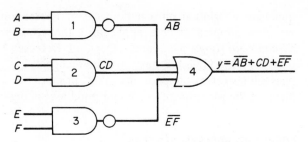

FIG. 4-11   Combinational gating logic.

is inverted to $\overline{EF}$ before it is applied as an input to OR gate 4. The output of OR gate 4 is then

$$y = \overline{AB} + CD + \overline{EF}$$

where $+ = $ OR.

The above process is an example of finding the equation from a gating diagram when given a logic layout consisting of AND gates, OR gates, and inverters.

$\overline{CD}$ not$= \overline{C}\overline{D}$

Converting from Equations to Logic

The reverse problem of finding the logic diagram from the equation is not difficult. Consider the equation

$$y = (A + B)CD + \overline{C}\overline{D}(A + B)$$

$A + B$ is obtained by "ORing" (OR gating) A with B. The $A + B$ term generated is "ANDed" (AND gated) with CD, and also separately ANDed with $\overline{C}\overline{D}$. Finally the expressions $CD(A + B)$ and $\overline{C}\overline{D}(A + B)$ are ORed together to yield the output. The logic diagram is shown in Fig. 4-12.

Unfortunately, no common standard of logic symbols has received un-

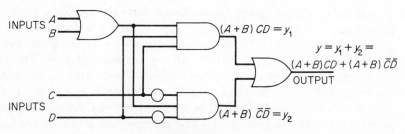

FIG. 4-12 Logic expansion of $y = (A + B)CD + (A + B)\overline{C}\overline{D}$.

qualified recognition on a nationwide or international basis. In this text, we have adopted (where applicable) the symbolism used in *Graphical Symbols for Logic Diagrams* (Dept. of Defense, MIL-STD-806B). Although MIL-STD-806B has yet to be recognized as the universal standard, possibilities for its adoption are good, primarily because of the influencing factor of the government as a major purchaser of digital devices.

LOGIC AND BOOLEAN ALGEBRA

In the mid-1800's, an algebra which simplified the representation and manipulation of propositional logic was developed by the English mathematician, George Boole. It became known as *Boolean algebra*. Its use provides an economical, straightforward approach to the design of relay and other types of switching circuits. This development is of interest here because of its application to the design of two-state switching circuits. These circuits were proposed in 1938 by Claud Shannon, while a research assistant at Massachusetts Institute of Technology, in his thesis, *A Symbolic Analysis of Relay and Switching Circuits*. The familiar terms AND *gate* and OR *gate* originated in Shannon's work. He adopted the terms from the Boolean algebra vernacular.

Only a brief treatment of propositional logic, symbolic logic, and an associated Venn diagram will be given in this chapter. Boolean algebra postulates and theorems will be stated and an example will be given to show how a particular theorem is proved by a Venn diagram. This is considered background material, and the student is referred to established texts for more detailed treatments.

THE VENN DIAGRAM APPLIED TO PROPOSITIONAL LOGIC

The Venn diagram is an aid in proving the theorems of Boolean algebra. As an example of a Venn diagram, assume that all the tournament tennis players in the United States, England, and Australia are being graphically represented as a subclass of all sportsmen in these countries. Such a diagram is shown in Fig. 4-13, where area A is all the United States players, B is all the English players, and C is all the Australian players. The use of A, B, and C to represent subclasses within a total class is an example borrowed from *symbolic logic*. The Venn diagram is one of the tools of symbolic logic. It would be used in the following way. Assume that tennis matches are held in a given area. For example, two players in the United States play each other. Their match has no international implication except that it might help determine who would eventually make up the Davis Cup team entry of the United States. The intersection of all three areas conceivably represents an international tournament. Here, it represents the class of players of each nation competing against each other (e.g., at Wimbledon).

In general, all the tennis players in all three countries are represented by the circular area bordered by the heavy line. All the sportsmen in the three countries who are not tennis players are represented by the area within the square but outside the bordered area just described. The total group of sportsmen is called the *universe K* from which the individual subsets were drawn.

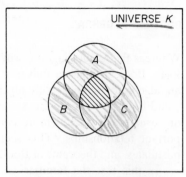

K=ALL SPORTSMEN IN USA, ENGLAND, AND AUSTRALIA

FIG. 4-13 Example of Venn diagram.

In Boolean algebraic notation, a true condition is represented by a "1" and a false condition by a "0." All tennis players in the countries mentioned are represented as

$$A + B + C \qquad (4\text{-}1)$$

On the Venn diagram, the total shaded area encompassed by *A*, *B*, and *C* represents Eq. (4-1) symbolically. All international players competing at Wimbledon are represented in Boolean notation as

$$A \cdot B \cdot C \quad \text{or} \quad ABC \qquad (4\text{-}2)$$

Equation (4-1) is represented on the Venn diagram by the crosshatched section. Equation (4-1) is an example of a Boolean OR expression, and Eq. (4-2) is a Boolean AND expression.

The meaning of these expressions is the same as discussed in the earlier section devoted to AND and OR circuits. The OR condition represented by Eq. (4-1) means that, if any one of *A* or *B* or *C* is true, or any combination of them, the entire expression is true. To return to the Venn diagram, tennis players are represented by areas *A* or *B* or *C*, or any combination thereof. Symbolically, the representation is equivalent to the electrical circuits employing three single-pole relays *A*, *B*, and *C*. Their connections vary depending on whether the AND or OR condition is to be demonstrated.

At this point, the student is correct in questioning the usefulness of Venn diagrams as an aid in designing circuits. The Venn diagram (as shown here) is merely an aid in *proving* the theorems of Boolean algebra. A modified Venn diagram, called a *Veitch diagram* or *Karnaugh chart,* will prove useful in reducing Boolean functions and accomplishing other feats, as will be seen in Chapter 5.

BOOLEAN ALGEBRA

Whereas the Venn diagram provides a graphical representation of symbolic logic, Boolean algebra makes it possible to represent logical situations in an algebraic manner with algebraic symbols. Although Venn diagrams could be used to represent switching circuits, Boolean algebra expressions are usually considered more convenient and easier for visualizing the important relationships. This section concentrates on some of the axioms, postulates, and theorems of Boolean algebra itself.

In this text the familiar $\cup$ and $\cap$ of propositional logic will *not* be used to represent AND (intersection) or OR (union) conditions. The author's use of ABC to represent the AND of A, B, and C rather than $A \cup B \cup C$ and $A + B + C$ to represent the OR of A, B, and C rather than $A \cap B \cap C$ is usually preferred for writing Boolean algebra terms by logic designers today.

The basic elementary rules of Boolean algebra are called *postulates*. These ground rules have Venn diagram equivalents. By combining and juggling the basic postulates, several other usable theorems are derived. The postulates and theorems together make up the working formulas of Boolean algebra. The basic postulates credited to E. V. Huntington are stated as follows:

1a. If the subset A is within the universe K, and the subset B is within the universe K, then A and B (represented as AB) are within the universe K.†

1b. If the subset A is within the universe K and the subset B is within the universe K, then A *or* B (represented as $A + B$) is within the universe K.†

2a. There is an element "0" such that $A + 0 = A$, for every element A in K.

2b. There is an element "1" such that $A \cdot 1 = A$, for every element A in K.

In order to simplify the remainder of postulate and theorem expressions, assume A, B, and C are always within K. Then, we can write:

3a. $A + (B + C) = (B + A) + C = (A + C) + B$, etc.

3b. $(A \cdot B)C = A(B \cdot C)$, etc.

† This postulate can easily be modified to include C in additional subsets. Only A and B are used for the sake of simplicity.

4a. $A + (B \cdot C) = (A + B) \cdot (A + C)$

4b. $A \cdot (B + C) = A \cdot B + A \cdot C$

5. If "0" and "1" are unique, then, for element A, there is an element $\bar{A}$ such that $A \cdot \bar{A} = 0$ and $A + \bar{A} = 1$

6. A, B, and C are such that $A \neq B \neq C$

Although the theorems apply to more than two or three variables, for the sake of illustration, most texts limit the discussion to two or three as needed.

Given the above postulates, the theorems which emerge are as follows:

7. $A + A = A$

8. $A \cdot A = A$

9. $A + 1 = 1$

10. $A \cdot 0 = 0$

11. $A + AB = A$

12. $A(A + B) = A$

13. $\bar{\bar{A}} = A$

14a. $\overline{(A + B)} = \bar{A}\bar{B}$ ⎫

14b. $\overline{AB} = \bar{A} + \bar{B}$ ⎬ De Morgan's theorem

15. $(A + B) + C = A + (B + C)$

16. $(AB)C = A(BC)$

17. $A + \bar{A}B = A + B$

18. $A(\bar{A} + B) = AB$

19. $(A + B)(\bar{A} + C) = AC + \bar{A}B$

20a. $\overline{AC + B\bar{C}} = \bar{A}C + B\bar{C}$

20b. $\overline{(A + C)(B + \bar{C})} = (\bar{A} + C)(\bar{B} + \bar{C})$

The last two expressions (20a and b) are examples of applying De Morgan's theorem (14a and b) and are not always included in a list of theorems. Other theorems may be developed. A good and challenging exercise for the reader is to prove these last two theorems correct.

Example 4-1: Prove two Boolean expressions are equivalent using the above postulates and theorems.

Given: $y_1 = \overline{\bar{A}B}(\bar{A} + AC)$

                 $y_2 = AC + \bar{A}B$

Prove: $y_1 = y_2$

Solution:

Step 1

$$\overline{\bar{A}\bar{B}} = (A + B) \qquad \text{by De Morgan's theorem}$$

Step 2

$$\bar{A} + AC = (\bar{A} + C) \qquad \text{by theorem 17}$$

Therefore,

$$\overline{\overline{A}\,\overline{B}}(\overline{A} + AC) = (A + B)(\overline{A} + C)$$

Step 3

$$(A + B)(\overline{A} + C) = AC + \overline{A}B \qquad\qquad \text{by theorem 19}$$

Therefore finally,

$$\overline{\overline{A}\,\overline{B}}(\overline{A} + AC) = AC + \overline{A}B$$

The use of a Venn diagram to prove a Boolean theorem can be demonstrated by proving this example:

$$A(\overline{A} + B) = AB$$

Draw a Venn diagram. This proof technique will show that the left-hand and right-hand expressions of the above equality, when plotted, encompass the *identical* area in corresponding Venn diagrams.

The right-hand expression is easy to plot. It is merely the intersection of A and B, as shown in Fig. 4-14.

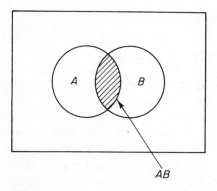

FIG. 4-14 Venn diagram for right-hand side.

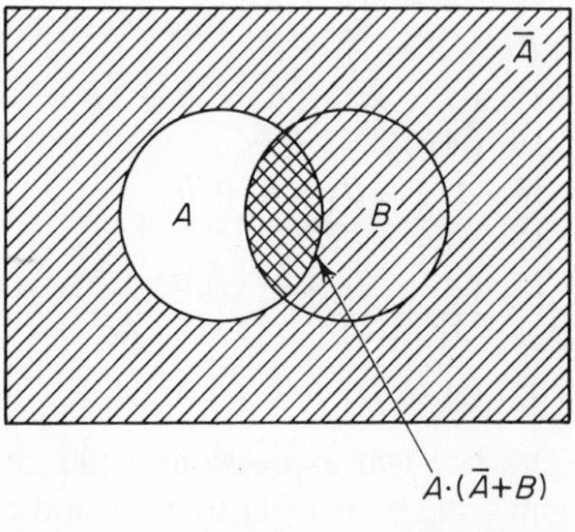

FIG. 4-15 Venn diagram for left-hand side.

The left-hand expression is somewhat more complicated. What must be expressed in the diagram is really $A \cdot (\overline{A} + B)$. The function $\overline{A} + B$ is the total crosshatched area shown in Fig. 4-15.

Performing the AND operation with A leaves the same shaded areas in Fig. 4-15 as are encompassed by AB in Fig. 4-14. The crosshatched area of Fig. 4-14 is the same as the crosshatched area of Fig. 4-15. Thus, by using a Venn diagram, the two expressions are shown to be equivalent.

Another way to prove the equivalence of a Boolean expression and a method that could possibly appeal to the experimenter would be to examine the equivalence of two circuits reported to yield similar switching paths

As determined previously, AB is represented by two series contacts of relays A and $B,$ both energized, and the electrical path under these circumstances is completed between input and output. With the use of the same basic ground-rules, $A(\overline{A} + B)$ is represented by Fig. 4-16.

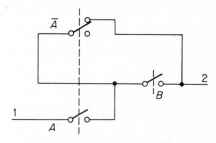

FIG. 4-16   Relay logic for $A(\overline{A} + B)$.

Note that the complete circuit 1 to 2 can only be completed when A is energized and B is also energized. The contact of relay A, labeled $\overline{A}$, does not affect the resulting connection in any way and hence is redundant and unnecessary to the switching operation. Therefore, it may be left out of the system. When this is done, the remaining contacts are identical with the AB circuit. Although this appears to be a trivial example, it does illustrate another approach to the proof of Boolean theorems.

The same results could, of course, have been deduced directly from the application of two simple theorems of Boolean algebra. This example illustrates that, if the switching circuit can be expressed in simple Boolean form, application of the postulates and theorems is probably the most efficient way (at least of those covered to date) to reduce the expressions representing the relays to the minimum number of contacts. Note the following reduction of the expression $A(\overline{A} + B)$:

$$A(\overline{A} + B) = A\overline{A} + AB$$
$$A\overline{A} = 0 \qquad \text{by postulate 5}$$

Therefore,

$$A(\overline{A} + B) = AB$$

and the relationship is proved. Is not this a simple process? It is truly simple in this case, but remember the illustration is not an involved one.

This brief example, showing that $A(\overline{A} + B) = AB$, illustrates the practical use of Boolean algebra to simplify the large equations which represent complex combinations of switching circuits. Reducing the equations leads directly to reductions in the number of paths, relays, contacts, etc. Boolean algebra axioms are ideally applied to the switching-circuit equation before designing the relay or circuit network.

The Boolean theorem proved previously by both the Venn diagram and by application of other Boolean theorems can also be proved by associated truth tables. If the circuit functions described by the truth tables are identical, the two forms are equivalent. See the truth tables for the two components of the equation, AB and $A(\overline{A} + B)$, shown here. Since the truth table results are identical, the two sets of terms must be the same; therefore, the two sides are again proven equalities.

<table>
<tr><td colspan="3" align="center">AB</td><td colspan="3" align="center">$A(\overline{A} + B)$</td></tr>
<tr><td>A</td><td>B</td><td>AB</td><td>A</td><td>B</td><td>$(\overline{A} + B)A$</td></tr>
<tr><td>0</td><td>0</td><td>$0.0 = 0$</td><td>0</td><td>0</td><td>$(1 + 0)0 = 0$</td></tr>
<tr><td>0</td><td>1</td><td>$0.1 = 0$</td><td>0</td><td>1</td><td>$(1 + 1)0 = 0$</td></tr>
<tr><td>1</td><td>0</td><td>$1.0 = 0$</td><td>1</td><td>0</td><td>$(0 + 0)1 = 0$</td></tr>
<tr><td>1</td><td>1</td><td>$1.1 = 1$</td><td>1</td><td>1</td><td>$(0 + 1)1 = 1$</td></tr>
</table>

These three examples serve to prove that there is more than a single way to prove a Boolean theorem or reduce a Boolean expression. The algebraic method or the truth table method at this point appear to be somewhat more convenient to apply than either the Venn diagram or the relay circuit. This is basically the consensus of most experts. However, the approaches have not yet been exhausted, and one of the more popular charting methods will be developed. This will be done in Chapter 5 but only after a discussion of exactly what a Boolean function is.

THE DISTINCT AREAS OF A VENN DIAGRAM

Before leaving the discussion of the Venn diagram, it is essential to emphasize that each area of the Venn diagram represents a specific combination of variables. We have already seen that the intersection of the three areas represents the AND condition $A \cdot B \cdot C$. Now, consider the two variable Venn diagrams, and note that the areas unbroken within their subboundaries represent the variable combinations shown in Fig. 4-17.

This area equivalence can be proven for the area $\overline{A} \cdot \overline{B}$ by combining the elemental single-variable Venn diagrams of $\overline{A}$ and $\overline{B}$ on the right, as shown in Fig. 4-18. If $\overline{A}$ is AND gated with $\overline{B}$, $\overline{A}\overline{B}$ results, as shown in

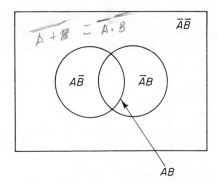

FIG. 4-17 Areas of a Venn diagram.

Fig. 4-18, which is the same as the $\overline{A}\overline{B}$ area of Fig. 4-17. In a similar manner, areas $A\overline{B}$ and $\overline{A}B$ are defined as areas encompassed by the individual circles.

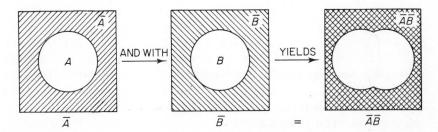

FIG. 4-18 Combining a Venn diagram.

Similarly, a three-variable Venn diagram breaks down into discrete areas, as shown and defined in Fig. 4-19.

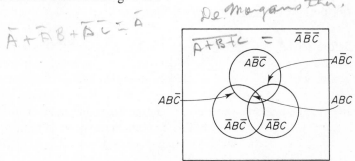

FIG. 4-19 A three-variable Venn diagram.

These representations will become important when the make-up of the Karnaugh chart and Veitch diagram are discussed. A Venn diagram and either of these other two charts are all equivalent.

SUMMARY

This chapter started out by discussing an algebra representing the action of relay contacts. The AND and OR relay circuit was described, followed by a circuit which combines both types of connection. Then AND, OR, and inverter logic representation was introduced, and a relationship to gating circuitry outlined. The basic conversions from equations to logic diagrams and vice-versa were also covered briefly.

Following the discussion of switching-circuit logic, the Venn diagram and Boolean algebra expressions were introduced. Three distinct methods for proving a Boolean theorem were discussed, and attention was directed to other facts concerning the organization of a Venn diagram.

REVIEW QUESTIONS AND PROBLEMS

4-1. Draw the relay circuits that represent each of the following switching equations:

   a. $y = A + \bar{B} + \bar{C} + D$.
   b. $y = AB\bar{C}\bar{D}$.
   c. $y = AB + \bar{B}\bar{C}$.

4-2. Draw the relay circuit which represents

$$y = A + BC + \overline{ACD} + C\bar{D}$$

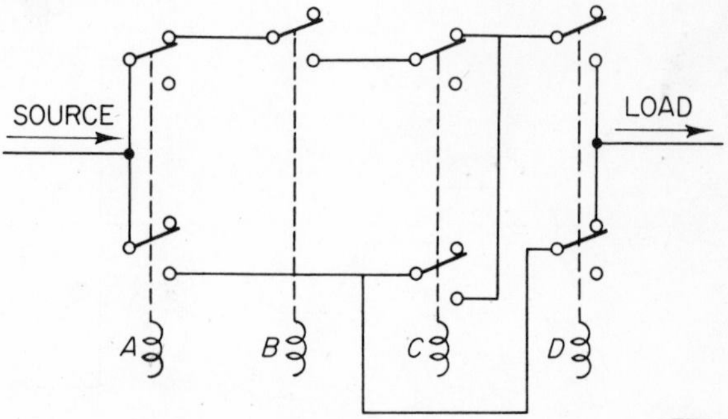

FIG. 4-20

4-3. Draw the logic diagram for Problem 2.

4-4. Given the relay network shown in Fig. 4-20, write the logic equation.

4-5. Convert the above equation to an AND–OR logic network.

4-6. Prove by Venn diagram that

$$\overline{XYZ} = \overline{X} + \overline{Y} + \overline{Z}$$

all area outside of all 3 rings is not

$$\overline{X} + \overline{Y} + \overline{Z} = \overline{X + Y + Z}$$

4-7. Draw $AB\overline{C}$ on a Venn diagram.

4-8. Simplify

$$y = \overline{A + B + C} + AB\overline{C} + (\overline{A} + \overline{B})C$$

4-9. Prove by truth table that

$$XY + YZ + XZ = (X + Y)(Y + Z)(Z + X)$$

4-10. Prove by truth table that

$$\overline{AC + B\overline{C}} = \overline{A}C + \overline{B}\overline{C}$$

4-11. Simplify the Boolean expression

$$y = A\overline{B}C + AB\overline{C} + \overline{A}B\overline{C} + \overline{A}BC$$

4-12. Prove by three methods

$$\overline{\overline{A}\,\overline{B}} \neq AB$$

4-13. Prove the theorem

$$(A + B)(\overline{A} + C) = AC + \overline{A}B$$

4-14. Draw the relay circuit and also the logic for

$$y = \overline{AB + B\overline{C} + AC}$$

use De Morgan t
$$= \overline{A}\left(\overline{B} + C + B\overline{C}\right)$$

4-15. Prove by Venn diagram

$$\overline{A} + \overline{A}B + \overline{A}\overline{C} = \overline{A}$$

4-16. Write the logic equation for the relay circuit shown in Fig. 4-21.

$$y = A \cdot B + A \cdot \overline{D} + \overline{B} \cdot \overline{C} + \overline{B} \cdot \overline{C}$$

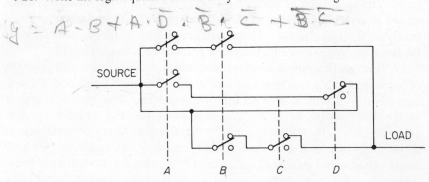

FIG. 4-21

BOOLEAN FUNCTIONS AND SWITCHING-CIRCUIT DESIGN 5

The application of Boolean functions today lies primarily in the development and simplification of switching circuits for computer or digital device logic. The expression of computer logic in the form of algebraic equations makes it possible in many instances to apply the techniques illustrated briefly in the last chapter. These techniques lead to the simplification of the Boolean expressions and, therefore, point to less complex logic.

A Boolean function is an expression which contains sums and products of variables having two states or conditions. The minus sign and division sign have no definition and no use in this system. The variables appear as the *true* variable or as the *complement* of the true variable (or just complement). The variable, sums of variables, products of variables, in all combinations, in true or complement form may be employed. Not only single variables but groups of variables can be defined in complement form. Although, a Boolean function can be a very complex structure, most often it will be stated or reduced to a basically simple form.

Two basic forms of Boolean functions are of special interest because of their common occurrence and symmetrical form. These are the two *canonical* forms: (1) the *product-of-sums* form, often called the *maxterm* form, and (2) the *sum-of-the-product* form, often called the *minterm* form. In order for either form to be in canonical form, all variables involved must appear in all terms of the expression in either the *true* or *complement* form only. A *minterm* is a product containing all variables involved in either the *true* or *complement* form. No multiple complements (a complement of two or more variables together) are permitted by the definition. For three variables there are eight possible minterms; for four variables, sixteen possible minterms, etc.

Maxterms are constructed from the sums of all the variables involved. Again all variables must appear in each term in either its true or complement form, and no multiple complements are permitted by the definition. There are also eight maxterms for three variables, sixteen for four variables, etc. A Boolean function, if it is canonical, will be composed solely of either maxterms or minterms.

Canonical expressions can often be simplified into forms which do not contain all the variables in all terms. Other types of Boolean functions, not necessarily canonical, can likewise be simplified. This simplification process is the underlying subject of this chapter. A topic that may assist at times in the process is an easy method for deriving a *complement* of a complete Boolean expression. This is explained in the next section.

THE COMPLEMENT OF A BOOLEAN FUNCTION

The complement of a Boolean expression or a part of any expression can be found by employing De Morgan's theorems. Two steps are required to accomplish this, as follows:

1. Replace the addition symbols with multiplication symbols, and the multiplication symbols with addition symbols.
2. Replace all variables with their complements.

As an example, consider finding the complement of the expression

$$A\bar{B} + C = y$$

By applying the above two rules,

$$(\bar{A} + B)\bar{C} = \bar{y}$$

The expression $\bar{y}$ is the complement of the expression y. This can be proven by a truth table or plotted on a Veitch diagram, as shown later in this chapter.

Another method of determining or proving the complement of a Boolean expression is to observe that the reciprocal or complement of a Boolean function is the reciprocal area on a Venn chart. For instance, $\overline{AB}$ is related to AB as shown in Fig. 5-1. Compare this diagram with Fig. 4-17, noting diagrammatically that $\overline{AB}$ does not equal $\overline{A}\overline{B}$.

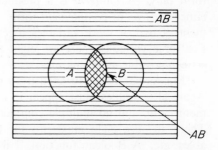

FIG. 5-1 Complementing via the Venn diagram.

SWITCHING-CIRCUIT DESIGN

At this point the relationships between Boolean functions and their usage in practice is explored briefly. The design of a normal switching circuit is achieved through an orderly series of steps which typically includes the following:

1. A precise statement of the conditions when the output circuit(s) must provide output(s).
2. The formation of a detailed truth table listing all possible positions of the relay switches or gates and the resulting output (*true* or *false*, 1 or 0) for each such position.
3. The formation of the necessary Boolean functions from the truth table.
4. A simplification of the Boolean function to its simplest apparent form.
5. The implementation of the final Boolean function with relays, switches, or gates.

This chapter details the design process and introduces the Veitch diagram (or Karnaugh chart), a modern substitute for Boolean algebra, now used for reducing two-level logic diagrams.

The first step, defining the details of the switching configuration, consists of the preparation of a detailed truth table. The particulars of this process depend upon the designer. They require that he have complete and exact details of the output needed for specific positions of the gates, switches, or relays. An orderly listing of the relay positions, with a true or false indication for each combination, is the basic ingredient of the resulting table.

For example, assume that, for three relays A, B, and C, a true output is desired at the three positions 4, 5, and 7 indicated by "1's" in the output column of the accompanying truth table.

Identity number	Inputs			Output	All three variable minterms	All three variable maxterms
	A	B	C	y		
1	0	0	0	0	$\bar{A}\bar{B}\bar{C}$	$A + B + C$
2	0	0	1	0	$\bar{A}\bar{B}C$	$A + B + \bar{C}$
3	0	1	0	0	$\bar{A}B\bar{C}$	$A + \bar{B} + C$
4	0	1	1	1	$\bar{A}BC$	$A + \bar{B} + \bar{C}$
5	1	0	0	1	$A\bar{B}\bar{C}$	$\bar{A} + B + C$
6	1	0	1	0	$A\bar{B}C$	$\bar{A} + B + \bar{C}$
7	1	1	0	1	$AB\bar{C}$	$\bar{A} + \bar{B} + C$
8	1	1	1	0	ABC	$\bar{A} + \bar{B} + \bar{C}$

NOTE: "1" means the gate is opened. In the y column it means a *true* output is required.

BOOLEAN FUNCTIONS APPLIED

A Boolean function is often made up of maxterms (or minterms) and forms an equation describing a desired switching function. The minterm form is an expression of a group of AND terms upon which the OR operation is performed.

In the minterm form, an equation is written describing the relay condition for three outputs, since the output (y) requires only three conditions of the relays

$$F(y) = \bar{A}BC + A\bar{B}\bar{C} + AB\bar{C} \tag{5-1}$$

The procedure is to write the AND condition of the relays for each place where a "1" appears in the output column. There are three AND conditions defined by the truth table in this example. These terms are then ORed together (i.e., the OR process is performed upon them) to complete the Boolean minterm function. This is the canonical form previously described.

The canonical form usually can be reduced to include fewer contacts. For instance, the Boolean theorems can be applied to this example as follows:

$$y = \bar{A}BC + AB\bar{C} + A\bar{B}\bar{C} \quad \text{(canonical form of the equation)}$$
$$y = \bar{A}BC + (B + \bar{B})A\bar{C}$$
$$y = \bar{A}BC + A\bar{C} \quad \text{(reduced form)} \tag{5-2}$$

The circuit may then be implemented, as shown in Fig. 5-2 by logical AND and OR gates.

when using the maxterm form remember that output = 0 (y = 0") page 65

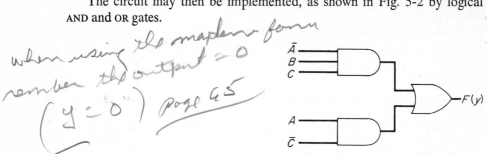

FIG. 5-2 The Boolean function $\overline{A}BC + A\overline{C}$.

Another approach to the same problem is the maxterm form. Here, the sum form of the terms is written rather than the product terms. The minterm form was written as a sum of three products, while the maxterm form is written as the product of the five sums occurring whenever there are zeros in the y column. It is important to note that the terms are written for those conditions, where the output $y = 0$, as follows:

$$y = (A + B + C)(A + B + \overline{C})(A + \overline{B} + C)(\overline{A} + B + \overline{C})(\overline{A} + \overline{B} + \overline{C})$$

maxterm identity number: **(1)**   **(2)**   **(3)**   **(6)**   **(8)**   **(5-3)**

This is also a canonical form. If there are fewer "0's" than "1's" in the right-hand column, it probably will be to the designer's advantage to write the expression in maxterms; otherwise, the algebra can be more tedious, as illustrated by the following solution to Eq. 5-3).

Rewriting Eq. (5-3) with identification numbers for the terms in parentheses,

$$y = (A + B + C)(A + B + \overline{C})(A + \overline{B} + C)(\overline{A} + B + \overline{C})(\overline{A} + \overline{B} + \overline{C})$$

     (1)   **(2)**   **(3)**   **(4)**   **(5)**

Combining (1) and (2) by multiplying and reducing according to the Boolean axioms,

$$AA + AB + A\overline{C} + AB + BB + B\overline{C} + AC + B\overline{C} + C\overline{C}$$
$$= AB + A\overline{C} + B + B\overline{C} + A + B\overline{C}$$
$$= A + B$$

Combining (3) and (4) in the same way that we did (1) and (2),

$$A\overline{A} + AB + A\overline{C} + \overline{A}\overline{B} + B\overline{B} + \overline{B}\overline{C} + \overline{A}C + BC + C\overline{C}$$
$$= (AB + A\overline{C} + \overline{B}\overline{C} + BC + \overline{A}C + \overline{A}\overline{B})$$

Combine (5) with a combination of (1) and (2)

$$(A + B)(\bar{A} + \bar{B} + \bar{C})$$
$$= A\bar{A} + A\bar{B} + A\bar{C} + \bar{A}B + B\bar{B} + B\bar{C}$$
$$= (A\bar{B} + A\bar{C} + \bar{A}B + B\bar{C})$$

This gives

$$(A\bar{B} + A\bar{C} + \bar{A}B + B\bar{C})(AB + A\bar{C} + \bar{B}\bar{C} + BC + \bar{A}C + \bar{A}B)$$

Multiplying out this entire expression and reducing at the same time,

$$A\bar{B}(AB + A\bar{C} + \bar{B}\bar{C} + BC + \bar{A}C + \bar{A}B)$$
$$(0 + A\bar{B})(AC + A\bar{B})(\bar{B}\bar{C} + 0 + 0 + 0) = A\bar{B}\bar{C} + A\bar{B}\bar{C} = A\bar{B}\bar{C} \qquad \text{(term 1)}$$

also,

$$A\bar{C}(AB + A\bar{C} + \bar{B}\bar{C} + BC + \bar{A}C + \bar{A}B)$$
$$AB\bar{C} + A\bar{C} + A\bar{B}\bar{C} + 0 + 0 + 0 = AB\bar{C} + A\bar{C} + A\bar{B}\bar{C} \qquad \text{(term 2)}$$

and,

$$\bar{A}B(AB + A\bar{C} + \bar{B}\bar{C} + BC + \bar{A}C + \bar{A}B)$$
$$0 + 0 + 0 + \bar{A}BC + \bar{A}BC + 0 = \bar{A}BC \qquad \text{(term 3)}$$

and,

$$B\bar{C}(AB + A\bar{C} + \bar{B}\bar{C} + BC + \bar{A}C + \bar{A}B)$$
$$0 + AB\bar{C} + AB\bar{C} + 0 + 0 + 0 = AB\bar{C} \qquad \text{(term 4)}$$

Gathering together the remainders designated term 1, term 2, term 3, and term 4,

$$A\bar{B}\bar{C} + AB\bar{C} + A\bar{C} + A\bar{B}\bar{C} + \bar{A}BC + AB\bar{C}$$

This reduces by using Boolean axioms to

$$A\bar{C} + A\bar{B}\bar{C} + \bar{A}BC + AB\bar{C}$$

$$A\bar{C} + A\bar{C} + \bar{A}BC$$
$$y = A\bar{C} + \bar{A}BC$$

[NOTE: This is the same equation as Eq. (5-2) but arrived at by the use of maxterms.]

5-3 A second and simpler method of reducing the maxterm form of Eq. (5-4) is to apply the complementation theorem twice to this equation. The first application of this theorem to Eq. (5-3) gives

$$\bar{y} = \bar{A}\bar{B}\bar{C} + \bar{A}\bar{B}C + \bar{A}B\bar{C} + A\bar{B}C + ABC$$

Reducing the above equation by the usual Boolean axioms gives

$$\bar{y} = \bar{A}\bar{B} + AC + \bar{A}B\bar{C} = \bar{A}(\bar{B} + B\bar{C}) + AC$$

[handwritten marginalia]

$$\bar{y} = \bar{A}(\bar{B} + B\bar{C}) + AC$$

$$A + \bar{A}B = A + B \quad (\text{THEO. } 17 \ P \ 55)$$

$$\text{OR } (\bar{B} + B\bar{C}) = \bar{B} + \bar{C}$$

$$\bar{y} = \bar{A}(\bar{B} + \bar{C}) + AC$$

SO

Now again complementing the above equation (the second complementation) gives

$$y = (A + B)(A + C)(\bar{A} + \bar{C})$$

Multiplying out the terms of this equation and simplifying,

$$y = (AA + AC + AB + BC)(\bar{A} + \bar{C})$$
$$y = (A + BC)(\bar{A} + \bar{C})$$
$$y = A\bar{A} + \bar{A}BC + A\bar{C} + BCC$$
$$y = A\bar{C} + \bar{A}BC$$

[The Eq. (5-2) again, arrived at by the use of maxterms.]

  The lengthy solutions above indicate that the minterm approach is the easiest to apply to this particular example. The student, after a little practice, will observe and use the form of expression that has the *least number of ~~terms~~*. This form is usually the easiest to reduce to the minimum number of variables and terms.

[handwritten: VARIABLES]

THE GOAT–WOLF–CORN PROBLEM

The complete process of starting with a problem and ending with a solution in terms of a device can be illustrated by a simple example used by W. Keister of The Bell Telephone Laboratories, Incorporated. This illustration was presented at a meeting of the Institute of Radio Engineers in Baltimore, Maryland, many years ago somewhat as follows:

  A farmer employs as a hired hand a man who is not too bright. The hired hand is to keep the farmer's goat out of the barn while the door is open, because the barn contains a pile of corn to be used as cattle feed. Also, a wolf, who considers the goat a tasty dish, lurks nearby.

  The farmer decides to design a box which has three buttons: one each for "door open," "goat in sight," and "wolf in sight." The hired man will merely punch the buttons according to what he sees at a given time. If the situation is "dangerous," i.e., the ingredients are such as to cause harm to one of the items to be protected, the combination of buttons pressed will ring an alarm and the farmer will take appropriate action.

  To design this device, the farmer fashions a truth table, putting a "1" the y column if the situation is dangerous and an "0" in the y column if the situation is safe. The assumptions are made that:

1. The situation is safe if the goat and wolf are not visible; in other words, the goat cannot go where the hired hand cannot see him and still be in danger from the wolf.
2. The wolf does not eat corn.

With these assumptions, the truth table is as shown here.

| Inputs | | | Output |
D	G	W	y
0	0	0	0
0	0	1	0
0	1	0	0
0	1	1	1[a]
1	0	0	0
1	0	1	0
1	1	0	1[b]
1	1	1	1[c]

KEY:
D = 1 means door open
G = 1 means goat visible
W = 1 means wolf visible

[a] Wolf could kill goat if they are not separated.
[b] Door is open so goat can get to corn.
[c] Combination of above dangerous situations.

The Boolean function representing this truth table is

$$y = \bar{D}GW + DG\bar{W} + DGW$$

This reduces by use of the Boolean axioms to

$$y = \bar{D}GW + DG = G(\bar{D}W + D) = GD + GW \quad \text{(Fig. 5-3a)}$$
$$= G(D + W) \quad \text{(Fig. 5-3b)}$$

The logic symbolic circuits represented by the final equations is shown in Fig. 5-3a and b. The designer has the choice of using either one. Either logic arrangement will accomplish the required protecting function. If

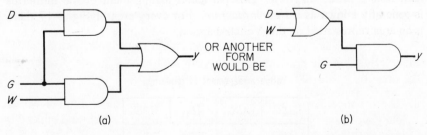

(a)   (b)

FIG. 5-3 Logic diagram: goat-wolf-corn problem.

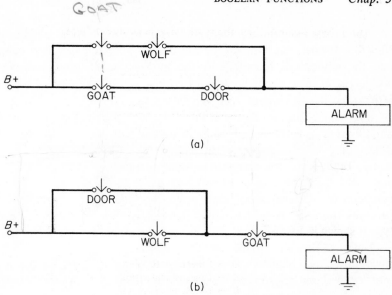

FIG. 5-4   Circuit diagram: goat-wolf-corn problem.

this logic were implemented with relays, the circuits may be as shown in Fig. 5-4.

Both circuits will do the job, but note that Fig. 5-4b has the advantage of using one less contact. This is an interesting fact. Although Boolean algebra will reduce the expression, it may not always achieve the smallest number of contacts possible. This occurs quite often in practice; hence, the ingenuity of the designer still has a place in deciding on an optimum solution.

THE VEITCH DIAGRAM (KARNAUGH CHART)

The Venn diagram of Fig. 4-17 can be arranged in the more usable form shown here in the diagram. This particular arrangement of the minterms is generally known as a *Veitch diagram*. For every area of Fig. 4-17 there is an area represented on this Veitch diagram.

Veitch arrangement of minterms

$AB\overline{C}$	ABC	$\overline{A}BC$	$\overline{A}B\overline{C}$
$A\overline{B}\overline{C}$	$A\overline{B}C$	$\overline{A}\,\overline{B}C$	$\overline{A}\,\overline{B}\,\overline{C}$

The overlapping of variables required to make the chart is indicated in Fig. 5-5. [NOTE: *Each square of the diagram corresponds to a minterm,* and the minterm is identified by the intersection of *three variables* for each square. For example, the lowermost right-hand square represents $\overline{A}\,\overline{B}C$. (It is the area where $\overline{A}$, $\overline{B}$, and $\overline{C}$ intersect.)]

The Veitch diagram shown in Fig. 5-5 and 5-6(a) will be used throughout this text. The *Karnaugh chart* is similar and differs only in the method of indicating coordinates. Both charts are used in the same manner and yield the same results. The chart used depends on the designer's individual preference and previous training. A four-variable chart of each type is shown in Fig. 5-6.

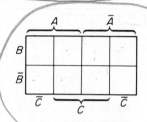

FIG. 5-5   Areas of a Veitch diagram.

Both the Veitch diagram and the Karnaugh chart provide a method of simplifying Boolean functions without referring to the simplifying theorems. They are essentially graphical methods of simplification. A chart is constructed as described in the following paragraphs and, by observing the pattern, a canonical form can be generated or simplified as was done previously by other methods.

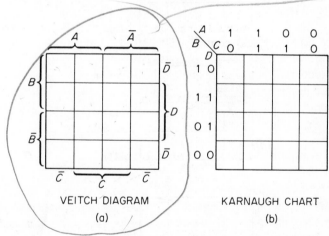

FIG. 5-6   Veitch diagram and Karnaugh chart.

As an example of the Veitch diagram, plot Eq. (5-2) by placing a "1" in each block where a minterm appears. The resulting plot is shown in Fig. 5-7. It can be noted that there is a "1" in both the $AB\overline{C}$ and $A\overline{B}\,\overline{C}$ positions which are adjacent on the diagram. It should be noted the $AB\overline{C} + A\overline{B}\,\overline{C}$ can be factored to $A\overline{C}(B + \overline{B})$. From Boolean theorems this reduces to $A\overline{C}$. On the Veitch chart this reduction possibility is identified by two "1's" in adjacent positions. Therefore, from the plot of Eq. (5-2) on the Veitch chart, the adjacent "1's" show that $AB\overline{C} + A\overline{B}\overline{C}$ reduces to $A\overline{C}$. The term $\overline{A}BC$ is all by itself and cannot combine with any other term. Hence, the final reduction is, as previously found by other techniques,

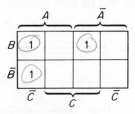

$$y = \overline{A}BC + A\overline{C}$$

FIG. 5-7 $\overline{A}BC + A\overline{C}$ in a Veitch diagram.

The general rule for reducing a Boolean expression by using the Veitch diagram is to look for groupings in either the row or vertical column. Diagonals do not count. Several examples are given in Fig. 5-8 to illustrate typical reductions. The chart can be considered continuous, i.e., squares on the outside can be combined with those on the opposite side.

The combinations illustrated so far concerned a reduction of three

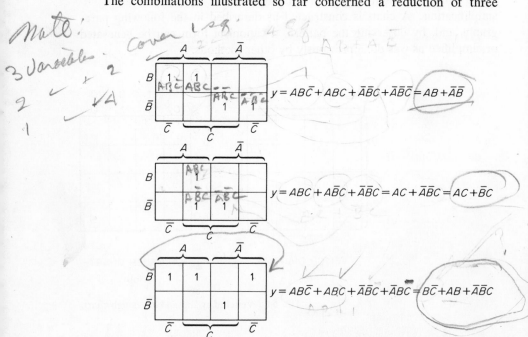

FIG. 5-8 Examples of Veitch reductions.

variables to two in a three-variable chart. If "1's" appeared in all four left-hand squares of Fig. 5-5, the variable represented would be A. If "1's"

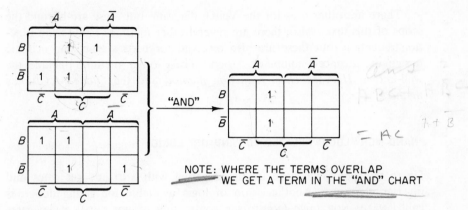

NOTE: WHERE THE TERMS OVERLAP
WE GET A TERM IN THE "AND" CHART

FIG. 5-9 ANDing Veitch diagrams.

appeared in a row completely across the bottom, the variable represented would be $\bar{B}$. Maxterms can also be represented on a Veitch diagram. For instance, $A + \bar{B}$ would be represented by "1's" in all positions except the top two left-hand squares. Other games can be played with Veitch charts as follows:

1. Boolean equations can be ANDed or ORed on the Veitch diagram merely by plotting one diagram over the other. Examples are given in Figs. 5-9 and 5-10, respectively. The procedure conforms to the definition of each function, respectively.

2. To find the *complement* of a Boolean function, plot the function on the diagram and *invert* the "1's" and "0's." Then read off the complement from the diagram.

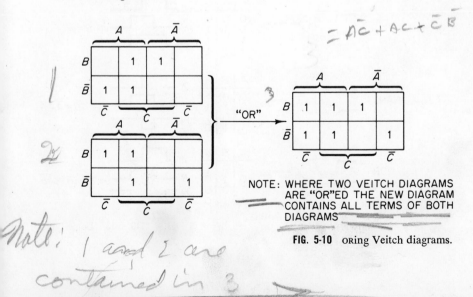

NOTE: WHERE TWO VEITCH DIAGRAMS
ARE "OR"ED THE NEW DIAGRAM
CONTAINS ALL TERMS OF BOTH
DIAGRAMS

FIG. 5-10 ORing Veitch diagrams.

There are other uses for the Veitch diagram, but these are beyond the scope of this text. Also, there are several other methods of Boolean function reduction, but these are also reserved for texts specializing in logic design or advanced computer design. These other methods include the well-known *Harvard chart reduction method* and the *Quine–McCluskey method*.

"NAND–NOR" LOGIC RELATED TO "AND–OR" LOGIC

Up to this point, we have discussed gating with AND and OR gates and inverter elements. Another form of logic available for gating design is called NAND–NOR *logic* (NAND is a contraction of *not* AND). NAND gates are constructed by merely combining an AND gate with an inverter element,

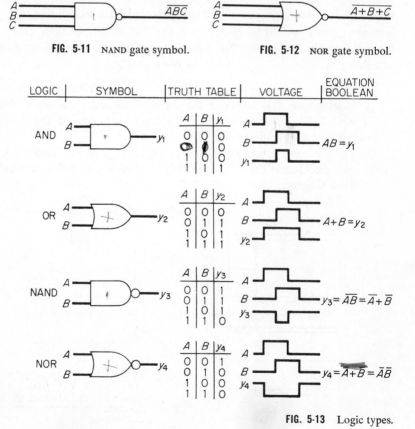

FIG. 5-11　NAND gate symbol.　　　　　**FIG. 5-12**　NOR gate symbol.

FIG. 5-13　Logic types.

as illustrated symbolically in Fig. 5-11. The circle at the gate output represents signal inversion.

A NOR gate is the corresponding combination of an OR gate and an inverter, as shown symbolically in Fig. 5-12.

Figure 5-13 summarizes the types of logic and shows their relationship. AND–OR logic, popular in the design of early computers, has one major disadvantage. After a string of gates in series (usually about three), it is necessary to restore power owing to degradation of the input pulse. This requires an amplifier with two inverting stages assigned periodically throughout the logic. With widespread use of diode circuit logic this was not a major handicap. Employing pulse logic (where a pulse represents a "1" and no pulse represents a "0") permitted the use of a single-stage amplifier along with a pulse transformer whose winding terminals were corrected to give a pulse output of proper polarity, as shown in Fig. 5-14.

With the advent of transistor logic, however, inversion of signal polarity was inherent in the circuit and could not be avoided in a single-stage circuit. This created a problem when a level type of logic was employed ("1" is represented by a level such as +10 volts and "0" by a second level, possibly 0 volts). Level logic has become very popular in transistor-circuit design. The increased importance in the use of NAND–NOR logic representation in today's digital devices can be attributed both to this change from

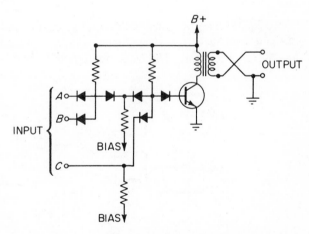

FIG. 5-14 Diode AND gate for pulse logic.

pulse to level logic and to the widespread change to transistor circuitry (and, more recently, to the integrated type of circuitry).

"AND–OR" LOGIC AND "NAND–NOR" LOGIC COMPARED

Some thought must be given to the conversion of AND–OR circuits to NAND–NOR circuits and vice versa; otherwise, erroneous results will be obtained. For example, suppose one decides to change from AND–OR logic to NAND–NOR logic merely by replacing AND gates with NAND gates and OR gates with NOR gates. A student might justify this change on the grounds that, for a simple AND–OR combination, there are two signal inversions. Hence, the direct substitution should not affect the output signal polarities. This substitution is shown here to permit evaluation of the results. First, the Boolean equation $y = AB + CD$ is represented by AND–OR logic as shown in Fig. 5-15.

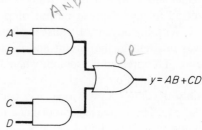

FIG. 5-15   AND–OR gate combination ($y = AB + CD$).

Replacing the AND gates with NAND gates and the OR gate with a NOR gate and feeding in the same logic quantities gives the circuit shown in Fig. 5-16. The term $ABCD$ is not equal to $AB + CD$; therefore, the

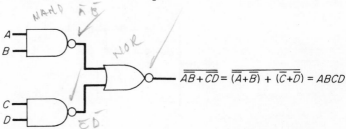

$$\overline{AB} + \overline{CD} = \overline{(\overline{A+B})} + \overline{(\overline{C+D})} = ABCD$$

FIG. 5-16   NAND–NOR gate combination.

direct substitution will not work. However, it is possible to use the set of gates shown in Fig. 5-17 to duplicate the result of the AND–OR gate combination of Fig. 5-15.

The same logic expression $(AB + CD)$ can also be constructed by

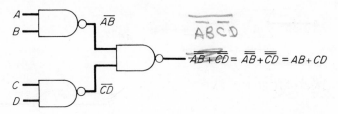

FIG. 5-17 NAND–NAND gate combination.

using NOR gates and inverters but at the expense of having to use additional circuit elements.

CONVERSION FROM "AND–OR" LOGIC TO "NAND" OR "NOR" LOGIC

One of the most direct methods of converting from AND–OR logic to either the NAND version or the NOR version is to substitute equivalent NANDS or equivalent NORS, with suitable simplifications, in the AND–OR logic diagram. Logic diagrams can be drawn directly from the Boolean equations in either NAND or NOR terms, but it is probably easier and more direct to draw the logic first in AND–OR notation, and then to transfer to either NAND or NOR. Because of the current trend to supply logic gates in either NAND version or NOR version, it is probably easier to make the design all NAND or all NOR rather than a NAND–NOR combination. Here again, both experience and the availability of packaged logic is a factor. The approach, therefore, varies with the circumstances. (Combination NAND–NOR logic is discussed in a subsequent section.)

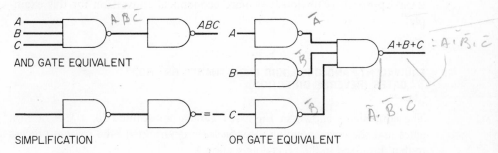

FIG. 5-18 NAND equivalents.

The NAND equivalents of AND–OR logic gating is shown in Fig. 5-18. The NOR equivalent of AND–OR logic gating is shown in Fig. 5-19.

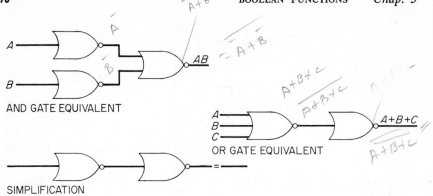

AND GATE EQUIVALENT

OR GATE EQUIVALENT

SIMPLIFICATION

FIG. 5-19   NOR equivalents.

The suggested technique for converting AND–OR to NAND or NOR logic requires drawing a logic diagram in AND–OR form first, followed by the application of the following steps:

1. Replace AND and OR gates with their equivalent NAND or NOR gates.
2. Perform simplifications where possible.
3. Redraw the final NAND or NOR diagram in its simplest form.

This straightforward approach is effective and also avoids use of the less familiar Pierce or Streffer stroke-function theorems in obtaining a logic diagram.

Beginning with the basic AND–OR circuit, the conversion to either a NAND or NOR version follows the simple progression illustrated in Fig. 5-20. Here, the NAND implementation uses eight gates compared with six gates plus an inverter for AND–OR circuit. The NOR version uses 14 gates. The NAND approach is obviously a more economical conversion for this example.

EQUIVALENT "AND–OR" LOGIC FROM "NAND" OR "NOR" GATES (REVERSE DIRECTION)

The equivalents shown in Fig. 5-21 can be substituted for NAND or NOR gates and the corresponding AND–OR logic determined (the reverse process to that discussed in the preceding section.)

An equivalent transformation can be made for a NOR logic diagram; but this exercise can be performed by the student, since it is comparable to the NAND to AND–OR transformation.

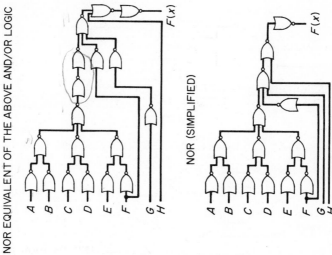

NOR EQUIVALENT OF THE ABOVE AND/OR LOGIC

NOR (SIMPLIFIED)

THE ORIGINAL AND/OR CIRCUIT

EQUATION: $(AB + CD + EF)F\bar{G} + H$

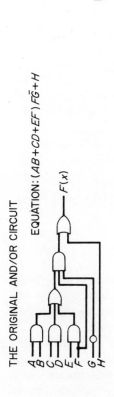

NAND EQUIVALENT OF THE ABOVE AND/OR LOGIC

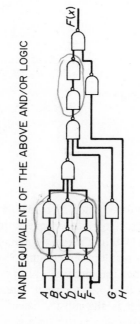

NAND (SIMPLIFIED)

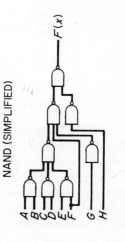

FIG. 5-20   Conversion for AND–OR to NAND or NOR.

EQUIVALENTS   EQUIVALENTS

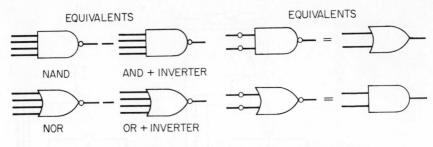

NAND   AND + INVERTER

NOR   OR + INVERTER

AS AN EXAMPLE CONSIDER THE FOLLOWING NAND CIRCUIT

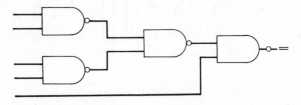

THIS CIRCUIT CONVERTS FIRST TO: AND FINALLY TO:

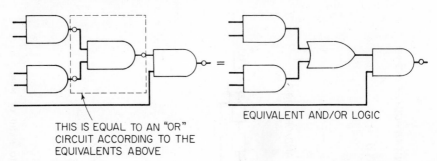

THIS IS EQUAL TO AN "OR"
CIRCUIT ACCORDING TO THE
EQUIVALENTS ABOVE

EQUIVALENT AND/OR LOGIC

FIG. 5-21   Equivalent circuits.

MIXED LOGIC

Although most logic systems are restricted by available circuitry to AND–OR, NAND, or NOR exclusively, there have been requests for logic systems employing *all* the above elements within a single system. Such a combination, if used properly, could possibly result in a minimum of circuits.

A brief study will show that the circuits represented in *minterm* form are best represented by a dual-level NAND circuit. Similarly, for a *maxterm* circuit, a dual-level NOR circuit is the most efficient representation. It is not unusual in logic systems to tie the output of a string of NORs to a NAND input, or vice versa. Such a connection is shown in Fig. 5-22a. Simplification occurs if a NAND gate is followed by a single NOR (or NAND) gate or if a NOR gate is followed by a single NAND (or NOR) gate. In the first case, a NAND followed by a single NOR (or NAND) can be replaced by a single AND gate. In the second case, a NOR gate followed by a single NOR or

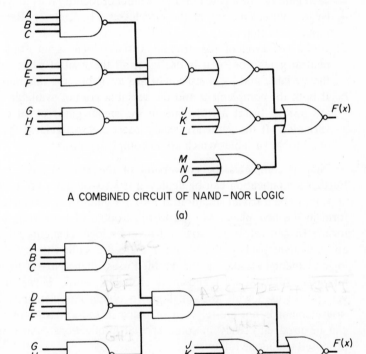

A COMBINED CIRCUIT OF NAND—NOR LOGIC

(a)

THE ABOVE CIRCUIT SIMPLIFIED BY SUBSTITUTING
AN AND GATE FOR A SERIAL
NAND—NOR COMBINATION

(b)

FIG. 5-22   Simplification of combined circuits.

NAND gate can be replaced by an OR gate. This makes it possible for Fig. 5-22a to be simplified to Fig. 5-22b directly.

Another systematic method of constructing a combination NOR–NAND logic that minimizes the total number of logic elements employed, follows these simple rules:

1. Obtain the minimum Boolean equation in the form of bars over single variables only.
2. Draw the logic in AND–OR form.
3. Remove the AND–OR symbols and replace with a neutral symbol for each gate (show a gate but do not label or identify it as to type).
4. Negate input entering at the *odd* levels (1, 3, etc.). Relabel all other inputs as in step 2.
5. If the last level of the original AND–OR logic is an AND, label all the neutral gates NOR; if it is OR, label all the neutral gates NAND. If both the variable and its complement are available, the diagram is complete.
6. If both the complement and the variable are not available and the gates are NANDs, insert a NOR gate in the signal paths of all complemented variables. If the gates are NORs, insert a NAND gate in the signal paths of all those variables which are in complement form.

Step 6 completes the conversion of the AND–OR logic to NAND–NOR. Further simplification can be achieved if AND–OR gates are permitted. This appears to be a trivial situation; if AND–OR gates were available in packaged form in the first place, why go to the trouble of converting to NAND–NOR form? In general, if AND–OR and inverter logic elements are available on an equivalent package basis and if there are sufficient power gains in the logic element to make up for circuit losses, then AND–OR logic implementation is usually simpler and more straightforward. However, because inverters are used with AND–OR logic to obtain complements, the NAND or NOR element is not entirely out of place in the AND–OR configuration and can be used effectively in some special applications. An example of the proposed technique follows:

Given:

$$F(x) = [(\overline{A + B})C + (C + D)\overline{A} + \overline{A + B + C}]E\overline{F} + \overline{C}DF$$

Determine: the simplest NAND–NOR logic for the above equation.

Step 1. Put into single-variable form, i.e., bars over a single variable only.

$$
\begin{aligned}
(\overline{A + B})C &= \overline{A}\,\overline{B}C \\
(C + D)\overline{A} &= \overline{A}C + \overline{A}D \\
\overline{A + B + C} &= A\overline{B}\,\overline{C}
\end{aligned}
$$

Step 2. Draw the AND–OR diagram.

Steps 3 and 4. Relabel with neutral symbols and complement inputs at odd levels.

Step 5. If the last level of AND–OR is OR, relabel the gates NAND. If both variable and inverted variable are available, the task is complete.

Step 6. If only the variable in true form is available, add NORs for the inverted variables.

The diagram (Fig. 5-23) is the final form of implementation.

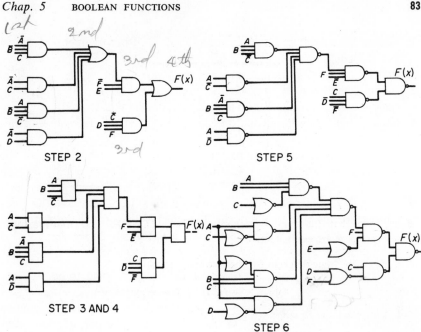

FIG. 5-23   Final circuit for the example.

SUMMARY

This chapter has extended a number of logic topics begun in Chapter 4. The first topic was the complementation of Boolean functions. This was followed by a summary of switching-circuit design illustrated by the classic goat-wolf-corn example. Terms such as *canonical, maxterm, minterm* were explained. An introduction to the Veitch diagram (or Karnaugh chart) showed how these methods can duplicate and improve the Boolean equation reduction techniques given in Chapter 4. The NAND–NOR logic representations of logic equations were presented and compared with AND–OR logic forms. The conversion of logic forms was also briefly outlined. An example of how to obtain logic in mixed form and its possible advantages in design concluded the chapter.

REVIEW QUESTIONS AND PROBLEMS

5-1. Assuming *ABC* are the only inputs [$\overline{A}$, $\overline{B}$, and $\overline{C}$ must be obtained by inverting (complementing) *A*, *B*, *C*] draw the logic which represents the accompanying truth table. Reduce the Boolean function where possible.

A	B	C	y_1	y_2
0	0	0	0	1
0	0	1	0	0
0	1	0	0	1
0	1	1	1	1
1	0	0	1	0
1	0	1	1	0
1	1	0	0	0
1	1	1	1	0

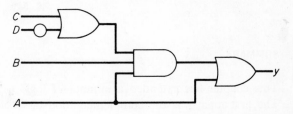

$y_1 = \overline{A}BC + A\overline{B}\overline{C} + A\overline{B}C + ABC$

$y_2 = \overline{A}\overline{B}\overline{C} + \overline{A}B\overline{C} + \overline{A}B$

5-2. Prove that the minterm expression $y = A\overline{B} + \overline{A}B$ and the maxterm expression are equivalent.

5-3. Draw the logic diagram for the following equation:

$$y = (A + \overline{BC})(A + \overline{B} + \overline{C})$$

5-4. Find the logic equation for the Fig. 5-24.

C
D
B
A
y

FIG. 5-24

5-5. AND together $f(x)_1 = AB + BC$ and $f(x)_2 = \overline{A}C + \overline{AB}$.

5-6. OR together the functions of Problem 5-5.

5-7. Find the quantity $\overline{f(x)_1 \cdot f(x)_2}$ of Problem 5-5.

5-8. What is the most reduced form of the Boolean equation represented by the Veitch diagram (Fig. 5-25)?

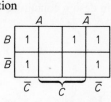

FIG. 5-25

5-9. What is the minimum expression for the Veitch diagram (Fig. 5-26)?

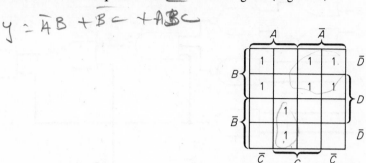

$$y = \overline{A}B + \overline{B}\overline{C} + A\overline{B}C$$

FIG. 5-26

5-10. Plot the following on a Veitch diagram and simplify:

$$y = \overline{A}\overline{B}\overline{C} + ABC + A\overline{B}C + \overline{A}BC + \overline{A}B\overline{C}$$

5-11. Convert the logic (shown in Fig. 5-27) first to NAND, then to NOR. Which method results in the minimum logic elements?

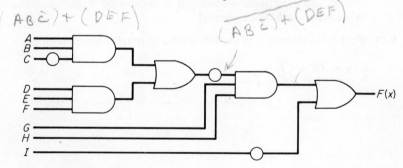

$$(AB\overline{C}) + (DEF)$$

$$(AB\overline{C}) + (DEF)$$

FIG. 5-27

5-12. Convert the following Boolean function to the minimum (a) NAND, (b) NOR, (c) NAND–NOR logic:

$$y = (\overline{A} + B)(\overline{C} + D) + AB\overline{C} + \overline{B}CD$$

$$y = \overline{\overline{A + \overline{B} + \overline{C}} + ABCD}$$

5-13. Convert to AND–OR logic the NAND–NOR logic of Fig. 5-28 (p. 86).

5-14. Draw the logic diagram for $F(x) = AB\overline{C} + A\overline{B}C + \overline{A}BC$ in NAND logic form.

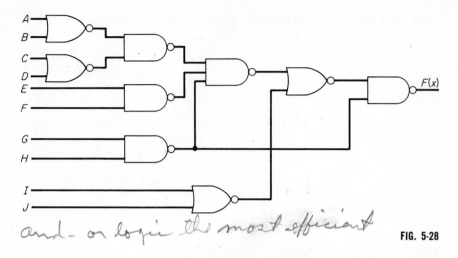

and - or logic the most efficient

FIG. 5-28

5-15. Draw the above logic in NOR logic form. Which logic form would you expect to be the most efficient in gate usage?

5-16. Draw the NOR logic diagram for $F(x) = \overline{(A + B)C} + \overline{C}\overline{AB} + \overline{(A + B)\overline{C}}$. Would you save logic elements if a NAND–NOR logic were available? What is the NAND–NOR diagram?

5-17. Find the complement of the following and simplify where possible:

a. $y = \overline{AB} + \overline{C}\overline{D}$.
b. $y = (A + B)C + \overline{C}D$.

CIRCUIT ELEMENTS AND OTHER LOGIC DESIGN 6

In the design of modern computers, many types of electronic devices are employed. Originally, vacuum tubes, diodes, and magnetic elements played a major role. The emergence of the more reliable transistor hastened the decline of the vacuum tube as a computer logic device. More recently, the transistor itself is giving way to the integrated circuit, which is currently undergoing evolution. Unquestionably, the field of logic circuitry is highly dynamic. Judging by past and present rates of evolution, the student should be prepared to accept and learn new approaches periodically. The future appears to rest on integrated circuit (I-C) technology. Field-effect transistor–metal oxide silicon (FET–MOS) devices and large-scale integrated circuits (LSIC) are extensions of this technology. The theory of these major electrical logic devices, both past and present, will be the major subject of this chapter.

LOGIC CIRCUIT EVOLUTION

Introduction

Logic elements in digital devices have always reflected the most advanced switching technology of the period. In the early 1940's, all gating was accomplished by relay contactors. It is not surprising that the first books on switching-circuit theory followed Shannon's theoretical lead and described connections in an alegbra illustrated by relay contacts. The early Harvard–IBM and Bell Telephone Laboratories machines generally employed the relay technology method.

Vacuum-tube switching circuits gave rise to vacuum tube computers. These included such memorable giants as the ENIAC, EDVAC, SEAC, ORDVAC, and early UNIVACs. Although relays provided ideal switching as a perfect conductor when closed to an absolute insulator when opened, they nevertheless were recognized as being relatively slow in operation. For example, the maximum number of cycles a typical relay can make is a few hundred opens and closures per second. Since many logical operations are sequential and dependent upon the opening and closing of the logic switches, the speed of a computer is limited, largely, by the rapidity of the switching.

Application of the vacuum tube and semiconductor diode to logic switching eliminated the relative slowness of relay switching. In the ensuing years, this circuit approach, too, was recognized as having deficiencies. These flaws involved the necessity to transmit information at rather high-voltage levels, which resulted in the expenditure of unnecessary power. The high-voltage levels led, occasionally, to undesired radiation of spurious signals or electrical noise to adjacent circuits and equipment—a phenomenon called *radio-frequency interference* (RFI) by electrical engineers. In addition, because of the electrical power required, the system was highly inefficient. The power drawn by the filaments of a tube (merely to heat them) amounts to about 50 per cent of the power drawn by the tube. This power serves no useful purpose in the switching or gating functions. Consequently, the vacuum tube as a computer logic element reached its zenith in the early 1950's and has declined thereafter as the transistor appeared on the scene.

The first transistor units were the point-contact type and were not dependable or uniform in their operation. With the development of the first diffused-junction process and later processes such as alloy junction and planar, the transistor rapidly began taking over the logic function of both vacuum tubes and diodes in the newly conceived "second-generation" computers. About 1955, transistor data processors were in operation in moderate quantities.

The transistor's two major advantages were (1) the lower power necessary for signal transfers and (2) their usefulness in replacing *both* vacuum tubes and diodes. Transistors needed no filament power; hence, this wasted power drain in the vacuum-tube systems was eliminated. Cooling could now be accomplished with blowers, and it was no longer necessary to provide air conditioning. This reduced the computer's energy consumption and operating cost considerably. In addition, transistors existed in both NPN and PNP types.† An NPN transistor behaves much as a vacuum tube does; i.e., it requires a positive voltage supply, and positive signals on the base cause the unit to conduct normally. In the PNP type, the basic power source is negative, and a negative level signal causes conduction. In other words, PNP transistors gave the designer a new tool, a device that in effect operates as a negatively powered vacuum tube. Such a type of tube never existed in the vacuum-tube family.

Nevertheless, transistors were not altogether satisfactory for computer logic circuits. They are temperature sensitive and require designs which take into account the variation in operating parameters over the expected temperature range. Although smaller in size than the vacuum tubes, more transistors may be needed to perform a given function.

About 1963, still another logic revolution took place. This involved the use of *integrated circuits*. An integrated circuit is basically a systems approach to circuitry, which allows not only the circuit transistors to be formed in a silicon or germanium chip but also the accompanying diodes, resistors, and even capacitors to be formed on the same chip at the time the transistor is formed. In essence, then, what was formerly a case enclosure holding a single transistor now became a case enclosure, or modular package, containing a complete circuit function such as an entire flip-flop or amplifier or perhaps four independent NAND gates. By combining modules, a complete logic system could be assembled. Integrated-circuit (I-C) bipolar technology has been expanded to several types or families, each with its own characteristics. This subject is discussed in detail in Chapter 8.

The FET–MOS technology is an innovation of the I-C technology which permits even greater concentration of circuit elements on the same size silicon chip as used for the earlier I-Cs. The concentration of components may be more than 10 to 1. Although the FET–MOS devices have great potential, they may not replace bipolar I-Cs entirely. The FET–MOS elements are close to ideal in certain serial logic applications, but it is difficult to bring out multiple parallel leads from the device in many parallel system applications.

The terms *unipolar* and *bipolar* often associated with I-C technology are important distinctions. The *bipolar* device generally refers to a *current*

---

† "NPN" and "PNP" are simply type designations.

amplifying device of the normal transistor type. The current in the emitter–collector path is a flow of electrons or holes or both (to be discussed below). This current path also encompasses two junctions and regions of both P and N material. Most I-C types, but not those employing FETs, fall into this class generally.

The *unipolar* device, on the other hand, is one in which the current flow is of one type, either holes *or* electrons. The current flows through only one type of semiconductor material, N or P. FET–MOS devices fall into this particular classification.

The next development appears to be the use of large scale integrated circuits (LSICs). Because technology of I-Cs is now better controlled and the yield of usable chips is higher, research effort is producing more elements on a single chip and larger chips. The indication is that *entire* arithmetic sections or control sections, may appear on a single chip. LSICs may be of either the bipolar or unipolar type.

The Operation of a Vacuum Tube

Thermionic emission, the phenomenon of electrons emitted from a hot filament to a surrounding positive electrode (all elements being located in an evacuated container) was observed by many experimenters, including Edison, toward the end of the last century. Such a flow of electrons (or charge flow) is defined as an electric current. This basic device, called a *thermoionic diode,* is still in wide use today. The observers noted that the density of the electron flow was both proportional to the temperature of the filament and the potential of the electrode (electric field) that attracted the electrons.

Lee DeForest, in 1906, added a third element to the diode structure. This third element, called a *grid,* was placed in the electron path between the filament and the positive electrode (anode). Generally, the wires of the grid were widely spaced and, if uncharged, produced little effect on the filament–anode electron flow. If, however, a negative potential (with respect to the filament) was placed on the grid, it caused a reduction of the filament–anode electron flow. A positive grid potential, however, caused an acceleration of electrons to the positive anode. De Forest demonstrated that the electron flow could be controlled effectively and a relatively small amount of power to the grid controls a much greater amount of power in the filament–anode path.

Modern tubes are more complex than the simple one just described. For instance, the electrons are not drawn from the filament directly but from an element in close proximity, called a *cathode.* The heat from the filaments literally boil off electrons from the cathode surface.

There are often other grid elements in the tube's electron cathode–

anode path besides the simple control grid discussed. These grids have special functions and are employed to control the electrical characteristics of the tube more closely than is possible with a single grid.

The vacuum tube has been used (see Fig. 6-1) to amplify weak sig-

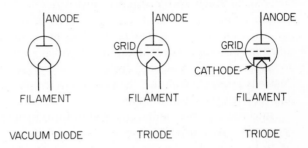

FIG. 6-1 Thermionic tube devices.

nals and produce sufficient power to operate a loud speaker, e.g. The signal driving the speaker must be a faithful reproduction of the original weak signal but greatly amplified both in voltage and current. The exact variation in signal amplitude and frequency should not be distorted from the original weak signal. This operation for the vacuum-tube amplifiers is called a *linear* operation.

When a vacuum tube is used to switch logic signals, it is *not* used in the linear mode. The electron flow will be turned fully (saturated flow) or turned completely off (cutoff) by the logic signal (1 or 0) on the grid. This operation is *nonlinear* (since a faithful reproduction of a varying signal is not required) and it is the proper mode of operation for a logic circuit switch.

The same remarks on modes of operation apply to transistors and integrated circuits. They, too, operate in a highly nonlinear manner in logic applications.

Semiconductors as Circuit Elements

The vacuum tube achieves power gain because a relatively small amount of power applied to the grid controls a larger amount of power in the cathode–anode path. The grid is said to *modulate* the stream of electrons that flows between electrodes. In semiconductor transistors, a similar modulation takes place, but in this case the signal current flow to the base corresponds to the changing grid signal and the modulated flow of electrons is between the terminals designated emitter and collector of the transistor. The electron path in the vacuum tube is a flow of electrons in free space, whereas, in the transistor, electrons drift through the crystalline structure of the semiconductor material (solid state conduction). Again, current through the semiconductor is defined as a charge flow of electrons, but it may also be defined as a positive charge flow called *holes.* Whether the current flow is electron flow or hole flow depends on the particular materials of which the transistor is constructed.

Semiconductor material, e.g., pure silicon, is neither a true conductor nor a true insulator but lies somewhere in between. The pure material, called *intrinsic,* is a crystalline solid in which electrons associated with the crystals may move erratically from crystal to crystal, but there are no more electrons available than just the number to satisfy the valence bonds necessary for a neutral intrinsic material.

Intrinsic material can be changed in form by addition of certain minute impurities. An intrinsic material so modified to have an excess of free electrons—i.e., there are more electrons in the material than necessary to satisfy the valence bond requirements—is defined as "N" material (Fig. 6-2). On the other hand, if the impurity added leaves a deficiency of elec-

INTRINSIC   —N—   —P—   NEUTRAL
(LIKE INTRINSIC)

FIG. 6-2   Semiconductor materials.

trons (the same thing as an excess of holes), the material is defined as "P" material. Antimony is an example of a *donor,* a material which when added in trace quantities to intrinsic material makes it N-type. Indium is an *acceptor,* which when added in trace quantities to intrinsic material makes it P-type. During processing of a semiconductor device, both donors and acceptors may be added to the same sample. Whether the material eventually is N- or P-type depends on whether donors or acceptors predominate. The techniques of manufacturing useful semiconductor devices requires that N- and P-regions be fabricated adjacent to each other in the same chip of material. The demarcation between two regions is called a *junction.* The semiconductor diode is such a chip containing a single N- and a single P-region with a junction between them. Current flow through this device is across the junction. If the N-region of the diode chip is made negative in relation to the P-end, the current will tend to flow easily across the junction, since the excess electrons in the N-region will be encouraged to flow toward the junction by the electric field set up across the chip. At the junction, the excess electrons combine with the holes in the P-area. The junction in this instance, is said to be *forward biased,* as shown in Fig.

6-3a. When the polarity is reversed, the junction is *reverse biased* and no appreciable current flows. The reason for the latter phenomenon is that both electrons and holes are urged away from the junction; hence, current flow across the junction is discouraged.

The transistor, on the other hand, is a three-region device with two separate junctions between the intersections of each region, as shown in Fig. 6-3b. NPN and PNP devices are both commonly used. In the NPN device the lower N-region is connected to ground (possibly through a resistor), as shown in Fig. 6-3c. This is generally called the *emitter* region and would correspond to the cathode in a vacuum tube. The upper N-region is called the *collector* and corresponds to the anode of the vacuum tube. This anode connects to the "B"-supply through a collector resistor in a typical practical amplifier. The region between the emitter and collector is a P-region. It is very thin and is termed the *base*.

The base connection, as shown in Fig. 6-3c, corresponding to the vacuum tube's grid connection, is made here. The base region joins the emitter through the emitter–base junction and joins the collector through the *base–collector* junction. The emitter–collector current is the primary load current. Its amplitude is a function of the base–collector current. In other words, when the base is supplied electrons, the emitter–base junction is forward biased and the electron flow between emitter and collector increases. When the base current is decreased, the emitter–base junction tends toward the reverse-biased condition and the emitter–collector current decreases.

In the region where the emitter–base is forward biased, the gain characteristics of the device are linear and it can be used for linear amplifier applications.

Just as the vacuum tube, the transistor may be used in the switching mode. Again, the unit is operated in a collector-current cutoff mode with the emitter–base junction completely reverse biased and alternately in a saturated mode when the emitter–base junction and often the emitter–collector junction, also, is forward biased.

Except for the reversal of polarities of both the power supplies and the signals, the PNP transistor (Fig. 6-3d) behaves in an identical manner. The emitter–collector current here can be described as hole flow, however. Circuit symbols for NPN and PNP transistors are shown in Fig. 6-3e.

Field-effect transistors are still another form of semiconductor device that has power-amplifying capabilities. Instead of having a *cathode, grid,* and *anode* like the vacuum tube or the *emitter, base, collector* of the bipolar transistor, field-effect transistors have corresponding elements called *source, gate,* and *drain* (see Fig. 6-4). One form of this device is also constructed on a silicon chip, as shown in Fig. 6-4a. The chip body, for example, is P-material. Within the chip, an N-channel (or corridor) is diffused

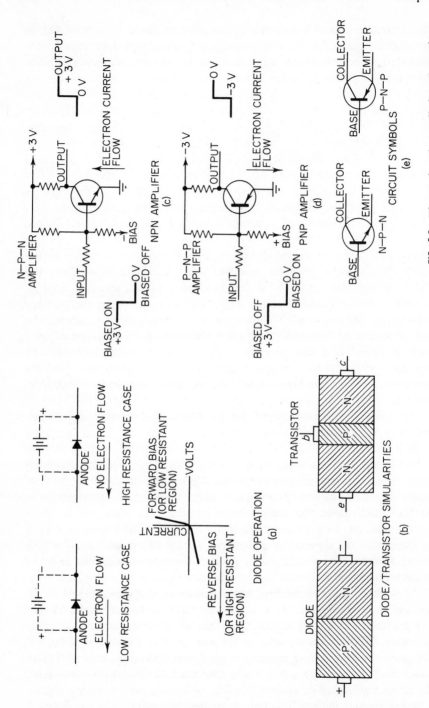

FIG. 6-3   The semiconductor diode and transistor.

with electrodes fastened to both ends. One of these electrodes is the *source,* the other is the *drain.* Normally the source and drain may be interchanged with little or no adverse affect on the unit's operation. The center portion of the corridor is made very narrow. Above this narrow

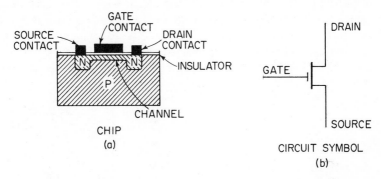

FIG. 6-4   Field effect transistors.

corridor section and insulated by a thin silicon dioxide layer is the gate electrode. A potential on the gate will create a field which in effect closes or opens the corridor to the electron flow from source to drain. This pinching operation represents the input signal and modulates the electron flow from source to drain and subsequently through the load resistor. The body of the chip is reverse biased from the corridor; hence, the channel remains isolated at all times during operation.

In its operating characteristics, the FET device is a much closer relative to the vacuum tube than the transistor is. This close operating similarity results from the insulation between the input signal circuit and the load circuit in both vacuum tube and FET. This degree of isolation is not obtainable in the bipolar transistor configuration.

Although the FET device described uses an N-corridor and a P-body (or substrate), an equivalent device can be fabricated with a P-corridor and an N-body. These FET–MOS devices, discussed in Chapter 9, are of the latter configuration.

Another required definition when discussing unipolar devices is the term *enhancement* mode. If a conduction channel occurs with the gate biased with the same polarity as the drain, the device operates in the enhancement mode. The types discussed here and in Chapter 9 operate in this mode. If an opposite polarity is required of the gate or if a channel exists when the gate is at the same potential as the drain, the device operates in a *depletion* mode.

Integrated circuit (I-C) is a term applied to a semiconductor device in which, as previously stated, several separate circuit elements are diffused on the same chip. The elements can be diodes, resistors, transistors, and capacitors—all separate and distinct. Interconnections between these elements is possible via conducting paths usually in the form of minute conductors deposited on the insulation silicon dioxide layer covering the top of the chip. A complete circuit subsection such as an amplifier, several gates, or a flip-flop storage element (to be described later in the chapter) may be constructed within a single 0.1-in. square semiconductor chip.

Because individual element isolation is less of a problem within unipolar FET–MOS structures, circuit elements can be packaged much more

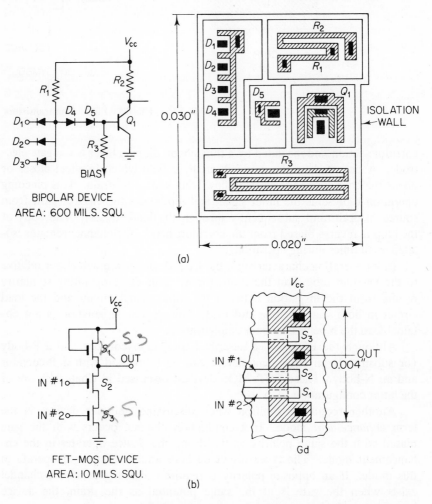

FIG. 6-5 Comparison of chip surface layout of (a) bipolar and (b) FET–MOS device.

tightly than within so-called bipolar integrated circuits discussed earlier in the chapter. For example, a bipolar chip might contain a single register element, while the FET–MOS equivalent-size chip contains 100 stages of a register.

Techniques of I-C fabrication are maturing with complete I-Cs of much higher complexity produced economically. Larger chips are also now available (instead of a few circuits being put on a single chip) with major portions of a computer section squeezed on a single chip. In early 1967, LSICs reached the point that, for instance, a complete arithmetic adder was available on a single chip. This chip is somewhat larger than the 0.1-in. square version previously described but still easily fits a standard transistor or standard 14-lead flat-pack. In addition, 40-lead flat-packs have been in use since 1966.

Examples of typical I-Cs are shown in Fig. 6-5. The upper chip (Fig. 6-5a) is a bipolar device containing 77 elements such as resistors, diodes, and transistors in a 60 mil square area. The lower device (Fig. 6-5b) is a FET–MOS chip containing 207 elements in a 43 by 69 mil area. Notice that because of the large connecting pads used for off-the-chip connections only about half the total chip area is used for active components.

Other Logic Techniques

It should be mentioned in passing that devices other than semiconductors are usable as logic elements. Logic can be built with relay switching, as described earlier. Some of the newer reed relays are used as logic elements, especially in equipment where high logic speed is not an important requirement. *Magnetic cores* have been used as logic elements in other

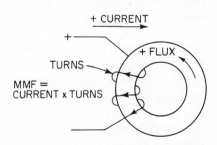

FIG. 6-6 Ring of magnetic material.

special applications. These magnetic elements (see Fig. 6-6) are larger toroids, and may have one to several separate windings. Diodes are sometimes used in conjunction to make a complete logic-element gate or register element.

Hydraulic and pneumatic gates, flip-flops, etc., have received a limited acceptance for very low speed applications. *Tunnel diodes* have also been proposed for some extremely high speed logic applications. Semiconductor logic devices, however, appear to be the logic of the future and, as a result, the remainder of this book will employ semiconductor logic.

MAGNETIC DEVICES   *chap 7 of Bartee*

Magnetic theory is important in the study of digital devices because many of the components employed are magnetic devices and their operation is explained by magnetic theory. Such devices include the small ferrite toroids that make up a typical memory plane, or the recording–read heads employed to transfer data to and from a magnetic tape, magnetic drum, or disk file. Magnetic logic elements were mentioned earlier, but their use is receiving less support now because of rapid solid state developments.

To demonstrate the behavior of a magnetic material sample, consider a ring of the material which is wound with several turns of wire, as shown in Figure 6-6. A current in the coil produces a magnetic flux, as shown. According to electrical theory, the current flowing through a wire sets up a magnetic flux at right angles to the wire whose intensity is proportional to the current. The magnetic material has higher permeability and less reluctance to magnetic flux than air. As a result, many more lines of flux form than would if the core were not included. A magnetic form of Ohm's law states in essence that the amount of flux is proportional to the magnetomotive force (ampere-turns) and inversely proportional to the magnetic material reluctance: flux = magnetomotive force/reluctance. Actually the reluctance is a complex quantity that varies with the current level, the frequency of current reversals, and a characteristic called *permeability*. Permeability is a term defining the reluctance of the material at low flux densities. The higher the permeability the lower the reluctance. Magnetomotive force is generally specified in terms of the product of the current (amperes) times the number of turns of wire in the coil. Flux is specified in terms of lines of flux or in terms of flux density, lines per square centimeter, etc. Permeability is often defined as the ratio of the lines of flux, when a nonsaturated sample of magnetic material forms the path, divided by the number of lines that would form if the path were air. The reluctance of the toroid core is much lower than air. When current flows in the coil, a high flux density is produced, saturating the core.

By cycling the current through the coil first positive then negative, a plot of the core flux versus the magnetomotive force (proportional to current) can be obtained, as shown in Fig. 6-7a. This plot, called a *hysteresis loop,* is representative of the core's flux characteristics, and its

general shape and limits tells a great deal about how the material will perform under bidirectional current flow. An example is furnished by Fig.
6-7a. This basic diagram has been used for many years by the designers of
heavy electrical equipment such as transformers, motors, and generators.

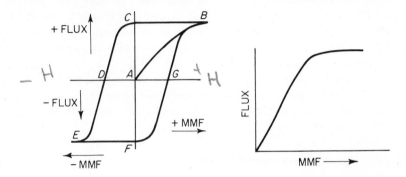

FIG. 6-7a Hysteresis curve.   **FIG. 6-7b** Magnetization curve
(magnetic flux versus magnetiz-
ing current).

When a magnetic sample is first magnetized, a plot of the actual flux
against the current through the winding is linear for a current near zero,
but then as the current increases the flux change per unit current increase
becomes less and less. When this phenomenon predominates the material
has reached a region of flux saturation. A typical magnetization curve
showing this saturation action is given by Fig. 6-7b. Flux builds up if the
material was at first in a completely unmagnetized state, i.e., under no
previous magnetic influence. Once a material has been magnetized initially
it does not retrace the initial path of Fig. 6.7a. In Fig. 6-7a when the initial
magnetizing current is reduced to zero the flux returns to C not point A,
the starting point. Point C represents the remaining flux in the core when
the magnetizing current returns to zero. It is called the *positive remanent
point* or simply *positive remanence*. To reduce the remanence flux to zero
the current must be made negative to point D. If the negative current is
increased to point E, the core is at negative saturation, and just as before
if the negative current is permitted to return to zero, a negative remanence
point F is reached on the curve. Continuing the positive current the flux
again reaches zero at point G, and the core again reaches a positive saturation at point B as in the first positive current excursion. This completes
a full cycle of the hysteresis loop; the sample has gone through during one
alternation of an a-c cycle of current.

The shape of a hysteresis loop is unique with the type of magnetic alloy
material used for the core. One way to explain the behavior of a mag-

netic material is to assume it is composed of elemental magnets. In the unmagnetized state these magnets are oriented in random fashion. As the magnetomotive force (mmf) builds across a region, more and more of these elemental magnets leave their random initial positions and align themselves in the direction of the force field, until, at saturation, substantially all these elements are aligned. This theory is generally supported by the observations of the crystalline domain structure existing in thin magnetic films. The domains can be observed to shift their alignment as the magnetic force intensifies.

Where a magnetic element is to be employed to store a point of data ("1" or "0"), the core should possess what is called a *square hysteresis loop* such as in Fig. 6-8a. The high saturation level is the important fea-

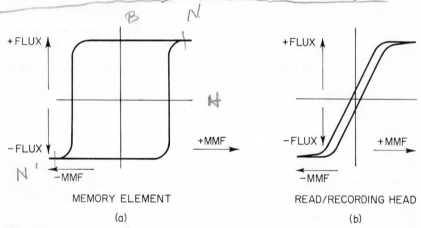

MEMORY ELEMENT
(a)

READ/RECORDING HEAD
(b)

FIG. 6-8 Hysteresis loop for a memory element and for a magnetic read–recording head.

ture. A "1" is stored by saturating the core in one direction, while a "0" is stored by saturating the core in the *other* direction. The flux that remains (residual magnetism) is the *storage medium*. Storage of data is achieved by pulsing the core past the knee (point N or point N'). A read-out of the stored data is achieved by pulsing it a second time past point N'. To read out a core, a second wire must thread the core. This wire is termed the *sense* winding. When a sensing pulse is applied to the data core, if a "1" has been originally stored, the sensing pulse past N' will cause a reversal of saturating flux. This reversal of saturation causes an instant reversal of flux linking the sense winding, and results in a pulse of current in this winding. If an "0" has been stored, the flux reversal during sensing does not occur; hence, the stored data here can be recognized to be "0" because no appreciable pulse of current has occurred in the sense winding.

Two important observations remain to be made. First of all, when pulsing a core to change its saturation state, the core-current pulse amplitude (mmf) must exceed the knee. Otherwise, if the current amplitude is less than the knee, the saturation condition will remain as it was. Secondly, the windings which carry the saturating current are not windings at all, usually, but merely a single wire (or dual wires) that threads through the hole in the toroid. The toroids employed are very small, often with an outer diameter on the order of 30 thousandths of an inch.

A different situation exists when considering the best magnetic material to use for a read–recording head. Here a high permeability (but low retentivity) and a high saturation level is desirable. The high saturation flux level means that a high flux level can be built up in the material; therefore, the lines of flux that protrude into the recording gap will tend to be high. This leads to a head that records efficiently. The permeability should also be high so that weak fluxes during readback will be sensed by the gap effectively. A low retentivity prevents the head's assuming a permanent magnetic bias or set. A material that would perform well in a head application should have a hysteresis loop as shown in Figure 6-8.

For more detail on magnetic theory on both a scientific and engineering level, the student is referred to established texts.

BASIC DESIGN OF LOGIC CIRCUITS

Generally speaking, the logic designer is not interested in the details of logic construction providing it has the correct levels, proper polarity, sufficient speed, etc. He relies upon the circuit designer to provide logic elements to meet his specifications and needs.

The logic symbols in MIL-STD-806B define the *function* rather than construction of the logic circuit. However, a major portion of a digital system design consists of designing the logic, in other words, *interconnecting* the elementary blocks to form a system. The logic designer is concerned with system economy and uses a Boolean function, Veitch diagram, or Karnaugh chart to determine the minimum number of digital circuit (AND gates, OR gates, etc.) blocks required.

One additional point on logic representation must be stated. Logical representation of numbers usually exists in one of two basic forms, *level* logic or *pulse* logic. Three examples of representing the number 11010110 in serial form are given in Fig. 6-9. In pulse logic, the "1" and "0" are represented by the existence or nonexistence of a pulse in a particular position. If the voltage excursion is between ground and a positive voltage, the logic is defined as *positive pulse logic*. It makes no difference whether either the "1" or the "0" is defined as the existence of the pulse. Likewise,

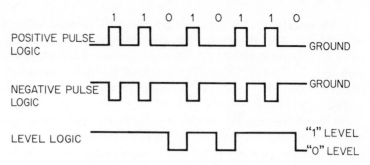

FIG. 6-9 Types of logic representation (pulse or level logic).

negative pulse logic is recognized as being a pulse excursion between ground and a negative voltage level.

On the other hand, level logic differs from pulse logic in that the level itself defines whether the bit is a "1" or "0." Changes in level occur only when going from a "1" to a "0" or vice versa. (Level logic can also be defined as negative or positive, or it can straddle ground.)

Inverter

The inverter is a primary logic element (universally required). This element performs the inversion function by converting A to $\bar{A}$ or vice versa. A transistor inverter is illustrated in its most elementary form in Fig. 6-10. The inverter is a single transistor stage whose output is the inversion

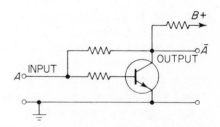

FIG. 6-10 The inverter circuit.

of the input. A positive level input will cause the transistor to conduct heavily via the emitter-collector path through the collector resistor. The collector will saturate to a voltage level slightly positive from ground. A negative level input, on the other hand, will cause the transistor emitter-collector current to cut off; hence, the collector voltage will now approach that of V_{cc}, since no appreciable current can flow through the resistor.

The inverter is necessary in order to invert function variables for level logic as discussed previously. In early AND–OR diode logics, dual inverters in tandem were employed as amplifiers. NAND–NOR logics have their own built-in power amplifiers; hence, separate power amplifiers would be redundant. Inverters for pulse logic will make use of *inhibit gates*—to be discussed later in this chapter.

It should be pointed out that logic modules rarely use combinations of vacuum tube and transistors. Presently the combinations of transistors and diodes or tubes and diodes are the most common arrangements, exclusive of integrated circuits or their extensions.

Consider the circuit design of the inverter used for level logic. It must be designed in such a way that it will provide a signal at the output of opposite polarity to that at the input at the time. As an example, if a "1" at the input is represented by $+10$ volts and a "0" by 0 volts, the output for the inverter is ideally zero volts when the "1" is at the input and $+10$ volts when the input is zero volts.

Ideally, it is desirable that logic levels be precisely defined as zero volts and 10 volts. However, in any practical system a tolerance must be assigned to each logic level. This may amount to ± 1 volt. In our example, a "1" is represented by a voltage level of $+9$ to $+11$ volts, and a "0" is represented by $+1$ to -1 volt. Any voltage level between the limits of $+1$ and $+9$ volts has no logical meaning and is likely to indicate a faulty circuit.

OR Gates

A basic element of any computer logic is the OR gate. As previously shown, this device gives an output if one or any combination of its inputs is actuated to the "1" level. Its use in a logic circuit is to *isolate* one input from another, i.e., to prevent the sources from affecting one another. As shown in Fig. 6-11, the diode circuit has a positive output if one, two, or all of the input lines are made positive.

The diode has low impedance in the forward-biased direction when driven positive on its input, which causes the top of R_1 to go positive. When this point is at a positive level, it cuts off all other diodes in the gate. Through the high back impedance of the other diodes, this effect isolates all other input sources. The OR gate, therefore, provides an additional state function of isolating each source from the other.

NOR Gates

Transistor gate circuits operate on the principle that the collectors are isolated from the base by a relatively large impedance; hence, interaction back to each source will be relatively slight and unimportant. A transistor circuit performing the NOR function is illustrated in Fig. 6-12. In the absence of any input signal, the output is at a positive voltage level, or "1." Any single "1" input at the base is sufficient to cause the respective

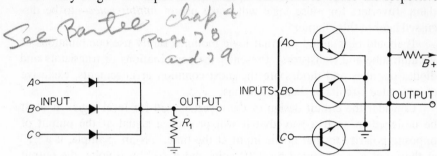

FIG. 6-11   The diode OR gate.   FIG. 6-12   The transistor NOR gate.

transistor circuit to conduct and thereby give a "0"-level output. Consider the collective output. A positive output will be obtained only when *A*, *B*, and *C* are all cut off. Any other condition of input will give a ground or low level on the output. Hence, this circuit serves as a NOR gate for positive logic (or NAND gate for negative logic).

AND Gate

The AND gate performs the operation of detecting a coincidence of two or more signals. In fact, *all* inputs must be turned-on in coincidence before an output is generated. A circuit using positive signals or pulses for its operation is illustrated in Fig. 6-13. Again, the diode version, a very popular form, is shown for the AND circuit.

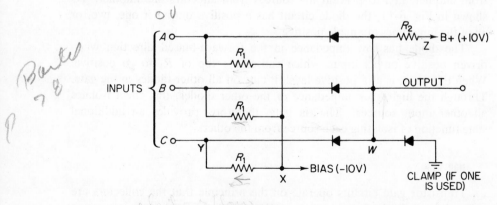

FIG. 6-13   Diode AND gate.

For the diode AND gate shown in Fig. 6-13, assume that "0" is represented by zero volts and "1" by +10 volts. Consider the electron flow from X to Y to W to Z. This shows that all diodes are conducting in the absence of input signals at A, B, and C. The resistor R_1 equals R_2, and the diode has a small forward resistance in its normal conducting state. Point W (the output) is at ground potential (zero volts) since the voltage drop across R_1 equals the drop across R_2.

The output will stay at zero volts even if one input is forced positive, because, as the input goes positive, the diode associated with that input is cut off. The output is still held in the zero condition essentially by the current flow in the remaining conducting diodes. Only when *all* inputs go positive will a valid "1" output be generated. In a practical gate circuit the resistance of R_1 is made lower than that of R_2. A clamp diode is included which sets the negative level that can occur on the output. The circuit is designed so that the clamp will always draw current and this "sets" the negative level of the gate output. In Fig. 6-13 this level is ground, or zero volts. In the transistor version of this circuit, the forward-biased base–emitter diode serves as the negative clamp. In the logic previously described in this chapter, a clamp level of ground is probably a good choice.

NAND Gate

A transistorized NAND gate using PNP transistors is shown in Fig. 6-14. Recall that the operation of a PNP transistor is the reverse of the NPN

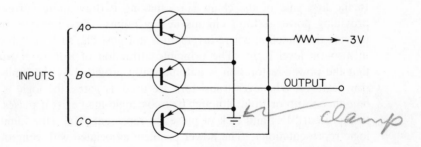

FIG. 6-14   The transistor NAND gate.

transistor employed in the NOR gate. Conduction of the transistor occurs with a negative input signal level on the base. Therefore, a positive going output occurs whenever any transistor conducts, and the output is positive for any "1" input signal. The output is negative whenever *all* inputs are high (all "1"). Hence, this circuit gives the NAND function for positive logic (or NOR function for negative logic).

A special type of AND gate called an *inhibit gate* is often used. It is like a normal AND gate and operates as such except when an inhibit signal occurs. The inhibit signal blocks the normal AND gate operation whenever it appears, thereby cutting off the gate's normal function. For the diode AND gate described, the normal or inhibited input would be positive at the input diode when no inhibit action is required. This input becomes negative when an inhibit is required. A normal AND gate with an inverter on the input inhibit channel is a common way to construct inhibit gates. Although the term *inhibit gate* is not as widely used as formally, it still describes a function that logic designers employ gates to accomplish.

Compound Gates

AND gates and OR gates are very seldom used by themselves. Most often they occur in combination, and many times there is more than one layer of gating (as is common for most Boolean function representation). For instance, $AB + CD$ is a two-level logic. This infers serial or successive gating. Where gates are used in succession, it is often necessary to stack them, such as AND–OR–AND and OR–AND–OR. Consideration must be given to the timing of signals through these chains, so that proper coincidence is maintained.

Another consideration is the power levels. Gates that drive other gates must have the necessary power capabilities. For instance, in an AND–OR–AND sequence of diode gates, the first gate must be able to drive the last AND gate. The necessary power is obtained either by adding more power to the first gate of the chain (i.e., making it draw more current) or by providing power-restorer circuits at key points. Two inverters in tandem provide this function where inversion is not possible, such as that occurring in AND–OR level logic. The principle attraction of NOR or NAND logic is that the power restoration is automatically provided by the built-in inversion feature. Whenever transistors are used as gates, the logic is likely to be either NAND or NOR, although AND–OR logic may exist if pulses are used to represent "1's" and lack of pulses to represent "0's" (the familiar pulse logic representation). The power problem associated with compound gates is therefore restricted primarily to AND–OR diode logic and is another reason for other logic systems having superseded diode logic.

THE FLIP-FLOP STORAGE ELEMENTS

Constructing logic for a digital device requires a variety of elements other than gates. It may be necessary to store a digit for a period of time. For instance, a memory cell essentially stores a bit until it is needed in a transfer or arithmetic operation. Some high-speed memory devices (e.g., a register) may make use of a storage device called a *flip-flop*.

Flip-flop is the general name for a circuit which exhibits either of two stable states and has two complementary outputs. When one output is positive, the other is negative, and vice versa. The state to which the circuit adheres is chosen by triggering either one of two inputs (defined as the *set* and *reset*). The diagram for a flip-flop is given in Fig. 6-15.

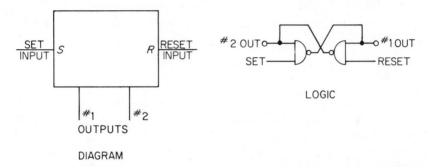

FIG. 6-15   Set-reset (*R-S*) flip-flop.

Normally the flip-flop circuit is completely symmetrical. If the circuit receives a set signal (often a pulse), it will assume a condition with output 2 positive, say +10 volts. At the same time, output 1 will be zero volts. When the circuit receives a reset pulse, side 1 will become +10 volts and side 2 will become zero volts. The circuit is said to be set in the first instance and reset in the second position. A set circuit receiving a set trigger remains indefinitely in the set position. A similar situation occurs on the reset side. This particular type of flip-flop is called an *R-S* (reset-set) *flip-flop*.

The logic element described previously as the basic flip-flop circuit is only one of several varieties of flip-flop. Another important type often used is called a *toggle circuit*. This circuit changes state whenever a pulse appears at its single input. Effectively, a toggle action is obtained by pulsing the set and reset inputs of a normal flip-flop simultaneously. In any practical circuit, steering diodes added in series with an *R* or *S* lead and connected together at the toggle input point permit the common pulsing of *R* and *S*. In some designs the toggle pulse is injected to a point common to the two-stage transistors in another way. In any case, the circuit is so designed that a pulse at the diode junction, just described, or other common point, causes it to reverse its state, i.e., toggle.

Flip-Flop Circuit

Figure 6-16 is a schematic diagram of a transistor and discrete component flip-flop circuit suitable for computer applications. This circuit is characterized by a clock input which allows the circuit to change state only at the end of the clock pulse.

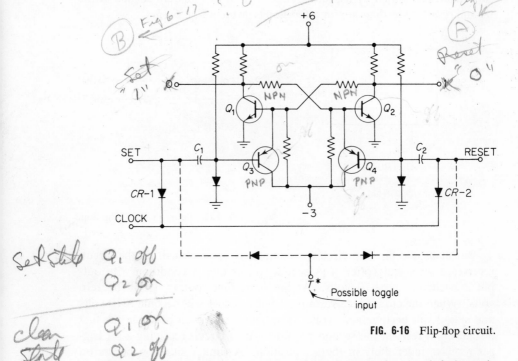

FIG. 6-16 Flip-flop circuit.

If the circuit is operating so that Q_1 is turned on, the circuit balance is such that Q_2 will be turned off. This is the normal way a flip-flop behaves, i.e., one side is turned on when the other is off. The bias generated by the cross-coupling network ensures this condition.

When the set line is made positive, the clock pulse line (at 0 volts) prevents the charging of capacitor C_1. When the clock pulse appears, C_1 charges through CR-1. At the end of the clock pulse, C_1 discharges, which generates a negative pulse that turns on Q_3 and drives the base of Q_1 negative. This turns off Q_1 and turns on Q_2. In other words, Q_1 and Q_2 reverse their functions. If the set line had not become positive, the charge–discharge cycle on C_1 would not occur and the circuit would remain in its previous condition.

The identical operation occurs on the reset side when the reset line is made positive and C_2 is permitted to go through a charge–discharge cycle.

This type of switching is typical of modern semiconductor flip-flops. Any noise occurring on the set or reset lines is ineffective in triggering the circuit, except during the unlikely time of the clock pulse interval.

The Family of Flip-Flops

Although logically the flip-flop can be represented as two NOR or NAND gates connected back to back, in reality they are much more complex devices. As a brief description of the usual members of the flip-flop family, the following types of flip-flops are defined (a tabular summary is given in Fig. 6-17).

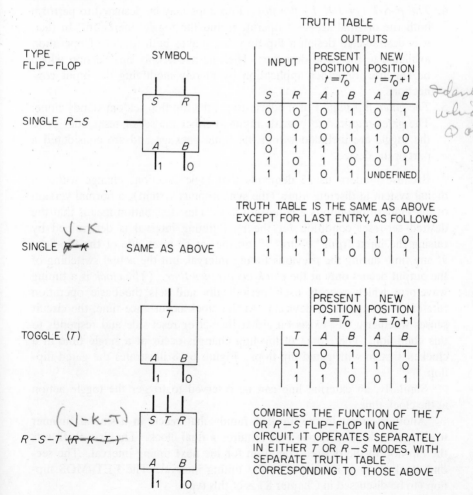

FIG. 6-17 Summary of flip-flop types.

1. *R-S flip-flop.* This device is the elementary two-way switch described in the introduction to flip-flops. It may be set or reset by a pulse at the appropriate input. If a set and reset pulse occurs simultaneously, the output is equally likely to assume either polarity; there is no way to predict exactly which way the circuit will set.
2. *The T flip-flop (Toggle).* This flip-flop has one input that toggles whenever there is an input pulse. (Its action was explained previously.)
3. *The J-K flip-flop.* The circuit behaves similarly to the *R-S* flip-flop, except that the circuit toggles when both a set and reset pulse occur simultaneously and thereby changes its polarity to the opposite of what it had been.
4. *The R-S-T (or J-K-T) flip-flop.* Flip-flops may be designed to perform both the original set-reset operation and the toggle operation. In fact, it is desirable to design a flip-flop that makes both modes of operation available to the logic designer. Then he needs only one version which he can use for either application by merely modifying the input connections.
5. *The gated flip-flop.* For modern usage, the flip-flop seldom stands alone. The gates required to provide input to either the set or reset sides or to the toggle are included within the same package and are considered a part of the device.

Because modern usage demands that logic functions change within a digital system at discrete times (the synchronous system), a normal version of the modern flip-flop is a *gated flip-flop.* This designation means that the desired set-reset condition for the next timing interval is determined by raising the input from "0" to "1" on the set or reset side of the flip-flop; at any time during the previous timing interval, but the actual switching of the output occurs only at the *clock occurrence time.* (The *clock* is a timing waveform which repeats itself periodically and sets the basic operation rate of the computer or device.) At the clock occurrence time, the circuit senses whether a "1" exists on either the set or reset side and responds to this condition. Therefore, all flip-flop changes occur at a single time in a clocked system with gated flip-flops. Figure 6-18 illustrates the gated flip-flop.

Similarly, an external line can be reserved to trigger the toggle action at the clock time.

Another circuit in the flip-flop family that reacts in a similar manner to the gated flip-flop is one that requires a dual clock. The first clock sets the flip-flop to the desired condition for the next timing interval. The second clock triggers its output at the timing interval. The FET–MOS flip-flop (to be discussed in Chapter 8) is of this type.

Other variations in flip-flops include the version that has a separate in-

TRUTH TABLE

SYMBOL

CLOCK –
CONTROL
FLIP – FLOP

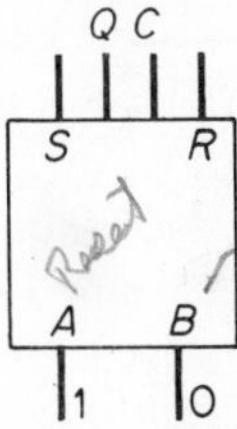

INPUTS CLOCK				PRESENT POSITION $t = T_0$		NEW POSITION $t = T_0 + 1$	
S	R	C	Q	A	B	A	B
1	0	1	0	1	0	1	0
1	0	1	1	1	0	0	1
0	1	1	0	0	1	0	1
0	1	1	1	0	1	1	0

NOTE: THE CIRCUIT ONLY CHANGES AT CLOCK TIME
($C = 1$) THE INPUT Q DETERMINES
IF THE CIRCUIT WILL RESPOND TO
R AND S WHEN $C = 1$

FIG. 6-18   Gated flip-flop.

put available for determining whether or not the flip-flop is to set or to reset (or react to other inputs). Whenever this second input Q is "1," the circuits respond as would a normal flip-flop. If Q is "0," it is unaffected by changes at R, S, or T inputs.

OTHER LOGIC CIRCUITS

One-Shot Multivibrator

This logic element controls the timing of an output by the internal design of the circuit. It can be designed to give:

1. a gating pulse of controlled length;
2. a lengthened or stretched pulse; or
3. an output pulse that is delayed for a time interval built into the circuit.

These three types are shown in Fig. 6-19.

The basic one-shot multivibrator circuit is illustrated in Fig. 6-20. The design allows Q_2 to conduct current normally via the emitter–collector path. When the circuit is at rest, Q_1 is cut off by the bias on its base. The change of status of this circuit occurs suddenly when a positive going pulse appears at the Q_1 base. This action causes a sudden conduction by Q_1 and a resulting drop in its collector voltage level. Capacitor C_1 couples this voltage drop to the base of Q_2, and the Q_2 collector current flow now cuts off. This causes the voltage on the Q_2 collector to rise immediately to V_{cc}. In the process of transferring the voltage drop from the collector of Q_1 to the base of Q_2 via C_1, the capacitor C_1 assumes a charge.

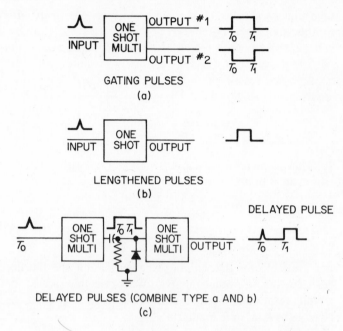

FIG. 6-19 Uses of one-shot multivibrators.

The only way for C_1 to lose the charge is for it to dissipate through R_1. This requires a period of time proportional to five times the time constant R_1C_1. As the charge in C_1 discharges, the time is eventually reached when

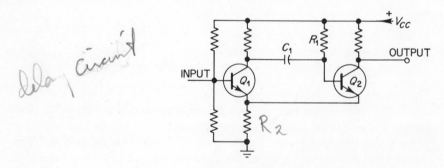

FIG 6-20 One-shot multivibrator circuit.

the bias on Q_2 is too low to hold Q_2 in a nonconducting condition. When this occurs, Q_2 restores its conduction mode and the collector voltage returns to its low point. This last step completes the cycle. The period of time that Q_2's collector remains positive is the *delay interval* of the one-shot multivibrator. Q_1 cuts off at the time Q_2 starts to conduct because the voltage level rise at R_2 effectively biases Q_1 off again.

The accuracy of the delay is normally about 5 to 10 per cent. This can be improved by use of clocking pulse injection, but basically these circuits are used only when a large tolerance in the delay can be tolerated.

Free-Running Multivibrator

This element is a variation of the one-shot element just described. However, it operates in a free-running mode and requires no input pulse to trigger it into operation. The circuit oscillates at a frequency dependent upon values of components used in its internal design. The output is a square wave. If designed to be compatible with the previous gates, this level will alternate between zero and 10 volts.

The free-running multivibrator is not a precision circuit, and its frequency may vary as much as 20 per cent with temperature changes, voltage variations, etc. Its use is restricted to special situations such as the generation of a square wave continuous waveform as in a square-wave oscillator or voltage calibrator. It is generally used in generating nonprecise timing signals in computers.

Other circuit types, such as blocking oscillators, also generate timing waveforms and may be employed in the same manner as free-running multivibrators.

The free-running multivibrator is shown in Fig. 6-21. Essentially, it

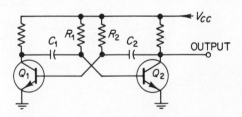

FIG. 6-21 Free-running multivibrator circuit.

is an oscillatory flip-flop circuit with each transistor conducting alternately. The time-constant product of R_1C_1 sets the cutoff time on Q_2, whereas the product R_2C_2 sets the cutoff time on Q_1. These particular networks charge and discharge in the same manner as on the one-shot circuit previously described, and the output is a square wave.

Delay Element

Delay lines that delay a pulse for a fixed period of time are very useful
in many applications. When delay lines are combined with gates they can
widen pulses, shorten pulses, generate many pulses from a single pulse, or
decode pulse patterns. A more direct logic application is a pulse that may
be delayed one clock-pulse period or an integral number of clock-pulse periods. To accomplish this delay function, a flip-flop is often combined with
gates and possibly a small delay element (such as a delay line). For example, consider how one might use a flip-flop to delay an output pulse one
clock period later than an input pulse. A circuit logic that would perform
this function is illustrated by Fig. 6-22. Pulse 1 on the pulse input sets the

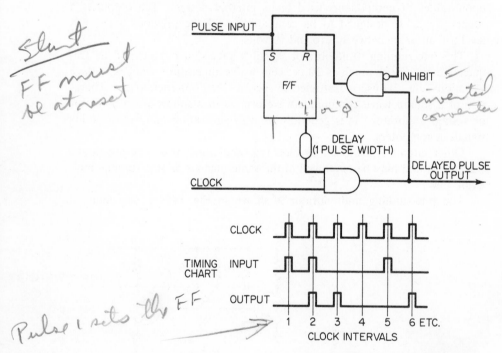

FIG. 6-22   Flip-flop used as a delay element.

flip-flop. Setting the flip-flop opens the AND gate and allows the clock pulse
(delayed one pulse period from input pulse 1) to pass through the gate to
the output. This is now delayed pulse 1. This pulse is gated via the inhibit gate to the flip-flop's reset side, and will reset the flip-flop if the next
pulse (input pulse 2) is a "0." If pulse 2 is a "1" the reset pulse is pre-
vented (inhibited) from resetting the flip-flop. As a result the output pulse

train is identical to the input pulse train but delayed one clock period. The delay element at the flip-flop output prevents a partial clock pulse to slip through the gate as the flip-flop sets. A gated flip-flop could be employed here so that no delay element would be necessary.

Interface Circuits

Normally, the logic of one circuit design will not match that of another. A variety of circuits may be required to fit (or, in computer parlance, *to interface*) one logic system to another. Pulses must be lengthened, shortened, inverted in polarity, or changed in level, and these requirements can occur in any combination. Quite often the impedances in the two interfacing systems are completely different. At times, the one-shot multivibrator is used to lengthen a pulse, or an inverter is used to reverse polarity. Circuits that can change levels are provided when needed. Unless the complete interface between the two systems is known, the design of these circuits is difficult and uncertain. Engineers for both systems must confer freely to establish a reasonable series of interface coupling circuits.

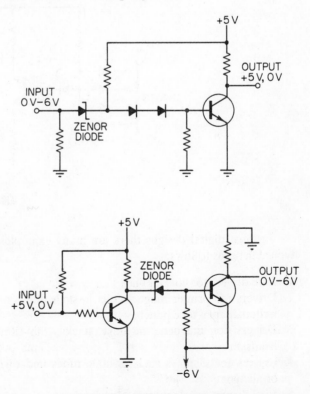

FIG. 6-23 Typical level change circuits.

An illustration of typical interface circuits called *level changers* is shown by Fig. 6-23. Their operation depends on the use of a *zener* diode. The *zener* diode has the ability to maintain a fixed voltage drop across itself over a wide current range and, hence, will serve well in a level-change application, as illustrated in the figure.

Driver Circuits

Driver circuits are a class of adjunct circuits necessary to augment logic circuits in any physical hardware program. When matched coaxial cables are employed between cabinets, the impedance level of such cables may be 50 to 100 ohms. To drive a pulse or logic level (+10 volts) through such a line requires 1 watt of peak power (10 volts through 100 ohms). A logic element such as a flip-flop may not be able to supply this amount of power, so special driver circuits (power boosters) are provided. A NAND gate with a line-driver output stage is shown in Fig. 6-24.

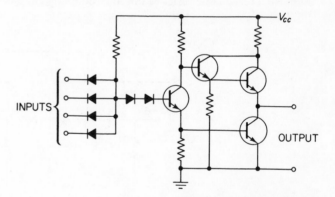

FIG. 6-24 Line-driver circuit.

In most digital designs there are many examples of special drivers. A typical list is as follows:

1. Line drivers for coaxial lines
2. Drivers for printer magnet coils in such things as digital printers, type-writers, paper-tape punches
3. Drivers for magnetic memory stacks, thin-film memories, recording heads, etc.
4. Drivers for displays such as nixie tubes and digital numerical displays of all types
5. Line drivers for clock-pulse distributors

These circuits come under the general classification of *output interface circuits*.

Input Circuits

Since inputs from equipment outside the computer must be used, there are areas where input analog signals must be converted to logic levels if a digital system is used. It is hard to define the needed circuits unless the circumstances are known, but such a typical circuit would be a *level detector*. Such a circuit assumes a positive, or "1," logic state, if the input threshold level is exceeded. Below this level the circuit is in the opposite, or "0," state. After exceeding the specified level and going into the positive state, the circuit remains in this state until the input level drops below the original threshold, at which time it returns to the "0" state. A typical circuit is shown in Fig. 6-25.

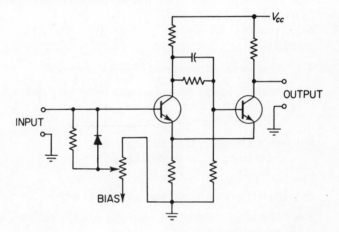

FIG. 6-25   Level-sensor circuit.

Another typical circuit of this kind is the read amplifier required to read the output of a recording head, a magnetic memory core, or a thin-film memory. This class includes circuits required to read photoelectric cells or phototransistor outputs from a paper-tape reader or the outputs from photoelectric cell–sensed punched cards.

SUMMARY

In conclusion, it should be noted that the elements discussed in this chapter are generally used in all logic systems whether they are tube, transistor, magnetic core, or other previously mentioned types. Design techniques may vary greatly, but the end result must always be the same. The individual elements must be compatible with each other in a given logic system. The design must be such that elements designed and constructed individually will perform together reliably and not require any individual circuit interfaces between them. The usual spread of production tolerances must not affect reliable operation, nor may the normal circuit noise on grounds, $B+$, or bias supplies. The specified variations of the $B+$ and bias supplies, the specified variation of circuit characteristics with temperature changes, and other specified environmental conditions must not cause circuit failures. In other words, a satisfactory tolerance or safety factor should be designed into all successful logic systems.

REVIEW QUESTIONS AND PROBLEMS

6-1. Trace the development of logic types from the relay to the present LSIC's.

6-2. What are the advantages of FET–MOS devices?

6-3. Compare the operation of a vacuum-tube amplifier with
a. Bipolar transistor.
b. FET–MOS device.

6-4. What is meant by the following terms:
a. Intrinsic.   c. Reversed bias.
b. Bipolar.   d. Junction.

6-5. Explain in your words what a hysteresis loop is.

6-6. What characteristics of a magnetic material make it usable for a memory-storage element.

6-7. What is the utility of the flip-flop circuit? Discuss several versions of the flip-flop. Why is each type useful?

6-8. Explain the operation of a diode AND gate.

6-9. Why is NAND–NOR logic becoming more popular than AND–OR logic?

6-10. From Example 5-4 pick a logic circuit type and draw the circuit diagram for this logic.

6-11. What is the function of interface circuits? Give some examples of interface problems that are likely to exist between two systems.

6-12. Construct a delay circuit using flip-flop, gates, etc., that will delay a serial pulse train two clock intervals.

6-13. Can you propose uses of one-shot multivibrators in a digital device? If so, demonstrate its use(s).

6-14. Design the logic which will delay a serial-level logic binary train, one clock interval. Assume the clock in this case to be a square wave clock (one complete reversal for each pulse period).

6.5. Hysteresis Loop — a curve showing the magnetic force (flux) in a forward and reverse direction. Looks somewhat like a box with its two opposite corners trailing out. [(saturated). @ −H and +H on the B−H diagram.)]

uses binary addition

$$0 + 0 = 0$$
$$1 + 0 = 1$$
$$0 + 1 = 1$$
$$1 + 1 = 0 \text{ with a carry of } 1$$

Half adder cant add a carry!

check on Half adder

COMBINATIONAL CIRCUITS— THE NEXT HIGHER LEVEL 7

In this chapter, the principles of the past chapters will be demonstrated, and the fundamental logic blocks combined to form the next higher set of logic elements. Basic elements such as the half-adder, full adder, buffer, register, matrix, and counter are described. As in the previous chapters, the discussion is confined to the block diagram (*logic block*) level. In following chapters, actual circuit combinations will be discussed. The reader will be introduced to ways in which transistors, diodes, magnetic cores, etc., are combined to construct the logic elements physically.

THE HALF-ADDER

This element is a fundamental building block composed of three AND gates and a single OR gate. It basically performs approximately one-half of the addition process, and its action can be described by the truth table shown here, in which S refers to a *sum* output and C refers to a *carry* output. Another way of stating its action is to say that it performs elementary binary addition.

$S = \bar{A}B + A\bar{B}$

$C = AB$

Truth table*

binary addition

Inputs		Outputs	
A	B	S	C
0	0	0	0
0	1	1	0
1	0	1	0
1	1	0	1

* NOTE: For this circuit, there are two separate outputs as well as two separate inputs.

As outlined in the previous chapter, the first step is to form the Boolean functions. The two functions are:

$$F(S) = \bar{A}B + A\bar{B} \qquad (7\text{-}1)$$
$$F(C) = AB \qquad (7\text{-}2)$$

The complete circuit (as required by the truth table) can be represented by the logic shown in the Fig. 7-1. The gate combination which

EXCLUSIVE OR

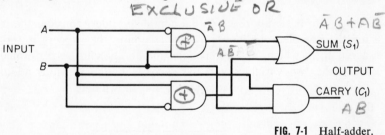

FIG. 7-1   Half-adder.

generates $F(S)$ is employed so often it has a distinctive name. It is called an *exclusive* OR gate.

By connecting two of these circuits, as shown in Fig. 7-2, and incorporating a delay element, a complete adder for performing serial binary addition may be constructed. The first half-adder compares the binary bits of the two 5-bit binary numbers (to be added one bit at a time) beginning with E and continuing at one-bit intervals to A. Whenever the A

and B bits are different, a "1" occurs at S_1. If the A and B bits are the same, a "0" occurs at S_1. If both A and B are "1," a bit at C_1 is also generated. This result is shown in Fig. 7-1 at the output of the first half-adder.

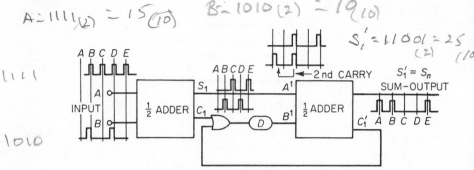

(handwritten annotations) $A = 1111_{(2)} = 15_{(10)}$ $B = 1010_{(2)} = 19_{(10)}$ $S_1' = 11001 = 25_{(2)}$

1111 1010

FIG. 7-2 Two half-adders combined to give a complete adder.

The second half-adder performs the same process once again but on the S_1 and on the carries C_1 and C'_1 ORed together (processed through the OR gate) and delayed one bit time. If the process is carefully checked, one bit at a time, through both half-adders in turn, it will be seen that the total sum is formed at S'_1, as shown in Fig. 7-2.

THE FULL ADDER

As a more basic approach to the complete adder, consider the truth table for the complete addition process, assuming the process is serial binary addition, in which, at a given time, the addition to be performed may include the two variables and the carry from the previous addition. The truth table under these circumstances is as shown here.

(handwritten note: teachers way to make TT)

(handwritten truth table)

A	B	C_{N-1}	S	C
0	0	0	0	0
0	1	0	1	0
1	0	0	1	0
1	1	0	0	1
0	0	1	1	0
0	1	1	0	1
1	0	1	0	1
1	1	1	1	1

A	B	C_{n-1}	S	C_n
0	0	0	0	0
0	0	1	1	0
0	1	0	1	0
0	1	1	0	1
1	0	0	1	0
1	0	1	0	1
1	1	0	0	1
1	1	1	1	1

The C_{n-1} term is the carry from the previous addition process, and C_n is the generated carry for the process being carried out. The Boolean function is written as in previous examples. The only difference is that C_{n-1} is the C_n of the previous summation, delayed one operation. In the case of serial add, C_{n-1} is the binary carry from the previous operation and, in the case of parallel add, the next lower bit carry. For simplicity, the serial case is assumed here. By writing the Boolean function from the truth table,

$$F(S) = \overline{A}\overline{B}C_{n-1} + \overline{A}B\overline{C}_{n-1} + A\overline{B}\overline{C}_{n-1} + ABC_{n-1} \tag{7-3}$$
$$F(C_n) = \overline{A}BC_{n-1} + A\overline{B}C_{n-1} + AB\overline{C}_{n-1} + ABC_{n-1} \tag{7-4}$$

These functions can be used to derive the required circuit directly. But is there any simplification that can be shown? It so happens that the sum term $F(S)$ is not easily reduced; although it may be rearranged to obtain other forms. However, some reduction can be accomplished in the $F(C_n)$ term. For instance, adding ABC_{n-1} twice gives

$$F(C_n) = \overline{A}BC_{n-1} + ABC_{n-1} + A\overline{B}C_{n-1} + AB\overline{C}_{n-1} + ABC_{n-1} + ABC_{n-1}$$

This factors to

$$F(C_n) = (\overline{A} + A)BC_{n-1} + AC_{n-1}(B + \overline{B}) + AB(C_{n-1} + \overline{C}_{n-1})$$
$$F(C_n) = BC_{n-1} + AC_{n-1} + AB$$

The simplified circuit is shown in Fig. 7-3.

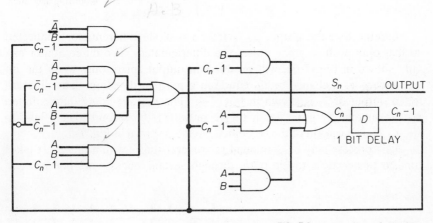

FIG. 7-3 Logic for a full adder.

An interesting exercise of taking equations for the half-adder and applying them to Fig. 7-2 logic is left to the student. If done correctly, the final set of equations for S and C_n will be identical with those found in the ful-adder truth table [Eqs. (7-3) and (7-4)]. The technique is to apply Eqs. (7-1) and (7-2) as the inputs to the second half-adder section.

USE OF FLIP-FLOP STAGES

The section above subtly implied that all switching will not occur at a single instant of time. In other words, present switching events may be influenced by events occurring at previous times. For example, consider the C_{n-1} pulse being applied at C_n time within the serial adder during the binary addition process described in the previous section.

A purely sequential circuit (the binary counter) will now be described. The previous chapter introduced the toggle form of the flip-flop, which has the ability to change state every time an input pulse is applied. Its outputs S_1 and S_2, resulting from a steady stream of input pulses, are shown in Fig. 7-4.

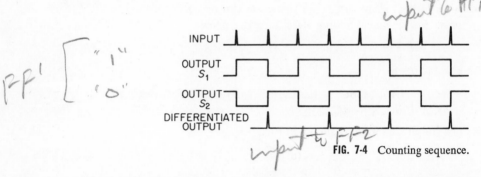

FIG. 7-4   Counting sequence.

Assume that the output S_2 is fed to a diode differentiator connected so that only positive going pulses are differentiated. The differentiator circuit, shown in Fig. 7-6a, will produce an output spike, only when the input undergoes a change in amplitude in a positive direction. The differentiated output of S_2 is shown in Fig. 7-4. The positive going differentiated waveform thereby generates a toggle pulse for the second toggle flip-flop stage. The waveform of the combined circuit is shown in Fig. 7-5.

This process may be continued for several stages within limits. It takes time to propagate a toggle pulse through several stages, and, hence, there

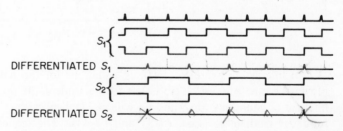

FIG. 7-5   Two toggle circuits in tandem.

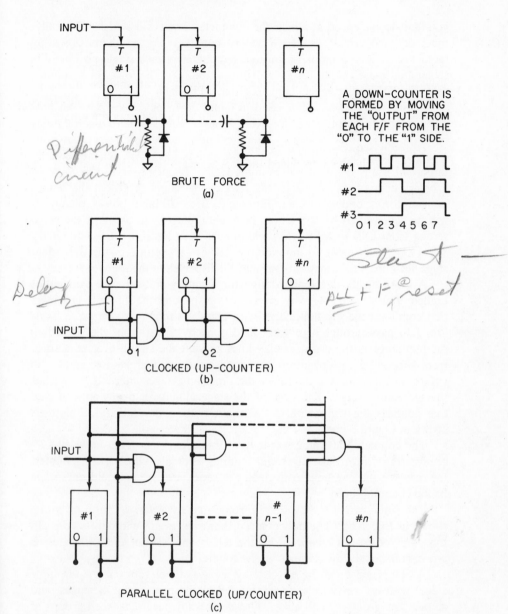

A DOWN-COUNTER IS
FORMED BY MOVING
THE "OUTPUT" FROM
EACH F/F FROM THE
"0" TO THE "1" SIDE.

BRUTE FORCE
(a)

CLOCKED (UP-COUNTER)
(b)

PARALLEL CLOCKED (UP/COUNTER)
(c)

FIG. 7-6 Up counters.

is a limit to the speed at which the complete circuit will switch. Basically, the individual circuit (called a *binary counter*) toggle counts down by factors of 2. For example, a four-stage counter gives a single positive differentiated pulse output for every 16 input pulses. The logic for a counter using the differentiating technique is given in Fig. 7-6a.

Binary counters are often used to count down pulses and give an output pulse at the output stage for every 2^n input pulses (where n is the number of stages). In other words, binary counting is a division operation with a single output occurring every 2^n input pulses ($\frac{1}{2}^n$). A second, equally important use is to count pulses numerically. If one observes the count in a binary counter, the flip-flop states set by the count represent the binary number corresponding to the input count. After 10 input pulses, binary 10 will be represented by the setting of counter stages. Looking at the stage setting from LSB to MSB, they will appear in order as 1 0 1 0—or binary 10. Using neon lights to monitor the "1" or "0" setting of the individual stage flip-flops, the binary number may be displayed to the user.

A more highly developed design for a binary counter, one that is not limited after several stages by the switching speed of the flip-flop, is a logic that combines the flip-flop stages with gates. An input toggle pulse is allowed to pass through AND gates held open by the state of the preceding flip-flop stage in the chain. Delay lines prevent the switch-over of a stage from affecting the propagation of the pulse through the chain of gates. As before, in Fig. 7-6a the output of the preceding stages alternately switches the succeeding stage. The state of the stage inhibits or opens an AND gate that controls the trigger pulse. A counter using the gating technique is shown in Figure 7-6b.

The counters illustrated so far have transferred the count between successive stages in a basically serial manner. For a multiple stage counter, the delay of the clock pulse through the series AND gates would determine its top counting speed.

The gating could be speeded up somewhat by a *parallel* form of gating shown in Fig. 7-6c. The added speed, however, is not without its cost. In this case the cost is measured by the telescoping size of the AND gates as one continues stage by stage down the counter.

A compromise can be effected by using parallel gating for a group of stages with the carry pulse from this fed to the next group of stages, and so on. The groups are all alike. The clock delay occurs between groups of stages rather than at each individual stage.

OTHER TYPES OF COUNTERS

All counters in Fig. 7-6 are examples of *up-counters*. That is, for each pulse counted, the binary number content increases by 1. By interchanging the output of each stage, each counter becomes a downcounter, i.e., each additional pulse counted subtracts 1 from the present sum. By adding the necessary gates (see Fig. 7-7), a counter can be assembled that will count either up or down, depending on which line carries the input pulse.

Counters can also be built so that they do not count through the entire sequence of the numbers available. For instance, Fig. 7-8 illustrates a four-

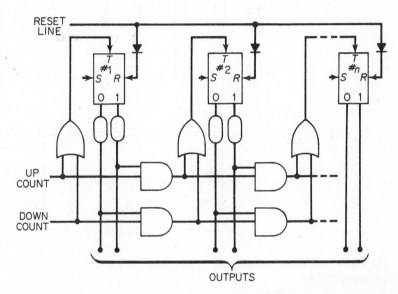

FIG. 7-7 Up-down counter.

bit counter that counts through 10 states. After count 1 1 1 1, the next count is not really a count but a *reset*. The counter is reset to 0 1 1 0 from which it counts in a normal manner until again reaching 1 1 1 1. This four-bit counter therefore counts through 10 states rather than the normal 16, which illustrates a binary counter counting in a decimal fashion. These units may be connected in tandem to count tens, hundreds, etc.

One of the other methods of obtaining counts of 10 from a four-bit binary counter is by resetting to 0 0 0 0 on the next count after 9 (1001). This achieves the same effective result as the one illustrated by Fig. 7-8.

Counters can be made to count any sequence of numbers by adopting this technique of *forced feedback*. Forced feedback means forcing a preset to an assigned count, after reaching a specific count. For example, a counter that counts 12 steps may be derived from a four-bit binary counter by causing a forced reset to four (0 1 0 0) from its 1 1 1 1 count position.

Reset to 0110

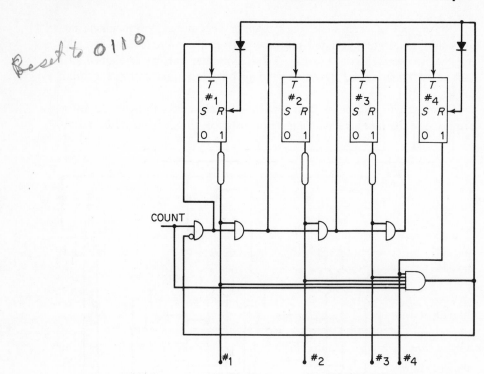

FIG. 7-8 Decimal counter.

Normally, without forced feedback, the count position following 1 1 1 1 would be 0 0 0 0.

Ring Counter

A ring counter is a type of counter that has as many distinct states as there are counting elements. These counters are most often formed by n circuit elements with only one of the n elements turned on at a given time. With every count, the n element turns off and the $n + 1$ element turns on. Usually the end of the counter ties to the beginning so that the counter steps around the circle (or *ring*). For example, a five-element ring counter would count: 1, 2, 3, 4, 5, 1, 2, 3, 4, 5, 1, 2, ..., etc., with only one of the five elements active at any one count.

Ring counters have been constructed of glow tubes, thyratrons, magnetic elements, and the like. They can be constructed by using individual logic elements but often they are made from individual circuit components. A possible design using logic elements is shown in Fig. 7-9; often a selection of the right logic element will make possible a ring-counter design that is simpler than a standard binary counter, especially for low-number

CLOCK

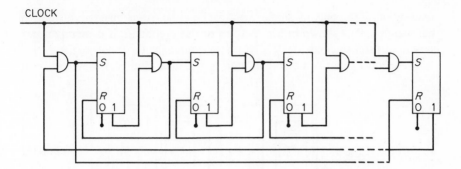

FIG. 7-9   Ring-counter implementation.

counts. Another advantage of the ring counter is that there is no logic required in order to obtain discrete count leads for control applications, as is the case for a binary unit.

BUFFER REGISTER

Assume that a binary counter is counting pulses and it is desired to read the output at specific times yet not to stop the counter from counting pulses. In other words, it is desired to read the counter during operation. A common method of doing this is to read the counter *between* counts and store this number in a device called a *register*. Since the term register refers to many types of storage devices, the device into which the binary counter's contents are dropped is known as a *buffer register,* a device in which a binary number is temporarily stored until it is used in a later process. Therefore, the buffer register is a form of *temporary memory*.

The buffer register–counter is shown in Fig. 7-10. Its logic operates as follows: As the count pulses enter at A, they cause the counter to add in a binary manner. At any time (except when A and B coincide), a clock pulse B may be allowed to pass through the AND gate, which has a positive "1" level, from the associated flip-flop. Of course, A and B must never coincide or chaos will occur, since the counter would be changing counts at the time of A. The B clock pulse passing through the AND gates will cause each buffer stage to align itself to the same position of the corresponding counter stage at the instant of the clock pulse. The counter continues to count, but the captured number remains stationary in the buffer register.

If desired, the buffer may be reset to zero at the beginning of the operation by use of a reset pulse. However, in the case discussed here, since this buffer aligns itself to the counter at the B clock time, a reset is unnecessary. Thus, if a reset pulse is available and can be generated before any read-in of data, only a single AND gate per stage is needed instead of the two per stage shown in Fig. 7-10. For this condition, it is merely necessary to transfer the existing "1's" from the counter to the buffer register.

A second general method of storing a count (buffering) would be to

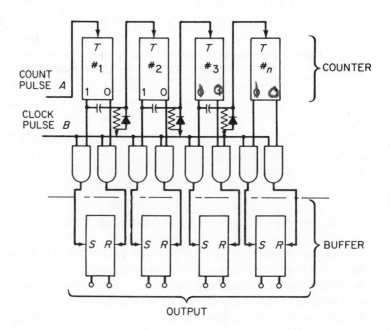

Fig. 7-10   Simple parallel buffer.

use the counter itself as the buffer register. For this type of operation, the input count is first accumulated and then blocked when buffering is desired. The continuing pulse count is shifted to a second counter, while the contents of the first counter are read out, displayed, or otherwise processed. The two counters alternate in function, each serving first as a counter and then as a buffer; hence, no loss in count will occur.

SHIFT REGISTER

The buffers illustrated, although useful, are quite limited. They permit a serial count to be captured, turned into a digital number, and transferred in parallel to other circuits; but this is the extent of their usefulness.

A more general device would be one in which a serial word (not count) could be inserted. Even more general would be a device in which a *serial* word can be entered and the same word shifted out in *parallel*. This, of course, permits a serial word to be made into a parallel word.

A shift register is a device that will accomplish this conversion. In fact, it can be designed to be even more versatile. It is the "gear" box of the computer and will perform any one and all of the following operations:

1. Permit a serial word to be shifted into the register, least significant digit (LSD) first, at one clock frequency, and shift the same word out of the register LSD first at a different clock frequency.
2. Permit a serial word to be shifted into the register LSD first at one clock frequency, and shift it out in parallel on command of a shift (or clock) pulse.
3. Permit a parallel word to be shifted into the register on command of an insert pulse, and shift this word out of the register LSD first in serial at a clock frequency.
4. Provide a planned number of bit shifts in the register either to the left or to the right.

Other operations, such as partial insertion of bits to any part of words, are also possible, but for the moment such specialized applications will be ignored, except to recognize their possibility.

As the reader may guess by now, the shift register is often the device that transfers words between the internal computer and the input–output or between the computer and the memory. As a result, its function is so important that it is used in all types of digital devices.

The shift-register organization is shown in Fig. 7-11. It consists of an array of flip-flops connected by *appropriate* AND and OR gates. To best explain how it works, assume a binary serial word's LSD is at point *A*. On the next clock pulse *B*, the LSD is inserted into the first flip-flop. If the LSD bit is a zero, the flip-flop is set to zero (actually, it stays at zero). If the first bit is a 1, the flip-flop is set to the "1" position. When the second bit appears at *A* one clock time later, it is shifted in the same manner into flip-flop 1. The bit that was in flip-flop 1 is simultaneously transferred to flip-flop 2. At the third bit time, the process is repeated. Both bits now in the first and second flip-flops are simultaneously shifted to the third and fourth flip-flops as the third bit is shifted into the first flip-flop. At every bit time, the bits are shifted. At the tenth bit time, 10 bits are entered in the register, etc. The delay lines shown are a temporary storage that permits the "old" state of the flip-flop to be remembered at the time it is being switched to the "new" condition. If gated flip-flops are employed as shift register stages, the delay is inherent in the circuit and no delay lines are required. Therefore, a gated flip-flop is preferred for this application.

Figure 7-11 shows both the serial input–output and the modification required of each stage to permit parallel transfer input–output. For parallel transfer, each flip-flop is set or reset by the corresponding data bit. This particular design provides for both serial and parallel transfers of data.

The relationship between the ring-counter and the shift–right-shift register is interesting. If a "1" is injected into the first stage of a shift

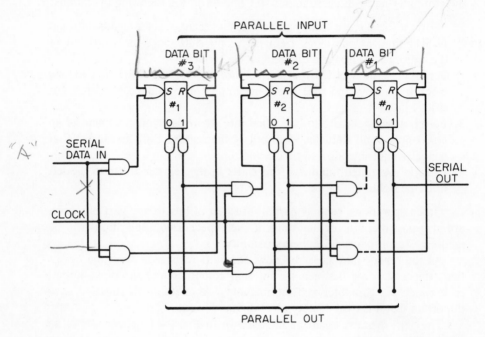

Fig. 7-11   Shift register.

register (all other bits being "0") and the tail of the shift register is hooked to the beginning, successive shift pulses would cause the "1" to progress around the resulting ring in the manner of a ring counter.

COMBINATION OF REGISTERS AND A FULL ADDER

The *full adder* may be combined with two serial shift registers to form a complete system for performing elementary binary addition. This combination is shown in Fig. 7-12. The contents of registers *A* and *B* are shifted sequentially to the input of the full adder. The output of the adder is shifted back through the *A* register on the tail of the original word going through the adder. At the end of a complete word shift through the adder, the new sum is stored in register *A*. This is an example of a fundamental serial adder.

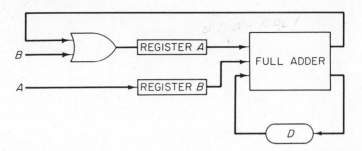

FIG. 7-12 Simple serial adder.

An example of a parallel adder circuit is shown in Fig. 7-13. A parallel adder requires a full adder for each digit to be added. Carries, as required, are generated and circulated in the MSD direction through the circuit. The three registers required to initially store word *A*, word *B*, and the results of the summation are not shown.

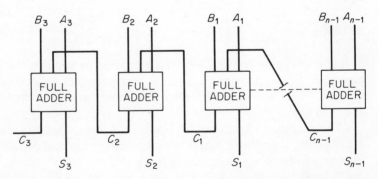

FIG. 7-13 Simple parallel adder.

SERIAL COMPLEMENTER

An interesting use of the flip-flop occurs in the *serial complementer*. This is a circuit that forms the two's complement of a serial binary number as it is passed through the circuit, as shown in Fig. 7-14.

The process starts with the flip-flop resting in the reset state. The number to be complemented starts through the upper AND gate, LSD first. The first and succeeding zeros pass through the upper AND gate unchanged until the first "1" appears. This "1" goes through the upper AND gate unchanged but also sets the flip-flop. From this point, all digits (both "1's" and "0's") are complemented. The lower AND gate now allows the digits

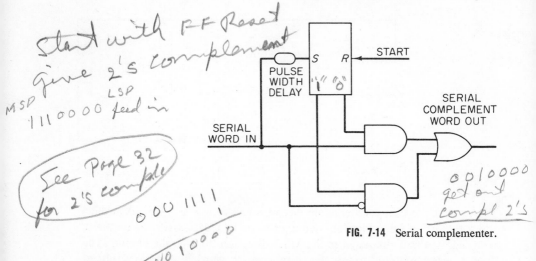

Handwritten notes: Start with F-F Reset — give 2's complement. MSP [down-arrow] LSP 1110000 feed in. MSP, LSP. (See Page 32 for 2's comple) 000 1111. 1010000. 0010000 get out compl 2's.

FIG. 7-14 Serial complementer.

to pass in complemented form, which results in the generation of the "2's" complement of the number.

MATRIX

A useful device to convert one type of coding to another (such as from binary to decimal or vice versa) is a group of gates collectively called a *matrix*. Logic for a matrix, often employed in coding applications, is shown in Fig. 7-15.

The operation of this logic is briefly as follows: Assume that the four flip-flops are acting as a binary counter—they count pulses. The state of the four flip-flops represents the binary count up to this instant. Note that the arrangement of the AND gate along with the inhibits permits outputs only on the 0 to 9 lines, according to the binary count in the counter. For example, the output for the "1" line is obtained when the first stage is "1" and all other stages are "0." An output for line 2 is obtained when stages 1, 3, and 4 are all "0" and stage 2 is "1." The same reasoning applies to all outputs. Therefore, this device truly converts a binary number to a decimal number.

The matrix conversion from a decimal number to a binary number is the reverse of the above, but just as straightforward. The design forces the flip-flops into the corresponding binary code when a digit is energized. One way to do this is shown in Fig. 7-16, which illustrates the conversion of the decimal digits 0 to 9 to binary form.

When more than one decimal digit is involved, it usually means that the binary code must be converted to BCD and then to decimal numbers. Con-

*See Bartel
page 78*

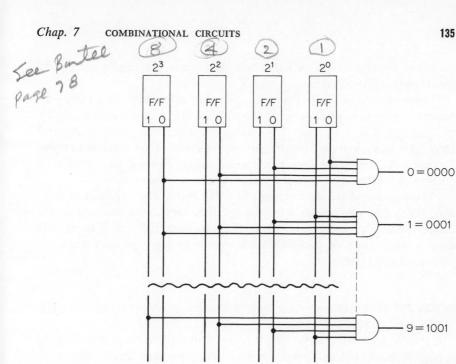

FIG. 7-15 Binary-to-decimal matrix.

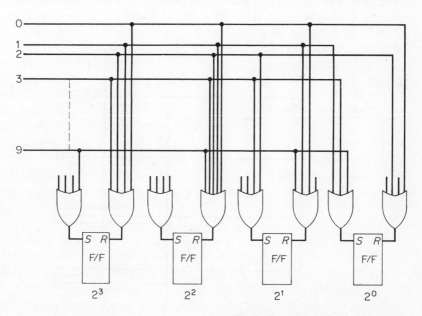

FIG. 7-16 Decimal-to-binary matrix.

sequently, the conversion for multiple digit numbers is generally more complex than that illustrated here.

Matrices may be expanded to any size, but to accomplish a binary-to-decimal conversion without going through the BCD conversion is usually not practical if it is necessary to display the number in multiple decimal form. To make a six-bit binary counter pick one of 64 lines is straightforward. To display 64 lines requires 64 display lights if its matrix is of the type discussed. This type of display is not usually feasible.

Matrices are also used to transform other codes, such as octal to decimal. They find application primarily in input–output sections and in the control section of computers, where they are essentially used to decode display information or provide control signals to other parts of the computer or digital system.

SERIAL DECODER

The matrix is primarily a *parallel decoder,* although with suitable clocking it may be converted to a *serial encoder.* An equivalent device, shown in Fig. 7-17, is sometimes called a *serial decoder.* It makes use of delay lines and will give an output only for the design input code. Naturally, it is used in decoding a portion of a serial digital word, as well as in decoding order

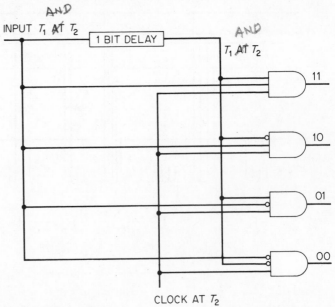

FIG. 7-17   Two-bit decoder.

(command) words in the control section. Briefly, depending on the sequence of digits, the circuit gives outputs on separate lines. For any code sequence, only one output is true. The output indication occurs at the time of pulse 2.

TO DESIGN A COUNTER FOR AN ARBITRARY COUNT

A counter for binary counting is not the only type of counter that can be designed. Counters that subtract as well as add are quite common and are called *up-down counters*. An up-down counter was previously shown in Fig. 7-7.

A more general term for circuits that change their state with time is *sequential circuits*. Such circuits are designed by considering each individual state in the sequence. Each change in state is considered in detail, and the overall circuit is designed to proceed step by step in the desired sequence of operation.

There are more sophisticated methods to accomplish this, but the discussion here will be limited to the so-called "brute-force approach." To understand this approach, consider a counter that will count (rather than the usual binary sequence of 000, 001, 010, 011, etc.) as follows:

$$
\begin{array}{c}
0\ 0\ 0 \\
0\ 1\ 1 \\
0\ 1\ 0 \\
1\ 0\ 1 \\
1\ 1\ 0 \\
0\ 0\ 0
\end{array}
$$

A table is drawn relating the state in which the counter is set at any particular time to the state at which it is to go during the next cycle. This method then permits one to "brute-force" the counter from its present state to the next desired state. The existing position of the flip-flop always guides the clock pulses in such a way as to set up the next state.

The following assumptions are made:

1. A "0" set means the counter stage is *reset*.
2. A "1" set means the counter stage is *set*.

The following sequence is then specified by the Table 7-1. Check this against the above tabulation of required counting. Starting at 000 and designating the counter stages as *A*, *B*, and *C*, it is now possible to tabulate the set and reset conditions through which the system must proceed.

TABLE 7-1

State n	State n + 1	S_A	R_A	S_B	R_B	S_C	R_C
000	→ 011			×		×	
011	→ 010						×
010	→ 101	×			×	×	
101	→ 110		×				×
110	→ 000	–	×		×		

Table 7-1 can be redrawn with the actual settings of the flip-flop replacing the crosses as shown in Table 7-2.

TABLE 7-2

	S_A	R_A	S_B	R_B	S_C	R_C
000			$\overline{A}\overline{B}\overline{C}$		$\overline{A}\overline{B}\overline{C}$	
011						$\overline{A}BC$
010	$\overline{A}B\overline{C}$			$\overline{A}B\overline{C}$	$\overline{A}B\overline{C}$	
101			$A\overline{B}C$			$A\overline{B}C$
110		$AB\overline{C}$		$AB\overline{C}$		

Now a tabulation can be made of the resets and sets for each side of each flip-flop, as follows:

$$S_A = \overline{A}B\overline{C} \qquad\qquad R_A = AB\overline{C}$$
$$S_B = \overline{A}\overline{B}\overline{C} + A\overline{B}C \qquad\qquad R_B = \overline{A}B\overline{C} + AB\overline{C}$$
$$S_C = \overline{A}\overline{B}\overline{C} + \overline{A}B\overline{C} = \overline{A}\overline{C} \qquad R_C = \overline{A}BC + A\overline{B}C$$

(NOTE: The only reduction possible is in the gating equation for S_C.)

To complete the logic, it should be recognized that a clock K must be added to each gate to generate the switching impulse. In other words, the count is clocked at all gates. The complete logic for the brute-force counter design is shown in Fig. 7-18.

SEQUENTIAL LOGIC DESIGN

The formal approach to the design of combination logic with the use of flip-flop elements involves combining the operational equations for the type of flip-flop employed and the application equations for the desired

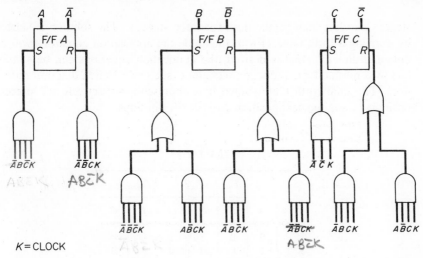

FIG. 7-18   "Brute-force" counter design.

logic on the set, reset, or toggle input of each individual flip-flop. The operational equation is in the form of:

$$Q_{n+1} = g_1 Q_n + g_2 \bar{Q}_n$$

where Q_{n+1} = condition of the Q flip-flop at time $n + 1$;

Q_n = "1" side of flip-flop Q_n;

$\bar{Q}_n$ = "0" side of flip-flop Q_n;

g_1 = application equation at Q_n input; and

g_2 = application equation at $\bar{Q}_n$ input.

The exact form of the equation differs depending on the type of flip-flop (R-S, T, R-S-T, J-K, etc.) to be used. The reader wishing to know more about this subject is referred to other texts, such as Phister,† for a detailed treatment. In this section, a simple example of the general approach is given only. The approach here is modified slightly from the formal one described in the reference cited.

The application equation is derived for *each* input to each flip-flop involved. It is generally found by comparing the truth table of the *present setting* of the flip-flop with the one that represents the *next* setting. The easiest way to describe this approach is by the simple example that follows.

Assume it is desired to design a counter that counts to 5 in sequence and then repeats. Also, assume the use of a T flip-flop at each stage. There will be three stages, since a count of 5 is more than 4 (the limit for two

† See the Bibliography.

stages) and less than 8 (the limit for three stages). The solution is started by drawing a truth table. From this table the application equations will be obtained directly. If it is desired, the application equations can be simplified by a normal logic reduction technique, such as a Veitch diagram reduction. The dual truth table shown here represents respectively the present position T_n and the next position T_{n+1} of the flip-flops.

TABLE 7-3

	T_n			T_{n+1}		
	A	B	C	A	B	C
1.	0	0	0	1	0	0
2.	1	0	0	0	1	0
3.	0	1	0	1	1	0
4.	1	1	0	0	0	1
5.	0	0	1	1	0	1
6.	1	0	1	0	0	0
7.	0	0	0	1	0	0
etc.						

Note that T_{n+1} is T_n raised one level position. The application equation for flip-flop A is obtained by noting every condition under which A *must toggle*. For the case here, it toggles at every step. In other words, at every count, flip-flop A will toggle to reach the T_{n+1} condition from T_n. Flip-flop B, on the other hand, will toggle at step 2 and step 4. Likewise flip-flop C toggles at step 4 and step 6. The application equations then will be respectively

$$T_A = \overline{A}\overline{B}\overline{C} + A\overline{B}\overline{C} + \overline{A}B\overline{C} + AB\overline{C} + \overline{A}\overline{B}C + A\overline{B}C$$

Since the toggle could also occur at steps 110 and 111 without affecting the results (these last two cases are "don't-care" conditions), the expressions for T_A could include all maxterms. Because this is so, $T_A = 1$.

In the same manner, T_B and T_C are determined, but here there are only two terms considered:

$$T_B = A\overline{B}\overline{C} + AB\overline{C} = A\overline{C}(\overline{B} + B) = A\overline{C}$$
$$T_C = AB\overline{C} + A\overline{B}C = A(B\overline{C} + \overline{B}C)$$

This approach, in a sense, is simpler than the formal one suggested in the introduction to this section, since the above equations can be applied directly to the terminals T_n of the flip-flop. From the equations, the logic

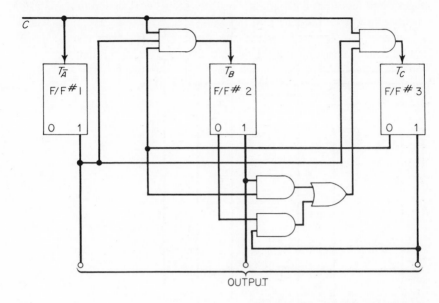

FIG. 7-19 Five-count counter design.

can be drawn directly, as is done in Fig. 7-19. The count clock K is applied to each stage and, in fact, ANDed with each simplified application equation. The final equations of the stage inputs are, therefore,

$$T_A = K$$
$$T_B = KA\bar{C}$$
$$T_C = KA(B\bar{C} + \bar{B}C)$$

USE OF HALF-ADDERS AS LOGIC ELEMENTS

Interesting logic can be constructed with half-adder circuits as logic elements, particularly if used as devices which recognize a coincidence between a specified number of half-adder elements. As a simple example, assume that one wishes to recognize when coincidence occurs between at least two out of six pulses (any two or more in coincidence satisfies the criteria). The circuit is constructed as shown in Fig. 7-20. It consists of six half-adders and an OR gate.

The equation for the outputs of the *half-adder* were given at the start of the chapter and are

$$f_1 = A\bar{B} + \bar{A}B \qquad f_2 = AB$$

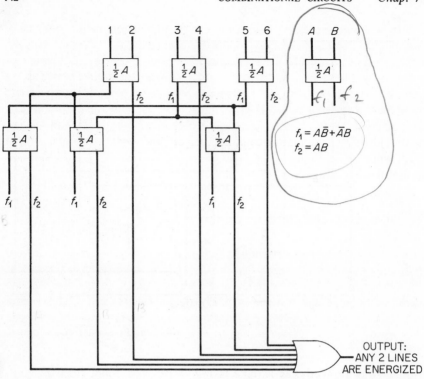

FIG. 7-20   Half-adders used as logic elements.

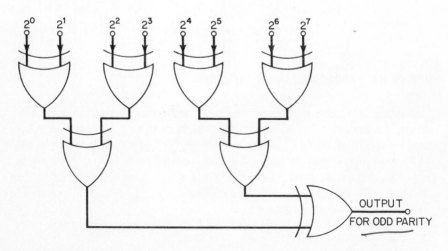

FIG. 7-21   Parity check logic (exclusive-OR gates).

It is merely necessary to review each combination in the outputs to see that any combination of two inputs will give an output.

A circuit for checking to see whether an "odd" or "even" number of "1's" occurs in a parallel code character makes use of the exclusive OR circuits. A complete circuit is shown in Fig. 7-21. In this example, any time two "1's" occur at the input of an exclusive OR gate, no output occurs. If a single input "1" occurs, an output "1" occurs. By checking the figure, it should be obvious that an *even* number of "1's" does *not* give an output "1," while an *odd* number of "1's" *does* give an output "1." This circuit is useful in checking the *parity* of a code character.

Adding a an extra bit. (detect a loss or gain a bit

SERIAL COMPARATOR CIRCUIT

It is often necessary to determine whether A or B is a larger number or if they are equal in magnitude. The logic required to accomplish this task is the *comparator*. The functioning of a simple form of comparator for two serial numbers A and B (LSD first) is shown in Fig. 7-22. Here A and B (LSD first)

(Feeding LSD or LSB first)

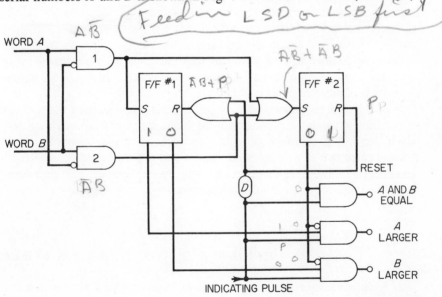

FIG. 7-22   Comparison logic.

are passed simultaneously through circuit gates 1 and 2. For equal "1's" or "0's," neither gate 1 nor 2 transmit the pulse through to the flip-flop. Gates 1 and 2 form the sum output of a half-adder. Flip-flop 1 is set or reset after the passage of the LSD digit, depending on which number (*A* or *B*) was larger. Flip-flop 2 remains reset if *A* and *B* are equal, since, then, there will never be a pulse through gates 1 or 2 during the comparison process. An indicating pulse will be clocked through the appropriate output, depending on the setting of flip-flops 1 and 2 at the end of the comparison process.

SUMMARY

Combined logic to perform the operations of addition, both by dual half-adders and a full adder was presented. The use of flip-flop (binary) stages to construct combination logic counters was followed by descriptions of three versions of straight binary counters, up-down counters, decimal counters, and ring counters. Buffer and shift registers, also composed of binary elements, received limited attention. A section demonstrated the use of brute-force techniques to design a counter that would count a *forced* (or controlled) *sequence*. This was an example of a more general form of sequential logic design.

Logic networks which convert from one code to another were covered briefly. These logic-circuit configurations have been called *matrices*. In addition, a decoder logic circuit was illustrated. In all cases, these logic examples combined gates and flip-flops and, hence, illustrated combinational logic of more complex capabilities.

Exclusive OR elements used as logic elements again showed the concept of combining the basic logic forms to build up combinational elements which perform a complete function. In these particular examples, logic that indicates two out of six coincidences and a parity-check device were demonstrated. The chapter concluded with an example of logic that compares binary numbers for relative magnitude.

REVIEW QUESTIONS AND PROBLEMS

7-1. Explain the operation of a count-down counter. Work up the first five sequences of such a three-stage counter.

7-2. Draw the logic for a half-adder in NAND form. In NOR form. Combine two such circuits (either NAND or NOR) to form a full adder. Explain its operation.

7-3. How many binary stages are required to represent decimal 8,192 in a binary counter?

14 stages $2^{13} = 8,192 - 1$ or

8,191

7-4. How many stages are required to represent the above number in BCD form? In octal form?

7-5. How can level logic be converted to pulse logic, and vice versa? What does it take to mechanize the above devices to change the type of logic?

7-6. Design a counter that counts in an arbitrary sequence, as follows: 110, 111, 000, 101, 001, 010.

7-7. Draw the logic of a serial full adder in NAND or NOR form incorporating a flip-flop delay element.

7-8. Is it more economical in circuits to construct a serial full adder working on level logic signals in the form of two half-adders or as a full adder.

7-9. Construct a counter that will count to 25 and then reset to 0.

7-10. Draw the logic for a shift register which will perform the following functions:

    a. Permit a parallel input of 10 bits at a particular clock time.

    b. Permit a serial output at 300 kc.

    c. Can be shifted left (one-bit shift of all digits simultaneously).

TRANSISTOR AND INTEGRATED CIRCUIT LOGIC 8

This chapter discusses in detail the various types of transistor logic, integrated circuit (I-C) families, examples of combination logic design with integrated circuits (I-Cs), and a brief discussion of the manufacturing of I-Cs and concludes with a condensed description of field-effect transistor–metal oxide silicon (FET–MOS) logic devices and large-scale integrated circuits (LSICs).

As previously pointed out, there are many ways of devising logic elements. In the early days of computers, the designers choice was limited to the relays, tubes, diodes, etc., available. With the availability of the transistor, the choice of logic types widened greatly, not only because of the two types of transistors available (NPN and PNP) but because these transistors could be used in so many ways to devise logic circuits with special characteristics. As the circuit designer learned more about this new circuit device, he was able to improve logic circuits. The original simple

DCTL circuits were shown to be lacking in some aspects; hence, the development of RTL, RCTL, DTL, TTL etc., followed in rapid order.†

The importance of studying both the development of transistor logic and the characteristics of the several types lies in the similarity of the transistor families of logic and the I-C families. Integrated circuits adopted generally one or another of the transistor generic forms. By understanding the transistor forms, the reader can then predict the performance of the I-C equivalents. In general the DCTL, the DTL, the TTL, and the ECTL forms have been reincarnated in the I-Cs with little change in theory of operation. The RCTL type has not been so fortunate because of the difficulty of forming capacitors with I-C technology.

The first section of this chapter will discuss in some detail the characteristics of some of the more popular families of transistor logic. Emphasis will be on the NAND gate elements in each logic, as they can be considered typical of the logic line as a whole.

TRANSISTOR LOGIC AND CIRCUITS

Directly Coupled Transistor Logic

Directly coupled transistor logic (DCTL) is one of the earliest and simplest of transistor logic concepts. Each logic gate output (the collector load–resistor junction) is directly coupled to the input of all the other gates it must drive (point A in Fig. 8-1). A serious defect of this logic circuit lies in attempting to drive parallel gates in the second level from a single first-level stage. The load current available from the first stage to the base of each second-level stage is a function of the beta gain (β) of that particular driven stage. Large β variations occur quite often, unless careful control of the parameters is achieved; in fact variations in driving requirements frequently do occur. In Fig. 8-1, the collector load of Q_1 is the load resistor and the base–emitter characteristics of Q_2, Q_3, . . . , Q_n are all in parallel. Because each of these input impedances can vary, the base current and therefore the collector currents of each second-level stage are subject to wide variation. Since transistor Q_1 is incapable of supplying more than its rated (safe) collector current, any DCTL stage at the second level which absorbs more than its fair share of base current deprives the other paralleled transistors of base current. This defficiency of DCTL is a factor which seriously limits its usefulness in new systems.

(current-hogging)

†*Abbreviations:* DCTL, directly coupled transistor logic; RTL, resistor-transistor logic; RCTL, resistor-capacitor-transistor logic; DTL, diode-transistor logic; TTL, transistor-transistor (dual transistor) logic; ECTL, emitter-coupled transistor logic.

A second disadvantage involves the small *noise margin,* i.e., the small difference between the saturated collector voltage of Q_1 and the turn-on voltage of Q_2, Q_3, or Q_n. As can be seen in Fig. 8-1, when Q_1 is cut off, a small negative noise voltage introduced between A and any of the paralleled loads will turn the particular transistor off since the base-to-emitter voltages are small.

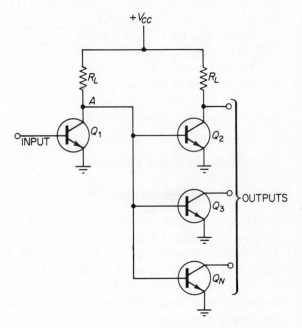

FIG. 8-1 DCTL NOR gate.

A third limitation of DCTL is that the β variations must be kept within a narrow range of values. If β is too low, Q_1 of Fig. 8-1 will not reach collector saturation in the "0" output state. If the β is too high, say on Q_2, it will turn on when, in reality, the stage should be off.

A final limitation on the operation of DCTL is high temperature. As the temperature is increased, the noise margin decreases since the collector-saturation voltage increases and the turn-on voltage threshold decreases.

In summary, DCTL is simple to construct in monolithic integrated form and has the advantage of making high production yields possible. It requires only one power supply and has moderate speed and power dissipation. However, it has three major disadvantages: a current-hogging problem due to base–emitter nonlinearity, an inadequate noise margin at higher temperatures, and a limited fan-out capability. The term *why are these only nor gates available ?*

fan-out means the number of identical parallel NAND gates of the next gating level that a particular NAND gate can successfully drive. The term *fan-in* refers to how many variable inputs are permitted to a single gate or circuit.

Resistor-Transistor Logic

If a small resistance is introduced into the base of the DCTL system, the coupling mechanism becomes *resistor-transistor logic* (RTL) and the base–emitter characteristics become more linear. An example of RTL is shown in Fig. 8-2. A 100-ohm base-coupling resistance reduces the logic

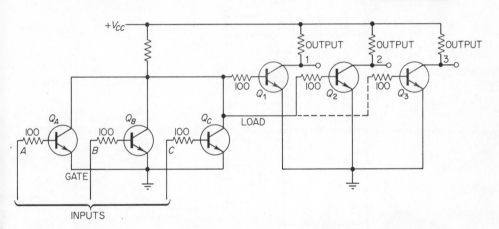

FIG. 8-2   RTL NAND–NOR gate.

response speed somewhat but increases the capability of DCTL to handle greater loads. Noise rejection will still be relatively low but is improved somewhat because the turn-on voltage is increased by the drop across the resistor. However, the circuit still is temperature sensitive. Operating speed is reduced below that of DCTL and high-level TTL. Logic swing is about 1 volt, and power consumption is a little less than DCTL.

Resistor-transistor logic retains the advantage of DCTL in that it is simple to manufacture and has one supply voltage. However, it also requires close control of β variation, and its fan-in and fan-out capabilities are limited.

Resistor-Capacitor-Transistor Logic

If the basic RTL circuit is modified to that of Fig. 8-3, the result is *resistor-capacitor-transistor logic* (RCTL). The high base resistance

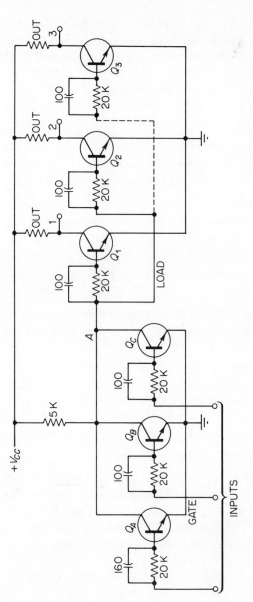

FIG. 8-3 RCTL NAND–NOR gate.

greatly reduces speed. The bypass capacitor increases the base current for faster turn-on and minimizes storage time by supplying a charge equal to that stored in the base. The value of C may be calculated as

$$\frac{Q_{\text{storage}}}{V_{\text{in}}} = C$$

where Q_{storage} is the maximum rated value of charge storage and V_{in} is the input voltage swing. The low base-current requirement permits relatively high fan-out. Operating power is typically low.

In summary, RCTL has slightly improved noise rejection over DCTL, low power consumption, high fan-in and fan-out capability and practically no base current deprivation. However, it has moderate speed and is relatively unsuitable for fabrication into silicon integrated circuits (even though one major semiconductor manufacturer is currently supplying large quantities of this device with reverse-biased PN junctions for capacitors).

Diode-Transistor Logic

The fourth type of I-C to be considered is *diode-transistor logic* (DTL) as shown in Fig. 8-4. If Q_1 is cut off, the voltage at A is almost equal to

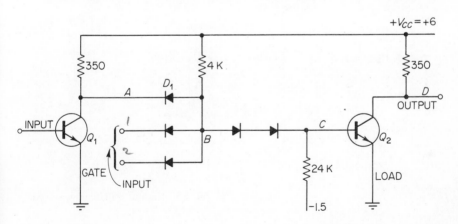

FIG. 8-4 DTL NAND gate.

the power supply. Current flows from the power supply through the two series diodes (point C), then through the parallel path formed by the 24,000-ohm resistor and the base to the emitter of Q_2. The voltage at point B is therefore 6 volts minus the drop across the 4000-ohm resistor, and the voltage at C is the voltage B minus the negligible forward drops of the two series diodes. Being well above ground, the voltage at C drives

Q_2 into saturation, and the voltage at D equals the collector saturation voltage in this situation (practically at ground level). A *positive* noise picked up between A and D_1 will *not* affect the operation of the gate since it will only increase the back bias on D_1. However, a negative noise will affect operation if sufficient to overcome the reverse bias, the forward voltage drop of D_1, and the voltage necessary to turn Q_2 off.

In the presence of a negative input pulse, Q_1 is conducting and Q_2 is cut off. The voltage at B is equal to the collector saturation voltage of Q_1 (practically at ground) plus the forward voltage drop of D_1 (practically negligible). The voltage at C is, therefore, at or below ground, and the base of Q_2 is back biased. The output voltage is a "1" at the V_{cc} level (the power-supply voltage). In this situation, a positive noise between A and D_1 must overcome the forward drop of the two series diodes and the base-to-emitter drop of Q_2 in order to drive Q_2 into conduction.

Figure 8-4 is not the only form of DTL available. More complex forms can be evolved, as shown in Fig. 8-5.

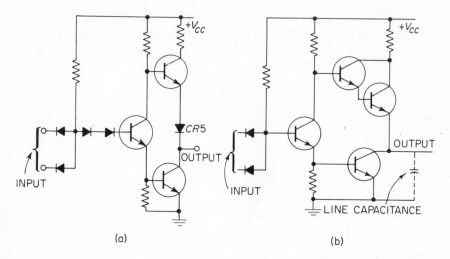

FIG. 8-5 Various DTL configurations.

The circuit of Fig. 8-5a shows greater DTL development. It incorporates many circuit improvements, including the addition of another transistor and a diode (CR_5). This diode charges line capacity between logic "1" and logic "0" states. Thus, high fan-out, good speed, and medium noise immunity are all realized. The sacrifice for these advantages is a higher power consumption, but this design is suitable for integrated microcircuits.

An even more elaborate version of the DTL circuit in Fig. 8-5a is shown in Figure 8-5b, where additional drive to the output-line capacity is produced by a dual-transistor combination, known as a *Darlington connection,* at the capacitance driving section of the circuit. The diode is superseded by a transistor—a natural result of converting to the I-C form. Higher power is consumed, as a result of these modifications, but high fan-out and excellent speed are worthwhile compensations.

To summarize, DTL has good noise immunity, good speed, and high fan-out at the expense of higher, but relatively moderate, power dissipation. Diode-transistor logic is inherently slower than TTL (described later) because of the relatively high impedance of the discharge path in the base of the first inverter. The first inverter in a TTL circuit discharges through the low impedance of the transistor gate. Attempts to speed up turn-off time of this inverter transistor leads to higher power dissipation (lower resistance) or a second power supply.

Emitter-Coupled Transistor Logic

Still another form of I-C logic is *emitter-coupled transistor logic* (ECTL). A typical ECTL circuit is shown in Fig. 8-6. The gate has a

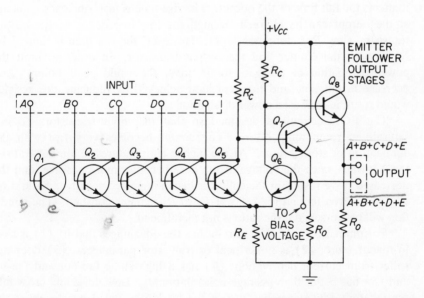

FIG. 8-6 ECTL OR–NOR gate.

maximum fan-in of five and consists essentially of six-transistor current mode switches and two emitter followers coupling the signals to the collector of the gate to the output. Five of the six switching transistors are used as input transistors with their bases connected directly to the input terminals. The sixth has its base connected to a fixed bias source (reference voltage). With no signal applied to any of the input transistors (Q_1 to Q_5), these units are cut off but Q_6 is conducting owing to the fixed bias applied. For any signal condition, there are two outputs available from the gate: one from the collector of the fixed bias transistor through emitter follower Q_8; the other from the common collector junction of the five input transistors through emitter follower Q_7. If, e.g., a positive signal representing a logical "1" is applied to any of the inputs, the common collector output goes negative while that of the fixed bias transistor goes positive. These two outputs simultaneously yield an OR and NOR function. It should be noted that, with this circuit, a signal and its complement are always available. Signals from the gate are coupled to the output terminals through emitter followers Q_7 and Q_8, which serve as d-c translators to make the output compatible with d-c level requirements of subsequent emitter followers and provide a large d-c fan-out capability.

In high-speed applications, the fan-out capability is necessarily reduced, since it is determined primarily by the capacitive loading of the succeeding stages. This circuit is particularly susceptible to capacitive loading in that it affects the fall time of the output. The rise time is fast, since any capacity at the output can be charged through the low impedance of the output transistor (low R–C time constant). However, the fall time is limited by R_0 in both the emitter and the output transistor. In order to limit the power dissipation of the gate to 35 mW, R_0 would be 2 kohm. Any decrease in fall time and time constant achieved by reducing this resistor would result in increased power dissipation.

The ECTL circuit is designed so that the input transistors do not saturate at room temperature. The circuit becomes very fast with the elimination of storage time. At the higher temperatures, the input transistors saturate, since the voltage at the base becomes more positive, and the decreased drive results in the collector becoming more negative. Saturation will occur even though the ratio of R_c to R_e remains constant. The condition will be worsened if the ratio is not maintained.

To summarize, the ECTL circuit has the advantages that it: (1) is easy to manufacture; (2) is noncritical of transistor parameters; (3) does not suffer from current deprivation; (4) has a high static fan-out and fan-in; and (5) has better than average noise immunity. Low noise and cross talk are inherent advantages because of the favorable impedance levels of the circuit. The high input impedance holds inductive cross-talk currents between adjacent signal lines to a minimum. Because output impedance is low, capacitive cross talk in the output is minimized. In addition, noise generated in power supply and ground lines is practically nonexistent because of the constant-current property of this type of design. Disadvantages, other than saturation and slow fall time, are the need for a reference voltage and potential oscillation in the emitter followers.

Transistor-Transistor (Low-Level) Logic

With the widespread use of transistors (as late as 1960 for silicon transistors), the use of all-transistor logic circuitry became economically feasible. Certain circuit-performance advantages accompanied this new type of circuit, known as *transistor-transistor logic* (TTL).

Figure 8-7 illustrates the operation of the typical low-level TTL

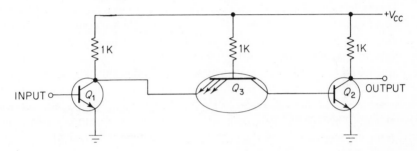

FIG. 8-7   Low-level TTL NAND gate.

NAND-gate circuit. Note the similarity to the previous DTL gate, shown in Fig. 8-4. The inverter Q_2 (or NOR part of the circuit) transistor remains as before, but the current-steering diode input gates are replaced with a transistor Q_1. The turn-off time of the inverter is now enhanced by transistor β of the input-gate transistors. In other words, the stored charge in Q_2, the inverter transistor, is removed from the base by β times the normal removal rate.

When Q_1 is turned off, the base current of coupling transistor Q_3 is steered into the base of the inverting transistor Q_2. In this condition, the base current goes out through the collector, and Q_3 acts as a forward-biased steering diode. When Q_1 is saturated, the base current of Q_3 is steered into the collector of Q_1, which clamps the base of Q_2 to a low potential. This cuts off Q_2, and the emitter of Q_3 is clamped at almost ground potential through saturated Q_1. In this condition, the base current of Q_3 would be steered through its emitter. This gate is capable of high-speed operation, requires only one power supply, and dissipates only a moderate amount of power.

To summarize, the TTL (low-level) circuitry requires rather tight control over transistor parameters in manufacture. Inverse β must be kept low to keep inverse β current low. This circuit has insufficient noise margin for high-temperature operation. The noise margin here is the difference between the collector saturation voltage of Q_1 and the minimum positive voltage applied to the emitter of Q_3 that will start Q_2 turning on. At a high temperature, collector saturation voltage increases; the threshold voltage decreases owing to increased β and lower initial turn-on voltage at higher temperatures. Thus the noise margin is reduced.

Transistor-Transistor (High-Level) Logic

The circuit shown in Fig. 8-8 overcomes most of the disadvantages the low-level TTL previously discussed. The Q_2 provides sufficient voltage

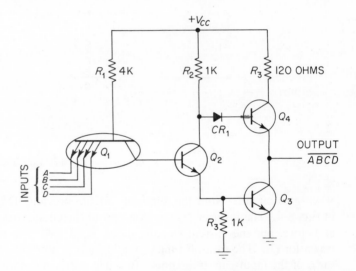

FIG. 8-8 Mechanization of a high-level TTL gate.

gains to drive transistors Q_3 and Q_4 out of phase. Together, Q_3 and Q_4 provide a positive drive to its line capacitance in both directions of operation (positive and negative).

To summarize, the TTL (high-level) circuit has a propagation time of less than 20 nsec over the temperature range of -55 to $+125°C$, with a fan-out of 10, and a moderate power dissipation of approximately 17 mW per gate. It has high fan-out capabilities and requires only a single power supply. Its fast switching speeds over the entire temperature range has been aided by gold dipping. In addition, the circuit has a noise margin of 50 mV over the temperature range of -55 to $+125°C$. An early disadvantage of TTL logic was the current pulse which occurred during switching because both output transistors were on at the same time. This limita-

TABLE 8-1

Comparison of logic systems for silicon integrated circuits

Logic system	Advantages	Disadvantages
DCTL (directly coupled logic)	Simple to manufacture Switching speed comparable to TTLs One supply voltage Low power dissipation	Current-hogging problem due to base–emitter nonlinearity Inadequate noise margin at higher temperatures Only logical NOR available Low fan-out
Modified DCTL, contains base resistor	Simple to manufacture Switching speed slightly slower than pure DCTL One supply voltage Reduced current-hogging problem Low power dissipation	Inadequate noise margin at higher temperatures Only logical NOR available Low fan-out
DTL (diode-transistor logic)	Fairly easy to manufacture Excellent noise margin Low power dissipation NAND–NOR mechanization possible	Two power supplies required (one for bias voltage) Somewhat slower than TTL owing to the higher input turn-off impedance Low fan-out
Single-output ECTL (emitter-coupled transistor logic)	Low power dissipation Higher switching speeds due to nonsaturating mode of operation	Two supply voltages and a temperature-tracking reference voltage required Critical ratio R_c/R_e needed to remain out of saturation Risk of emitter-follower oscillation Low noise margin due to logical signal of $V_{CE(sat.)}$ [a] for an "0" and $V_{BE(sat.)}$ [b] for a "1" Low fan-out Difficult to manufacture owing to stringent requirements placed on circuit parameters
Dual-output ECTL	Low power dissipation (but higher than saturating mode) Both logic OR and NOR available Higher switching speeds due to nonsaturating mode of operation Large fan-out capability	Critical ratio R_c/R_e needed to remain out of saturation One supply voltage and a temperature-tracking reference voltage required A risk of emitter-follower oscillation Possible transient saturation of input transistors due to emitter capacitance

TABLE 8-1 (Continued)

Logic system	Advantages	Disadvantages
TTL, low-level (transistor-transistor logic)	Simple to manufacture Good switching speed (but somewhat slower than ECTL) Low power dissipation One power supply Logical NAND–NOR mechanization possible	Inadequate noise margin at higher temperatures Low fan-out
TTL, high-level	Fast switching speeds due to low impedance output (speed approaching ECTL) Fairly easy to manufacture Excellent noise margin Large fan-out capability NAND–NOR mechanization available	Power dissipation slightly higher than low-level TTL

[a] $V_{CE(sat.)}$—Saturated voltage measured between collector and emitter.
[b] $V_{BE(sat.)}$—Saturated voltage measured between base and emitter.

tion has been corrected by further design. The magnitude of this pulse is limited by the 120-ohm resistor in the collector of the output emitter follower.

The conclusion of an investigation of the preceding logic-circuit mechanizations is shown in Table 8-1, which illustrates the advantages and disadvantages of each mechanization for use in future high-speed computers. The outstanding advantages of TTL over the other circuits are its high fan-out capability, high noise margin, and fast speeds over the entire temperature range of -55 to $+125°C$. The basic high-level TTL circuit and a set of I-C building blocks has been proposed for many modern computer designs.

APPLICATIONS OF INTEGRATED CIRCUITS FOR LOGIC

In recent years, circuits constructed of discrete components (resistors, diodes, transistors, etc.) have been superseded in some areas by *microminiature circuits*.

Extremely rapid changes have taken place in logic circuits since 1950. By 1961 the first complete logic line of integrated circuits was put on the market by Fairchild Instruments Corporation, followed shortly by Texas Instruments Incorporated. The technique employed by both companies (and many others later) involved building a complete logic circuit on a transistor chip, then packaging the circuit in a transistor can (similar to the standard TO-5 package but modified to have more output leads) or in a $\frac{1}{4}$-in.-square flat package, generally referred to as a *flat pack*.

These circuits are complete logic circuits. They can be united to form combination circuits of high complexity. (An example of a circuit chip, showing the many elements and interconnections, is illustrated in Fig. 8-9.)

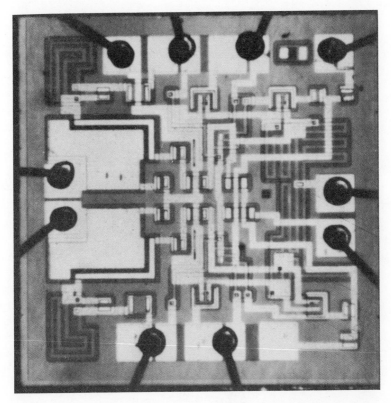

FIG. 8-9   SE150 integrated circuit.

By January, 1964, more than a dozen semiconductor manufacturers announced their entries in the I-C field with several of them capable of supplying devices in quantity. Therefore, it could be said that the age of microelectronic I-Cs had arrived.

Since this particular phase of the technology is advancing so rapidly, it is almost impossible to keep completely up to date. However, in Tables 8-2 and 8-3, a summary is given of a typical RTL logic and a popular DTL logic by Texas Instruments Incorporated.

A few samples of an RTL series are given in Table 8-2. These ele-

TABLE 8-2 A typical RTL logic family

Element	Positive logic	Circuit	Notes		
			Fanout	Pwr/Fu	Typ. Delay
1. Quad 2 gate	$y = \overline{A + B}$, etc.		5	3 mW	12 nsec

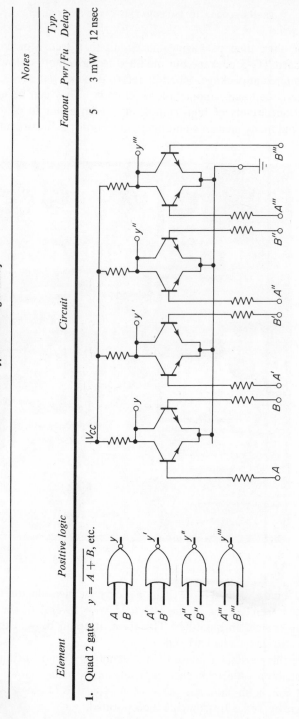

Element	Positive logic	Circuit	Notes		
			Fanout	Pwr/Fu	Typ. Delay
2. Dual 3 input gate	$y = \overline{A + B + C}$, etc.		5	3 mW	12 nsec
3. Half-adder	$y = (A + B)(C + D)$		5	10 mW	30 nsec

TABLE 8-2 (Continued)

Element	Positive logic	Circuit		Notes	
			Fanout	Pwr/Fu	Typ. Delay
4. Flip-flop (*S–R–T*)			5	45 mW	30 nsec
5. 4-input gate with extender input	$y = \overline{A + B + C + D \ldots}$		5	3 mW	25 nsec

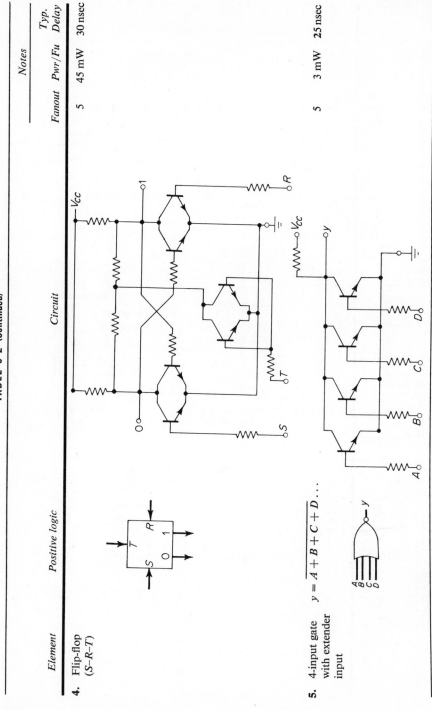

TABLE 8-3

Texas Instruments Incorporated, Series 1593 [a,b]

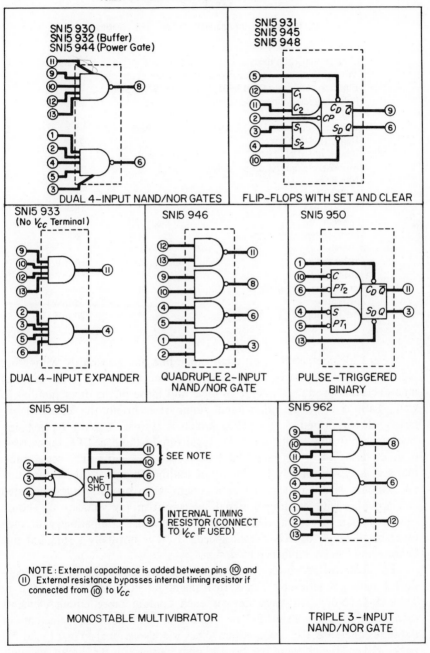

[a] Used with permission of Texas Instrument Inc.

[b] Typical operating characteristics, $T_A = -55$ to $125°C$, supply voltage $V_{CC} = 4.5$ to 5.5 volts. (*Continued on page 164.*)

TABLE 8-3

Texas Instruments Incorporated, Series 1593 (Continued)

Speed:

Gate propagation delay	25 nsec
Monostable multivibrator propagation delay	20 nsec
Flip-flop clock rate (SN15 931, SN15 945, SN15 948)	7 MHz
Pulse-triggered binary clock rate	20 MHz

Fanout capability:

Standard gates (SN15 930, SN15 946, SN15 962)	8
Buffer (SN15 932)	25
Power gate (SN15 944)	27
Monostable multivibrator (SN15 951)	10
Flip-flops:	
SN15 931	7
SN15 945	10
SN15 948	9
Pulse-triggered binary	8

dc margin:

at logical 1	500 mV
at logical 0	500 mV

Average power dissipation:

per gate	5 mW
per flip-flop	20 mW

ments are all compatible with each other but not necessarily with other logic types that are not of the RTL family, such as DTL or TTL. Several manufacturers produce this type of logic and those of the other families as well. Table 8-3, on the other hand, summarizes briefly the Texas Instruments, Incorporated, series 1593, which is typical of many types being manufactured now. This is a DTL logic family (had a TTL series been desired, series 54 or 71 would have been listed instead.) The series summarized is typical of any I-C family of building blocks to the extent that all elements will work together as a system when properly interconnected and provided with the proper signal levels and supply voltages. It should be noted that, in general, DTL and TTL logic are compatible with each other in all major aspects except speed. TTL is normally faster, but this factor again can be influenced by design.

To illustrate the newer trends in technology, examples of a semiconductor network series by Texas Instruments, Incorporated, are given in Table 8-4. Note that these devices each contain more circuit elements than those in either Table 8-2 or Table 8-3. The particular elements of the series cited are TTL compatible. They are also packaged in 14 lead flat packs. Even though there has been a great increase in the circuit elements packaged in a single pack (which provides higher efficiency in packaging), the use of these circuit elements will be more restricted because of their

TABLE 8-4

Semiconductor Networks Series 74N TTL[a]

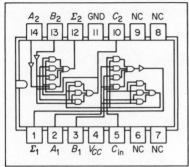

SN7482N 2-bit binary full-adder

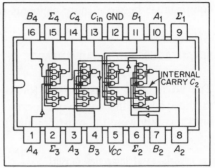

SN7483N 4-bit binary full-adder

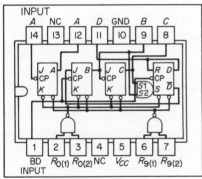

SN7490N Decade counter

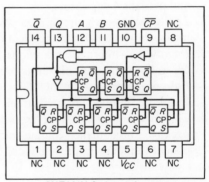

SN7491N 8-bit shift register

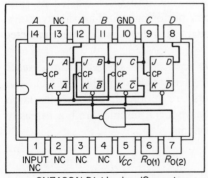

SN7492N Divide-by-12 counter

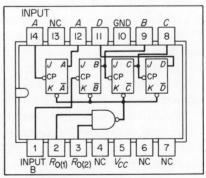

SN7493N 4-bit binary counter

[a] Used by permission of Texas Instruments Inc.

high degree of specialization. This is, of course, the basic nature of the compromise between more elements to the package versus more packages.

ADVANTAGES AND DISADVANTAGES OF INTEGRATED CIRCUITS

The advantages of using I-Cs for logic are many and should be obvious to those using the cord-wood or the printed-circuit-board versions which until recently were the most popular forms of logic circuit construction.

Advantages of Integrated Circuits

1. *Small size*—for example, one transistor size I-C package can typically replace up to 10 conventional transistors, 30 resistors, 6 diodes, and perhaps 4 capacitors.
2. *Low power*—each circuit uses power in the 3 to 40 mW range, depending on the circuit and the application, of course.
3. *Reliability*—internal connections between components are made under controlled conditions of transistor manufacture.
4. *Ease of assembly*—the interconnecting of I-C elements has led generally to a more simplified printed circuit board.
5. *Compactness on the final assembly*—functionally, many more can be packaged in a smaller volume for less weight than former discrete component versions. Improvement of 5 to 10 times is normal.

Disadvantages of Integrated Circuits

1. Integrated circuits were originally produced by a *limited number of sources*. The early circuits were expensive, and there existed no past experience against which to judge their performance. This disadvantage has almost entirely vanished, although in a few circles mistrust may still exist.
2. The major disadvantage is this: *users must accept the particular circuits that a manufacturer provides*. There is no way to modify an I-C. (In some cases expensive special circuits are required, but only in large production runs can these be justified. Special circuits are not as easily designed as those with discrete components.)

LOGIC DESIGN WITH INTEGRATED CIRCUITS

Generally, I-Cs can be combined easily to form relatively simple combination circuits. All manufacturers issue special sheets for their product (usually a series of application notes discussing special applications) giving examples of how their logic interconnects. At least one manufacturer provides the design engineer with a perpetual-life handbook. In Fig. 8-10,

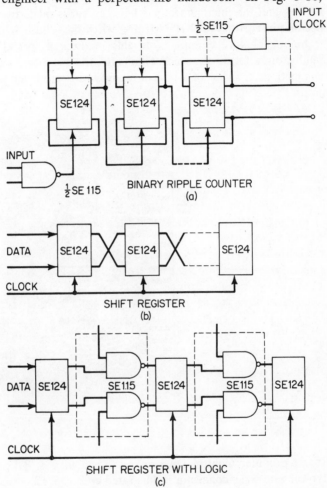

FIG. 8-10 Combining I-C units to form combinational circuits.

three typical combination circuits are shown as examples of how these components may be combined.

First efforts to package electronic equipment in integrated circuits involved the design of a new printed circuit board for each application. Because of the expense and processing delay caused by producing a new printed circuit board for each new design, a search for a less expensive and time-consuming method began. One solution, favored by a number of manufacturers, is to produce a line of standard plug-in cards. These cards, containing both I-Cs and discrete components, may be plugged into connectors and the interconnections between cards made by wires to the connector pins. New ways of fastening wires have been found, including the technique of wire wrapping. In this method, a special tool wraps wire tightly on a terminal, which eliminates the need for soldered or welded connections. A view of a typical module card produced by the Honeywell,

FIG. 8-11   Typical I-C module cards.

Inc., Computer Control Division, is shown in Fig. 8-11. The back of a typical wire-wrap connector is illustrated by Fig. 8-12.

The logic for an up-down counter of eight stages is given in Fig. 8-13a. The interconnections of the logic are demonstrated in Fig. 8-13b. Six logic cards of three types are required. The same three types can be used along with other cards as building blocks for innumerable other configurations. A table of typical card modules is given in Table 8-5.

In theory, design with I-Cs is a straightforward process. The design engineer, taking the equations or diagrams, will substitute for logic elements the best-fitting I-C elements at his disposal. Whenever possible, he will stay with one family of logic.

FIG. 8-12   Wire-wrap terminal connector.

Some of the ground rules which the design engineer must abide with or, at least, consider include the following.

1. Use of *power supplies* that are compatible with the logic involved: they should remain within specified limits. In general, I-Cs are tolerant of wide variations in supply voltages. It is important to consider decoupling the power supplies (add a low-pass filter at key locations) to keep noise generated by the switching of circuit elements confined to the area where the switching takes place. Without decoupling, noise filters into the power-supply B^+ system.

2. Adherence to *fan-out and fan-in restrictions: Fan-in* is the total number of inputs tied to a particular point. For instance, an AND gate might be limited to a fan-in of eight elements. Because of loading effects (capacitance added to a point), additional elements would slow the circuit response below specification. For *fan-out,* the problem is one of circuit response also but may in addition reflect a power limitation of the driving source.

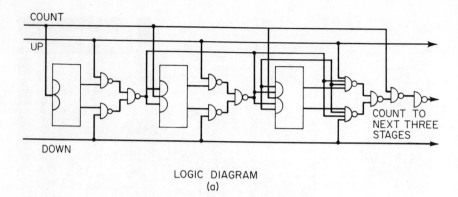

LOGIC DIAGRAM
(a)

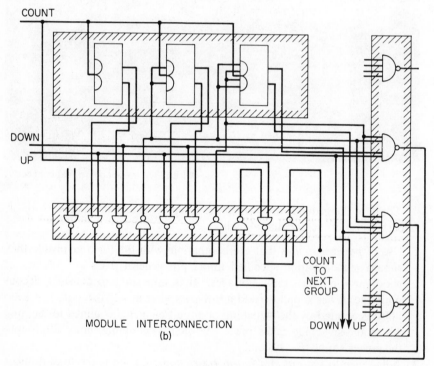

MODULE INTERCONNECTION
(b)

FIG. 8-13 Up-down counter with module cards.

3. Acknowledgment of the *inherent delay in each logic element* which cannot be ignored when using serially connecting elements: the *element delay* is defined as the time required for a change of state in the input to be propagated to the output of the element. The individual element delays added together will give the total delay of a chain of elements.

TABLE 8-5

Examples of integrated circuit module cards

Number	Function	Number of functions per card	Fanout per gate
1	Dual input NAND gate	10	8
2	4-input NAND gate	6	8
3	6-input NAND plus gate extender	2 gates plus two 4-bit extenders	8
4	3-input power NANDS	6	18
5	R–S flip-flop	8	8
6	Clocked flip-flop, type A	4	8
7	Clocked flip-flop, type B	3	8
8	4-bit up-down counter	1	6
9	D/A converter, 6 levels	1	
10	A/D converter, 6 levels	1	8
11	Dual one-shot multivibrator	2	8
12	1–10-bit counter	1	8
13	Line-relay drivers	6	
14	8-bit shift register	1	8
15	Bus dual NAND gate input-bus drivers	14	

In addition, the *rise and fall time of the signals* on the output of the gate element are criteria on which a logic element is judged. Technically, *rise time* is the time required for a signal to go from 10 to 90 per cent of its full amplitude. *Fall time* is the reverse process, i.e., the time for a signal to go from 90 to 10 per cent of its full amplitude. Rise time, fall time, and element delay must all be reduced to a minimum if the logic is to respond rapidly to high-speed signals. For example, a "3.0-MHz logic" means that the binary bits change at a 3.0-MHz rate. By present standards this is high-speed (I-C) logic.

4. Awareness that *noise immunity* is an important characteristic in any practical system: it determines the *safe-level sensitivity* of the logic elements and sets the signal-level limits that the designer must require for reliable operation of his logic. Noise immunity also determines whether he must use any form of signal filters.

5. Items 1 through 4 above are all *temperature-dependent*. Consequently, any design must be pretested for a temperature range over and somewhat beyond its intended operation.

6. *Reclocking:* this is a standard and much used technique for retiming and reshaping signals. A clock pulse is AND-gated periodically within the logic to improve pulse shape.

7. *Location of logic elements:* they should be arranged so that the elements may be interconnected as directly as possible. Short leads make for

fast response circuits with minimum of noise injection into adjacent circuits. Long leads are inherently high-capacitive, which leads to high-noise pickup potential and impedes signal rise and fall times between circuit elements as well.

These are a few of the design considerations. As in any other electronic circuit designs, the usual problems of power dissipation, driving proper loads, etc., must be taken into account.

FIELD-EFFECT TRANSISTOR–METAL OXIDE SILICON AND LARGE-SCALE INTEGRATED CIRCUITS

Field-Effect Transistor–Metal Oxide Silicon Logic

On a "per element" basis, FET–MOS logic has the ultimate potential of being less expensive to produce than the usual bipolar type of I-Cs. This advantage results from both the ability to put more circuit elements on a given-size chip and the production process which requires fewer total steps (approximately from 144 down to 43). The *higher number of elements* is achieved because the circuit elements are self-isolating. This self-isolation is a consequence of the production process. In a typical FET–MOS device, an active element may occupy a 2.0 square mills area; while, in the corresponding bipolar circuit, the same functional element would most likely occupy a 20-square mills area. One manufacturer estimates that a serial computer can be reduced in size by a factor of 10 if MOS elements are used rather than bipolar I-Cs.

Disadvantages of FET–MOS include higher and different levels of power-supply voltages and signal requirements than for the bipolars.

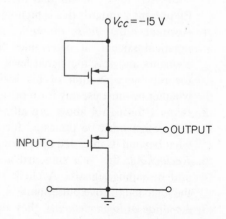

FIG. 8-14 FET–MOS inverter.

Therefore, mixed usage is difficult to impossible. Also, the need for two-phase, three-phase, or four-phase clocks is not compatible with the other class of I-Cs. Because the FET–MOS device itself is a voltage device and of higher circuit impedance generally, capacitances have a greater effect in slowing down its responses. Even with these defects the MOS–FET device has many uses, especially in logic configurations that are basically serial. A typical FET–MOS device is shown in Fig. 8-14. Note that the load resistor is replaced with an active FET–MOS device with a fixed bias. This form of load resistor is easier to make than a passive element and takes up much less space. An example of a gating element is given in Fig. 8-15 along with its logic description.

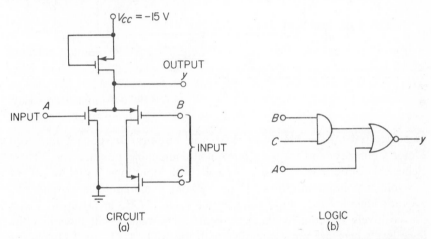

FIG. 8-15   FET–MOS gate.

Figure 8-16 illustrates a flip-flop or binary element requiring a dual (two-phase) clock. Clock C_1 initiates (readies) the flip-flop, and C_2 causes it to change state.

The logic speed of these devices is primarily a function of the circuit's capacitance, especially in the *gate* element. A popular method of increasing the logic speed of response is to precharge the circuit capacitance at clock time C_1 and propagate the signal to the next stage at C_2. Such a scheme is illustrated in Fig. 8-17. During C_1, the first stage is turned off and C_s is charged through S_2. If, when C_2 arrives, a "1" is stored, the charge from C_s is directed to C_t. If a "0" is stored, there is no charge to press into C_t. Because this device operates from higher impedance levels than bipolar devices, the capacitances associated have a greater relative effect in slowing the response speeds.

Table 8-6 lists a few typical FET–MOS logic packages. These are

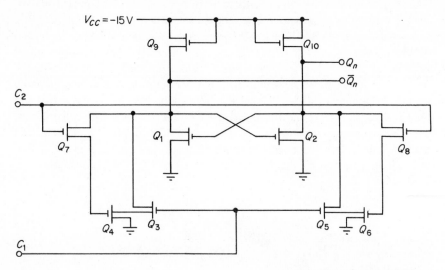

FIG. 8-16   FET–MOS binary.

manufactured by the Philco–Ford Microelectronics Division of the Ford Motor Company, and form an integrated compatible product line. These elements operate from −12 to −24 volts with input logic levels for "0" of −3 volts maximum and for a "1" of −9 volts minimum. The output voltages for logic levels is approximately the same. Noise levels up to 1 volt are positively rejected by these elements. The reader will note that the logic levels here are not compatible with the RTL, DTL, or TTL bipolar logic examined previously.

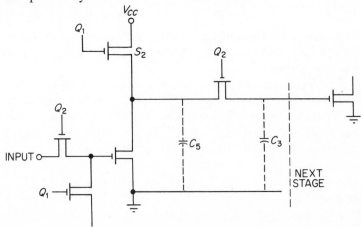

FIG. 8-17   High-speed MOS–FET logic.

TABLE 8-6

Monolithic integrated MOS subsystems[a,b]

Identity number	Logic or circuit	Function	Logic diagram
pL4C01	*BCD* decade counter	4-flip-flop *BCD* counter that will divide by 10; dc to 100-kc frequency range	
pL4G01	Dual 4-input gate	NAND–NOR gate. Each gate out is separate function; dc to 750 kc frequency range	
pL4G02	*BCD* to dec. decoder	Convert 4-line *BCD* to 10-line dec.; dc to 100 kc frequency range	
pLG04	3-input NAND	$\overline{ABC}$	

[a] Used with permission of Philco-Ford (Division of Ford Motor Company).

[b] NOTE: There are several other elements in this product line, but the above were considered to be typical. Shift register elements with up to 100 bits on a single chip are provided in one instance.

TABLE 8-6 (Continued)

Identity number	Logic or circuit	Function	Logic diagram
pL4G05	3-input NOR	$\overline{A + B + C}$	
pL4M01	Dual *J–K* flip-flop	2 individual flip-flops; dc to 500 kc frequency range	
pL4S01	4-channel analog switch	4-channel switches driven by four 3-input NOR decode gates	

Large-Scale Integrated Circuits

Large-scale integrated circuits (LSICs) are the next extension of I-C techniques for both bipolar and unipolar types such as the DTL, RTL, TTL, and the FET–MOS devices covered in the immediately preceding section. With better control of processing and larger chips, it is inevitable that the trend is toward more circuit elements on a single chip. The LSICs are proof of this trend.

If production demands are sufficiently great, a special LSIC can be developed and produced on order. However, when more and more logic is put on a single chip, the ability to satisfy more and more customers with this stock configuration diminishes. As a result, LSIC manufacturers seek methods to tailor-make the logic to fit consumer requirements. One approach is to build up a series of identical cells on the chip, each containing a quantity of independent circuit elements. The device is tailored by controlling the interconnections of these elements both inside and between the cells. There must be some plan to allow crossovers of interconnecting paths if maximum flexibility is to be obtained. Such a plan can be formulated if one level of connection is accomplished on the isolating layer immediately above the chip surface. A second insulating layer is laid over the first for the second layer of connections to be processed upon. Interconnections between the layers is by means of planned holes filled with conductor material.

Figure 8-18 is an example of an LSIC. The particular example is a 10-bit shift register with a parallel output. All the necessary gates and flip-flops for the 10 stages are included on this single ¼-in. square chip.

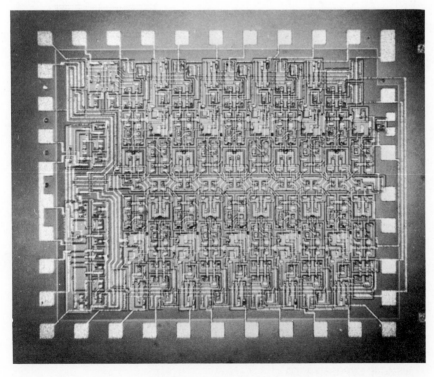

FIG. 8-18 Parallel-access shift-register counter (courtesy Honeywell, Inc., Florida Division).

Actually the flip-flop is a *master-slave design*† with 20 binaries and 30 gates included. The package is designed with 40 connecting leads. It is compatible with typical I-C bipolar logic of the DTL or TTL variety.

MANUFACTURE OF INTEGRATED-CIRCUIT CHIPS

The process used to form planar transistors is generally also used to form I-C chips, although manufacturers differ somewhat in the precise techniques.

In a planar transistor, a chip of silicon is coated with silicon oxide, then successively processed to form (within the individual chip) the emitter and base areas. Upon completion of this process, aluminum is deposited

† The term *master-slave design* is modern computer parlance for a two-stage flip-flop of the gated variety (previously discussed).

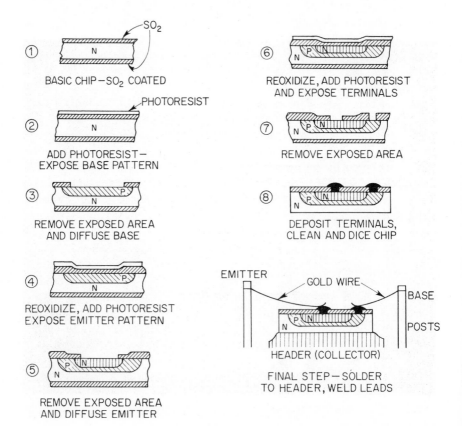

① BASIC CHIP—SO₂ COATED

② ADD PHOTORESIST— EXPOSE BASE PATTERN

③ REMOVE EXPOSED AREA AND DIFFUSE BASE

④ REOXIDIZE, ADD PHOTORESIST EXPOSE EMITTER PATTERN

⑤ REMOVE EXPOSED AREA AND DIFFUSE EMITTER

⑥ REOXIDIZE, ADD PHOTORESIST AND EXPOSE TERMINALS

⑦ REMOVE EXPOSED AREA

⑧ DEPOSIT TERMINALS, CLEAN AND DICE CHIP

FINAL STEP—SOLDER TO HEADER, WELD LEADS

FIG. 8-19 The planar process.

for the eventual connection of the terminal-post wire leads. These connections are usually made by compression bonding a gold wire to the chip pads. This wire is welded in turn to the terminal post. The entire process can be traced by referring to Fig. 8-19.

The exact process involves coating the silicon oxide with a photo sensitive material, photographing a pattern onto the oxide surface, and etching away the pattern. The chip is next placed in a diffusion furnace. At this point, an impurity is diffused into the chip to form a P-(N-)region. For example, a P-region will be formed if the chip is N. After the diffusion, the area is again coated with an oxide and the process repeated to end up with a second N-region within the diffused P-region in this example. The next step is to plate the diffused surface with a coating of aluminum at the point where leads are bonded for connections. Finally, the substrate is subdivided and the individual chips separated for assembly into the final package.

The process just described will result in an NPN transistor. The difference between the manufacture of a transistor and an I-C is the complexity of the surface pattern and the number of steps to the process. Individual transistors, diodes, resistors, and capacitors can all be diffused into a single chip. The separation of elements on the chip is generally accomplished by back-biasing areas within the chip, although complete isolation of the element cells is possible by special insulating processes. Interconnections between areas on the chip are accomplished by depositing aluminum paths over the surface of the oxide between contact points. A complete chip containing multiple circuits is normally 0.1 in. square or less. After the chips are completely formed, the substrate is subdivided and the individual chip is mounted in the header. The connecting wires are bonded to the chip pads and welded to the terminal posts. An example of a finished chip was given in Fig. 8-9. An example of the components that can be built into a chip is illustrated by Fig. 8-20.

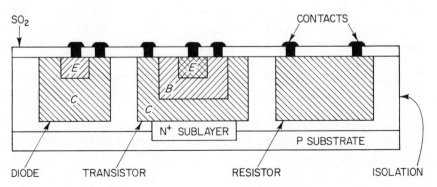

FIG. 8-20 Components on a chip.

OTHER PACKAGING APPROACHES

Although the I-C, in which one chip contains multiple circuits, represents a tremendous advance, yet further advantages in compressed packaging are expected. One proposed technique involves packing up to 25 chips under a single cover and providing interconnections between chips via conducting paths on a substrate. The connections are made by fingers welded to the chip pad on one end and to the substrate pad on the other.

Another method, termed *flip-chip,* involves placing minute soldered balls on the chip pads, turning the chip over (upside down), and applying heat to melt the solder for the connection. The result of this process is that the upside-down chip becomes soldered fast to pads on a substrate. The substrate paths make the necessary interchip connections. This method has been proposed and used by General Electric Company and Teledyne Inc., successfully.

Complete combinational circuits can be packaged in this manner with only a few external leads required to bring in power and for package interconnections. This approach should ease the problem of complex interconnect boards and should reduce required board interconnections drastically.

Other advantages of such a packaging technique include better heat removal characteristics, high reliability (because more of the processing is under clean-room control), and less noise susceptibility because of a built-in ground plane.

SUMMARY

In this chapter the discussion centered on generic forms of transistor logic. Examples of DCTL, RTC, RCTL, DTL, ECTL, and TTL logic were given along with their characteristics. The NAND gate element was usually considered, it being a typical example of the complete logic family. Examined briefly were FET–MOS, and LSIC devices. Their usage will tend to surplant the I-C chips so widely used in 1966 and 1967.

Examples were given of the way single I-C flat packs and also groups of these devices packaged on module boards may be used to create combinational logic.

An illustration of the process of creating transistor and I-C chips was outlined briefly. The subject was followed by a short treatment of future packaging techniques.

REVIEW QUESTIONS AND PROBLEMS

8-1. What are the advantages of DCTL logic? What are its disadvantages?

8-2. What are some of the advantages claimed for DTL logic? What are some of its disadvantages?

8-3. What are some of the advantages claimed for TTL (T^2L) logic? Evaluate DTL versus high-level TTL logic.

8-4. With what logic elements would you construct an up counter that counts at 5 MHz? Why?

8-5. Mechanize $f(x) = AB\overline{C} + \overline{A}BC + ABC$ with DTL logic. Repeat the exercise with another logic, such as FET–MOS logic.

8-6. What are some of the advantages of the *flip-chip* construction technique?

8-7. What is meant by the terms *fan-in* and *fan-out* applied to logic elements?

8-8. What is the relationship between fan-in, fan-out, and circuit speed (rise and fall times)?

8-9. The SE 110 and the SE 150 are made from the same chip. How is this possible?

8-10. Increasing the complexity (adding additional elements) of an I-C improves the circuits in some respects. Name some of these improvements. Give examples. Name some of the disadvantages of the more complex devices.

8-11. What is the reason that FET–MOS devices and bipolar I-Cs are not generally compatible?

8-12. Design a serial full adder using NAND logic such as the SN 930 series, and use an active device such as a flip-flop to give the necessary delay for C_n.

$+, -, \pm, \times,$ compare

THE ARITHMETIC
SECTION 9

This chapter and the following three deal with the *major subsections* of the data processor. This chapter discusses the *arithmetic section* of a simple binary computer. The following chapters consider in turn the memory, the control, and the input–output subsections of the processor.

The principal function of the arithmetic section is, of course, to perform computations. It is the section that adds, subtracts, multiplies, divides, compares, and (in some processors) performs square roots, floating-point operations, etc. We shall only consider here the more common operations of signed addition (an operation that permits subtraction, if one considers adding a positive and negative number to be subtraction), multiplication, and division. The hardware and methods used for square root and floating-point operations will not be covered in this text.

Arithmetic units may be either serial or parallel in their operation. Some designs are a combination of both. The serial form of arithmetic operations will be considered first, followed by a rather short example of a parallel organization. It will be shown that the principles applying to serial and parallel operation do not differ appreciably except in the detailed method of mechanization.

The early computers in general were serial machines. This approach was dictated by the desire to minimize hardware and by the memory types originally available. Those computers having a magnetic drum used the drum tracks both for memory and for the necessary circulating registers required in arithmetic operations.

Because serial computers require the use of recirculating registers, it is important to understand how these registers can be used to shift binary numbers to the right or to the left. Shifting operations of this type are required in computations. A *recirculating register* may be defined as a register in which the binary data are serially moved out one end (for instance, the right-hand end) and then transferred back into the left-hand side. The bits remain in their respective places. The recirculation may be better understood if viewed as if the bits were toy cars on a circular track. Such recirculating registers can be constructed from (1) delay lines; (2) a track on a magnetic drum, where a data word is read out by one head and read back on a second; or (3) a shift register, where the output end is fed back to the input. Although a shift register is unique (compared with the other two devices) from the standpoint that its logic can be designed to shift either to the right or to the left, the design generally employed is for right-hand shifts only. If a two-place right shift is desired, the word can be shifted by employing only two shift clock pulses—or, in the recirculating mode, a number of clock pulses equal to the register length (or a multiple thereof) plus two pulses. Similarly, a left shift in the recirculating mode can be achieved by applying shift clock pulses numerically equal to the register length (or a multiple thereof) minus two pulses.

The same basic approach applies when delay lines are used in the recirculation register, as shown in Fig. 9-1. Here a *left* shift is obtained by adding the required equivalent bit delay in the recirculation (feedback) path. For a one-bit left shift, an equivalent delay of one-bit time would be added to the recirculating path. By the same reasoning, a required right-hand shift in the recirculating mode is achieved by *reducing* the feedback path delay by the appropriate number of bit times. A one-bit right shift can be obtained by effectively *shortening* the register by one bit length. In this respect, the delay line register differs from the shift register. In order to obtain the right-hand shift with a delay line, a recirculation is necessary; whereas, in the simple shift register, only a single clock pulse is needed to accomplish the one-bit right shift.

Before beginning a discussion of the elements of a *serial arithmetic processor* and especially the arithmetic processes themselves, a representation for the numbers involved must first be adopted. For the sake of simplicity, only pure binary number processing will be used. (Although decimal numbers in coded form are processed in many digital computers, the basic arithmetic operations can be illustrated more simply if restricted to binary numbers.) In the simple illustrations to follow, binary whole number operations only will be assumed. The *magnitude* of the number will be represented by the magnitude of the binary number in the form used previously

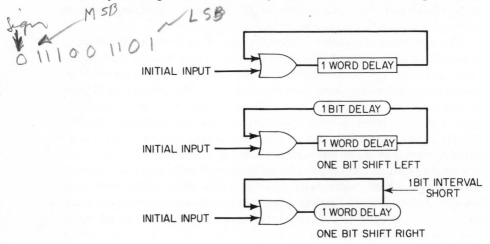

FIG. 9-1   Left and right shift by recirculation.

in Chapter 3. The *sign* of the number will be indicated by a "0" in the extreme left-hand bit position for a positive number (011011) and a "1" in the extreme left-hand bit position for a negative number (110110). The arrangement of bit magnitudes will be the LSB on the extreme right with the normal sequence of increasing bit magnitude proceeding to the left. The MSB possible occupies the adjacent position just to the right of the sign bit. Once the arithmetic process begins, the signs of the numbers involved must be sensed, remembered, and stored, but the sign bits are not necessarily recirculated in any serial processing. After an arithmetic process is completed, it is assumed that the computed results will be sent back to the memory or to other registers outside the arithmetic section in the same form the data were received—i.e., numbers will consist of a sign bit and a binary number representing magnitude. Internally it may also be necessary to *complement* the results of the computation before the number results are transported anywhere outside the arithmetic section. Usually, before allowing a number to leave the arithmetic section, the last step is to restore its proper sign. In multiplication and division, sign control is easy because the sign of the results depends strictly on the *initial* signs of the original numbers. In *signed addition,* the sign of the results depends on the sign of the original numbers and the results of the addition process as detected by the generation of an *overflow* pulse. Therefore, in signed number addition, multiplication, and division, one must consider the logic and organization that accomplishes the arithmetic operation, the logic that controls the sign, and the logic that controls and times the arithmetic process. All three of these logic groupings will be considered in the following sections, but most emphasis will be on the organizational section that does the processing. The sign control parameters and timing control functions will be touched on only briefly. There is some precedence for ignoring the control aspects altogether in a chapter devoted to arithmetic operations and lumping control functions separately (see Chapter 11). The level of treatment will be on the logic *block* level rather than on the circuit logic level. The interest now is: How does the arithmetic processor function? Previous chapters discussed the logic of the individual component building blocks. In this chapter, the blocks are used and combined to do the actual computing.

The presentation first covers the individual processes of signed addition, multiplication, and division with serial-mode hardware. With this background, the transition to parallel-mode hardware and to a total processing unit (one that does the total arithmetic function) will proceed more smoothly.

A SERIAL BINARY ADDER

The basic operation of serial addition with full adders is shown in Fig. 9-2. Here the two numbers to be added are directed to the respective *A* and *B* inputs of the full adder. The operations at individual bit times and the progressive build-up of the sum in the accumulator should be evident from the sequence of steps *a* to *e* in the figure.

The serial adder in general performs binary addition of *signed* binary numbers. The process of signed addition was discussed briefly in Chapter 3 and illustrated by Table 3-2. The student may find a review of this section helpful in following the steps of Fig. 9-2.

A block diagram showing how such an adder functions is shown in Fig. 9-3. Either or both numbers to be added may be positive or negative, as identified by their respective sign bits, 0 or 1. Consequently, words in and out of *memory* will always be in the form of a magnitude plus a sign bit. It will be assumed further that the serial word is always shifted through the adder LSB first. This sign bit is sensed by a special logic network called the *Sign Control Network* (SCN). This sensing determines which of the two (or whether both) serial complementers (1 and 2) are to be placed in the flow path during the actual addition process. These sign

bits are ignored when actually performing addition on the individual bits
of the two number words

The addition process will be described, but little explanation will be
given in this chapter on the generation of the pulse and waveforms re-

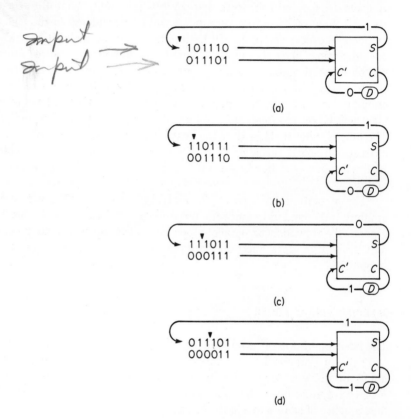

FIG. 9-2   Basic serial addition process.

quired to time and control the process. This will be discussed in Chapter
11. The adder shown in Fig. 9-3 operates in the following sequence:

1. The first number to be added is serially routed from the memory via
   the memory buffer register (MBR) to the register, often called the
   accumulator because the sums from separate additions may be permitted to build up in this register. For instance, during multiplication,
   the product is generated by successive additions. This product build up
   occurs in the A register (accumulator).
2. The actual addition process begins when the second word in the MBR
   is shifted out through the adder one bit at a time, LSD first; at the same

Sign · MSB   LSB

should have been
here   complementer

Memory Buffer
Reg.

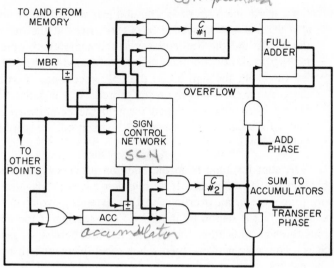

1. To add binary numbers the process is as follows:

A	10111	
MBR	11011	
A_1	110010	First sum
MBR	10001	
A_2	1000011	Second sum
MBR	10010	
A_3	1010101	Third sum, etc.

C #3
comp to
result

2. Assume numbers are stored in memory as magnitude
plus sign (that is, not in complement form if negative):

FUNCTION TABLE FOR COMPLEMENTERS
(ADD OPERATION)

A	B	Compl. 1	Compl. 2	Carry	Compl. 3	Sign output
+	+	No	No	No	No	+
−	−	Yes	Yes	Yes	Yes	−
+ > −		No	Yes	Yes	No	+
− > +		Yes	No	No	Yes	−
− < +		Yes	No	Yes	No	+
+ < −		No	Yes	No	Yes	−

NOTE: A similar table could be drawn for
subtraction

FIG. 9-3   Serial adder and subtractor.

Page 204
9-15   Logic Dia

time, word one from the accumulator is shifted to the adder, also one bit at a time. Each respective bit (2^n) arrives at the full adder from both the MBR and the accumulator at the same clock time. Thus the normal serial binary add operation is performed by the adder. The extreme left-hand bit, the sign bit, is the only exception. This bit is sensed initially by the SCN and the result stored. If a negative "1" is sensed, the binary word bits are routed through the *complementer* of the respective word channel. If a positive "0" is sensed, the word bits flow *directly* to the adder.

The sum resulting from the addition process is recirculated and stored back in the accumulator. If an overflow bit is propagated during the adding process, i.e., an overflow bit that extends beyond the MSB bit of the sum, this fact is sensed by the SCN. The sensing of the above overflow bit plus the sign indication for the original numbers is sensed together by the SCN. The logic network then sets the complementer in the output path to the memory so that the word in the accumulator (if in complement form) is changed back to the prescribed form of amplitude with sign indicated by the extreme MSB bit. Although the word could exist in the accumulator directly after addition in complement form, for the method chosen, it is converted back to the form of amplitude and sign bit before transfer back to the memory. The SCN sets complementer 2 properly when a complemented number appears in the accumulator. The student will note that complementer 2 serves two functions: (1) it provides a complementation of the initial accumulator stored word if that word is negative; and (2) it provides a recomplementation of a negative number word upon transfer back to the rapid-access memory.

The logic for the SCN is easily determined by converting the table of Fig. 9-3 to a truth table. At the proper time, as the result of its interrogation of the signals routed to it, the proper sign bit for output is generated.

(Since subtraction is essentially included in signed addition, it will not be considered further at this time.)

SERIAL BINARY MULTIPLICATION

The multiplication process sequence is shown in Fig. 9-4. It follows the process described in Chapter 3 for multiplication. If the multiplier decision bit is a "1," the multiplicand is directed through the adder and summed with the partial product then existing in the accumulation. A single bit right shift of the new partial product and multiplier follows directly. If the multiplier decision bit is a "0," a single right shift of the partial-product occurs along with a single right shift of the multiplier. After either of the above steps, whichever occurs, the next multiplier bit obtained by the above right shift is sensed for the next decision step. This second step and those following are identical with the first. The process continues until the multiplication process concludes.

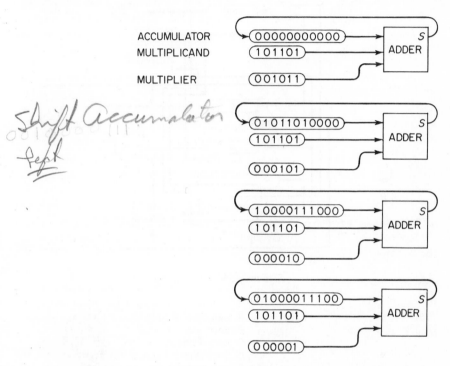

FIG. 9-4 Basic serial multiplication process.

As can be seen from the above, multiplication is really an extension of addition but with two additional registers for processing, as shown in Fig. 9-5. A basic difference between addition and multiplication exists in the sign problem. The sign of the resulting product is determined merely by noting the sign digits in the two *original* words to be multiplied (the multiplier and the multiplicand). Therefore, the sign control network (SCN) for multiplication is simple. It senses the two sign digits and instantly determines what sign must be added to the product. The complementers are *not* required in multiplication since product magnitude is *not* a function of the signs of the two numbers to be multiplied.

In the multiplication process, the multiplicand is shifted from the memory buffer register (MBR) to the M register and stored for further use. The multiplier is then shifted directly from the MBR to the Q register and stored. The multiplication then proceeds as shown in Fig. 9-5.

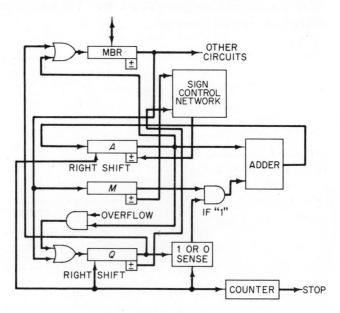

The multiplication process:

		110111
		x 1011
A.	Add multiplicand	110111
B.	Shift right 1 place	110111
C.	Add *A* and *B*	10100101
D.	Shift right 1 place	10100101
E.	Add 000...	000000
F.	Add *D* and *E*	10100101
G.	Shift right 1 place	10100101
H.	Add multiplicand	110111
		1001011101

FIG. 9-5 Serial binary multiplication.

The Q register contents is shifted right "1" bit, and the LSB of the multiplier is sensed to determine whether it is a "1" or "0." If a "1," the multiplicand is shifted into the adder and the partial sum builds up in the accumulator. For the first addition, all zeros are in the accumulator; hence, the multiplicand itself appears in the accumulator. The accumulator is now shifted "1" bit to the right.

If "0" is the LSB of the multiplier, the multiplicand addition is blocked by an open AND gate and only the partial product sum in the accumulator can flow through the adder. This points to a potential way to speed up the multiplication process. That is, whenever a "0" is sensed in the multiplier, the accumulator shifts one bit right. With discrete bit registers, no circulation is needed nor is any desired because of the time it requires. If the registers are delay lines and recirculation is required to perform the shifts, then the suggested shortcut is obviously impossible.

Continuing with the process, the next step following the above recirculation is a one-bit right shift of the multiplier. The former LSB is lost and the second multiplier bit now determines whether or not the multiplicand is to be added to the initial partial product.

This process continues until all bits of the muliplier are tested. As the partial product builds in the accumulator, it is repeatedly shifted to the right. Eventually, if both the original numbers approach the full complement of bits (large numbers), the shifted partial product will begin to spill out of the right side of the accumulator. When this occurs, the system operator has to make a choice. Either he ignores the bits lost because of right-hand spillover and accepts the product's most significant portion, or (if he cares to preserve the numerical accuracy) he may allow the spillover to overflow into another register. If the latter option is chosen (no loss of data accuracy permitted), it is customary in some designs to route the spillover into the Q register where it is temporarily stored. This procedure is possible because, as the multiplier is being shifted to the right in the Q register, it leaves bit positions open to the left, which can be used for this overflow partial product storage.

In this manner, only two registers have been added to the original adder to make it perform signed multiplication. Of course, quite an extensive addition has been made to the control logic to achieve this operation. (This will be explored later in Chapter 11.) In addition to this extra gating, to perform multiplication a counter is required to keep count of the right-shift sequences of the multiplier. When the proper number of shifts have been tabulated by the counter, the multiplication process stops.

answer for mult. of I - 6 bits = more than 6 bits

SERIAL BINARY DIVISION *two away to do it 1st throw away least significant bits*

The process of serial binary division, which simulates decimal long division, is shown in Figs. 9-6 and 9-7. The student will note some simplification of normal decimal long division inasmuch as the quotient digits are only "1's" and "0's." This leaves only two choices in determining the values of the divisor to be subtracted from the dividend, either the divisor times "1" or the divisor times "0." This leads to a relative simple division process in

or store answer for 2 reg. (i.e A + Q regs.)

principle, but one that still remains somewhat complex to mechanize. Again we assume shift techniques can be employed rather than the alternate method involving time-consuming successive subtractions.

To mechanize the process of the example shown in Fig. 9-7, the accumulator (which presumably contains the dividend) is shifted one place *left* after each subtraction.

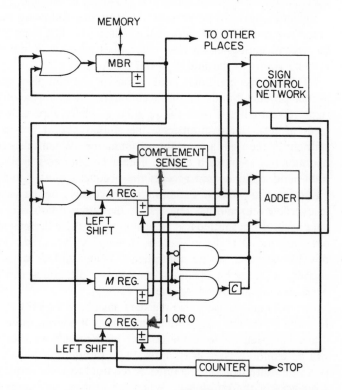

FIG. 9-6   Serial binary division.

The mechanism of division proceeds as follows: The dividend is first entered left to right serially LSB first into the accumulator. Directly following the loading of the accumulator, the divisor is similarly loaded into the M register. In the same manner as multiplication, the (SCN) determines the eventual sign by sensing the sign bits of the two numbers involved in the division. Again, only positive numbers are acted upon in this process, and the final sign is restored at the completion of the division.

The actual process begins (see Fig. 9-6) by routing the dividend (from the A register) and the divisor (from the M register) through the adder. The complementer in the M-register path is made operational so that the

Binary Division:

```
              01010 (quotient)
1110 | 10001100 (dividend)
       0000
       10001100
        1110
       00011100
        0000
       00011100
         1110
       00000000
           0000
```

The following steps are required:

① Compare: 10001100
              1110

The divisor is greater than the dividend.
Put "O" in the quotient. Do not subtract.
Shift dividend one place left. Put O in
quotient first slot.

② Compare: 10001100
              1110

The divisor is less than the dividend.
Put a "1" in the quotient (second slot).
Subtract divisor and shift remainder 1
place to the left.

③ Compare: 000111000
              1110

This is the same as ①. Do not
subtract. Shift dividend 1 place to left.

④ Compare: 00011100
             1110

This is the same as ②. Subtract and
shift the dividend 1 place to the left.
This leaves 0000; hence, the quotient
after this point has only "O"s entered;
01010 is in quotient at this point.

Fig. 9-7 Binary division example.

word from M subtracts from the accumulator word. If a valid subtraction
is obtained, i.e., the number remaining in the accumulator after the first subtraction is positive and not a complement, a "1" is inserted in the extreme
right-hand bit position of the Q register. The A-register remainder is now
shifted one bit to the left, and a second subtraction is attempted.

If the original subtraction was not valid, i.e., if the resulting number in the accumulator was a complement, this indicates the divisor is larger than the dividend, and (as in long division) a smaller product of divisor and trial quotient must be employed. In this case, the choice is limited to "1" or "0"; hence, the failure to provide a valid subtraction requires a "0" to be put into the extreme right-hand position of the Q register instead of a "1."

The tally of "1's" and "0's" in this Q register will be the quotient (the results of the division). On successive trials, it is necessary to shift the accumulator one bit to the left for each attempted division of the dividend by the divisor. At the end of the process, the quotient bits will be in their proper relative positions, e.g., the MSD is to the extreme left.

There now remains one problem. If a trial division is performed and the dividend in the A register appears as a complemented number, it is not a valid number. To return to the proper condition, it is necessary to follow each complemented result with a normal add of the divisor back to the accumulator.

This operation then restores the dividend to its position prior to the ill-fated subtraction attempt. After this routine restoration, the accumulator is shifted one place left and the next trial subtraction attempted. This second attempt is made, therefore, from a remainder twice the former magnitude because of the accumulator's left-hand 1-bit shift. (The reader should think about this point.)

Again, as in multiplication, a counter is required to record the number of subtractions to be performed so that the division process is stopped at the proper point. The build-up of the quotient in the Q register, along with the remainder in the accumulator after the proper number of subtractions, gives the final results required. As the final step, the proper sign is assigned to the quotient by the SCN.

The examples given above are only a few of the ways that the process may be mechanized with digital logic. Another approach to the division process is to circulate the dividend and divisor through a comparator first; there the decision is made as to whether or not to subtract the divisor before shifting the accumulator one step to the left. The processor time for this latter approach is longer because two-word circulations are necessary for each subtraction step.

The comparison process discussed in the last paragraph is shown in Fig. 9-7. The following tabulation further illustrates the process shown in Fig. 9-6.

Step 1. Subtract:

```
    10001100
  -     1110
  1 10101100    (carry 1)
```

Step 2. Note that the *carry* indicates an invalid subtraction. Put 0 in LSD of quotient. Now add back divisor:

$$
\begin{array}{r}
10101100 \\
+\ 1110 \\
\hline
1\overline{)10001100}
\end{array} \quad \text{(ignore carry)}
$$

Step 3. Shift accumulator and quotient one place left and try the next subtraction:

$$
\begin{array}{r}
10001100 \\
-\ 1110 \\
\hline
0\overline{)00011100}
\end{array} \quad \text{(carry 0)}
$$

Step 4. This subtraction is valid. Put a 1 in LSD of quotient. Move accumulator and quotient one place left.

Step 5. Subtract:

$$
\begin{array}{r}
000111000 \\
-\ 1110 \\
\hline
1\overline{)111001000}
\end{array} \quad \text{(carry 1)}
$$

Step 6. Note *carry* indicates an invalid subtraction; so repeat Step 2:

$$
\begin{array}{r}
111001000 \\
+\ 1110 \\
\hline
0\overline{)000111000}
\end{array}
$$

Step 7. Shift accumulator and quotient one place left and try next subtraction:

$$
\begin{array}{r}
000111000 \\
-\ 1110 \\
\hline
000000000
\end{array}
$$

Step 8. Subtraction is valid. Put 1 in LSD of quotient and shift both accumulator and quotient one place left.

(*This process continues until the division is complete.*)

In each of the above cases, we have limited ourselves to three registers (M, Q, and A) in the arithmetic process. The indication is that these are not simple registers and require rather unique shifting capabilities and multiple ways to enter or remove data (consider the Q register). However, the following facts stand out: The arithmetic unit can be constructed with few registers, but these registers serve different purposes during a given process at any given moment. Extensive gating, therefore, is required, and a rather complex control and timing of this gating is necessary.

Not all computers incorporate multiply and divide logic. If program time permits, these relatively complex processes may not be accomplished by hardware but by programming itself. In this case, the basic process of add, complement, shift left one place, shift right one place, and shift the entire word right accomplishes the process of multiplying or dividing completely.

On the other hand, the more complex automatic units not only will perform binary addition, subtraction, multiplication, and division but may have the logic to accept numbers in either octal or decimal form and perform the basic operations outlined on either octal coded or decimal coded numbers.

PARALLEL MECHANIZATION OF ARITHMETIC OPERATIONS

Addition

Parallel mechanization of binary addition requires a *parallel transfer* of the binary numbers from the respective A and B registers through a parallel adder, with the results placed back in register A. As in binary serial addition, the same problem of determining the sign of the addition sum remains and the sign to assign to it is specified by the same truth table. A block diagram for the parallel adder is given in Fig. 9-8. This process of

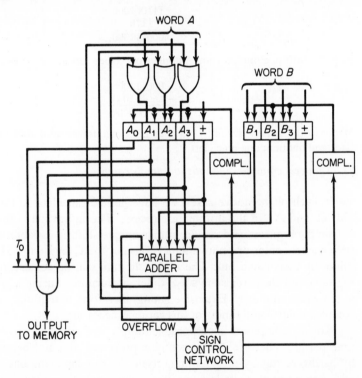

FIG. 9-8 Binary parallel adder.

parallel addition is similar to that of serial addition, except for the parallel data transfers and the different timing sequences appropriate to the parallel transfer process.

Multiplication

Parallel binary multiplication (Fig. 9-9) follows the same process as serial binary multiplication except, as the student may suspect, the transfers

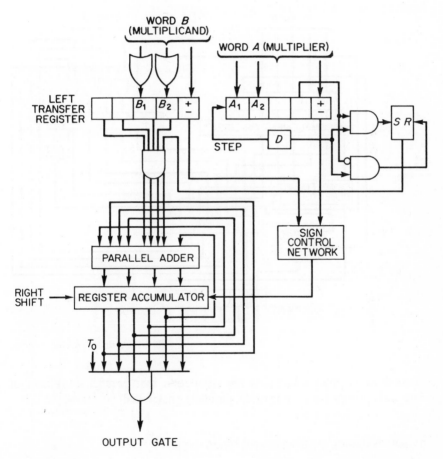

FIG. 9-9   Binary parallel multiplier.

from register to register are parallel. Again the extreme right-hand bit of the multiplier determines whether the multiplicand is added to the partial product or zeros are added. The shift right of the accumulator is accomplished by method appropriate to parallel devices. The register storing the partial or final sum is lengthened to take care of the right extension as the product builds.

Division

The block diagram of a parallel division processor is shown in Fig. 9-10. The steps performed are similar to those performed for the binary

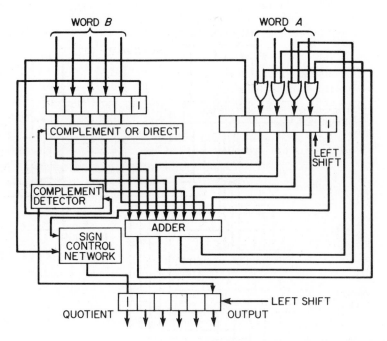

FIG. 9-10 Binary parallel divider.

serial division process but with the stipulation that parallel movement of data and appropriate shifting of the parallel register shall be provided.

OTHER REMARKS ON BINARY MULTIPLICATION

In performing machine arithmetic, many other compromise solutions are used. One of these involves the design of an adder to handle multiplication partly in serial and partly in parallel form. This modification has two advantages: (1) less hardware than in parallel organization, and (2) greater speed than in serial organization.

Another type of compromise that reduces multiplication time is the consideration of sensing two-bit increments of the multiplier. On the basis of how these two bits are sensed, *add* either one times the multiplicand, two times the multiplicand, or one-half times the multiplicand according to a previously determined truth table. This approach can be extended to three or four bits at a time and has been frequently applied.

As indicated above, multiplication is often accomplished by *two multiplier bits* at a time. This mechanization roughly cuts in half the time needed to perform a multiplication (with only a slight increase in hardware). The justification of this method is based on several simple rules according to the successive groupings right to left of the multiplication bits, as follows:

00 implies two right-hand shifts only of the partial product.

01 implies one addition of the multiplicand to the partial product, then two right-hand shifts.

10 implies one right shift, followed by one addition of the multiplicand to the partial product, followed by one more right shift. (This results in adding $2\times$ the multiplicand.)

11 implies one addition of the multiplicand, followed by a right shift of the partial product, plus a second addition of the multiplicand followed by a second shift. (This results in adding $3\times$ the multiplicand.)

The block diagrams of an organization that will do two-bit multiplying is shown in Fig. 9-11. The multiplier digits ($\times\times$) set up the gating according to the truth table (Table 9-1). The use of two adders reduces the time for processing the "11"; otherwise, additional switching and two circulations through the main adder would be required. As in the previous example of a serial signed-number addition, the mechanization is such that, rather than left shifts to the multiplicand, the partial product itself is shifted to the right, which substitutes for the required left shift to the multiplicand.

TOTAL ARITHMETIC UNIT

Serial Arithmetic Unit

The separate arithmetic operations described earlier in this chapter in most computers are all accomplished in a single computer subsection. This approach is possible since the basic operations of arithmetic involve signed addition, temporary storage, and word shifts within the registers involved. At the most, four registers have been used, and one of these, the MBR, is not normally considered a part of the arithmetic section. This leaves the A, Q, and M registers as solely associated with arithmetic functions. These

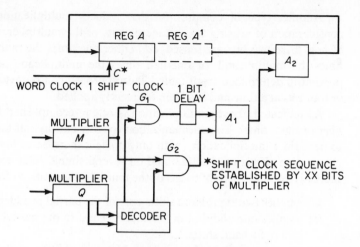

Serial Multiplication process 2−bit at a time:

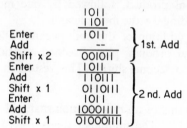

```
                    1011
                    1101
Enter               1011      ⎫
Add                  --       ⎬ 1st. Add
Shift x 2          001011     ⎭
Enter              1011       ⎫
Add               110111      ⎪
Shift x 1         0110111     ⎬ 2nd. Add
Enter              1011       ⎪
Add              10001111     ⎪
Shift x 1        01000111     ⎭
```

FIG. 9-11   Two-bit-at-a-time multiplier.

registers and their operation are controlled by timing signals originating within a control section. This control section may be either a separate and distinct subsection or part of the arithmetic subsection itself. The particular command specifying the arithmetic operation, when executed by the computer, sets in motion the proper sequence of timing signals. These se-

TABLE 9-1

Truth table for two-bit multiplier

Bit grouping	Multiplication to multiplicand	Use A_1	G_1	G_1
0 0	0	0	0	0
0 1	1×	0	1	0
1 0	2×	1	0	1
1 1	3×	1	1	1

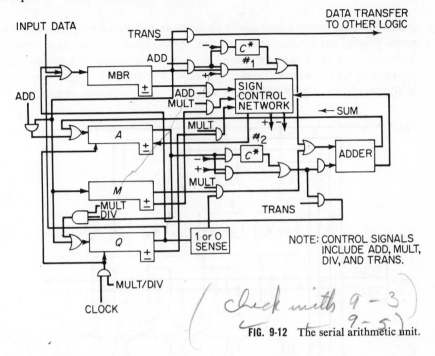

FIG. 9-12 The serial arithmetic unit.

quences, unique for each function, control the gates specifically for each respective operation the arithmetic unit is to perform.

A block diagram of a serial arithmetic unit is shown in Fig. 9-12. In this diagram, the operational control is derived from control signals to the respective gates. For addition, the MBR and A register are connected as they would be in Fig. 9-3. In this case, the M and Q registers are operated in the mode illustrated by Fig. 9-4. The gating associated with the registers and the timing signals generated by the control will effectively reproduce the system of Fig. 9-4. The same general statement can be made for the division process. In this case, the control gates and control signals reproduce the system of Fig. 9-5. The mode of the Q and A registers change radically from that of multiplication. To provide the A register with both left-shift and right-shift capability is often expensive in a serial system. As a result, the left-hand shift may be performed by a right-hand circulation with delay in the feedback path, as described previously. The same statement could apply to the Q register if the division quotient is built up by the left-hand shift process.

Parallel Arithmetic Unit

As previously shown, the parallel arithmetic unit differs from the serial arithmetic design in the way data are transferred between registers and, of course, in the adder itself. Other than this difference, however, the same general statements apply to the organization, timing, and control. Left and right shifts when required are either performed in two-way shift registers or by the use of transfer registers. The transfer register approach is illustrated by Fig. 9-13. Here the data word in upper register X, if

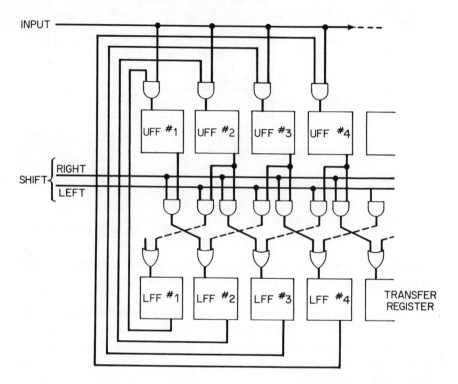

FIG. 9-13 Transfer registers.

shifted one place to the left, would be transferred via the dashed-line arrows. For a right-hand shift, the transfer would be via the solid-line arrows.

The organization of the parallel arithmetic unit is shown in Fig. 9-14. The similarity to the serial organization is easily noted. Again the control gating and timing segregates the operation into the processes illustrated by Figs. 9-8, 9-9, and 9-10.

Although the parallel transfer of data greatly speeds parallel arithmetic operations, the design of the parallel adder itself has a great influence on the speed of computations. In the parallel adder shown in Fig. 9-9, the *carry* under the proper circumstance could ripple down stage-by-stage from the LSB to the MSB end of the counter. This is a serial progression of the *carry* and is a moderately slow process. The way to speed up this *carry* propagation in a parallel adder design is to provide simultaneous carry between blocks of stages—two, three or four stages, for example. This technique then permits a carry from this block to the next higher block when the circumstances warrant. This design is followed in many of the more modern designs of parallel adders. Ingenious methods of carry anticipation

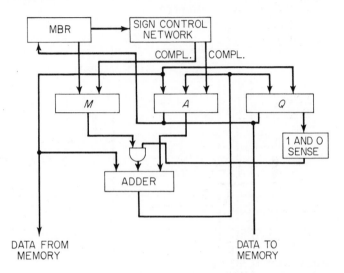

FIG. 9-14   Parallel arithmetic unit.

and propagation are used to reduce the limitation in adder speeds. A study of this aspect, although most interesting, is a subject in itself and would take more space to treat than would be reasonable in this text.

The composite SCN for the arithmetic unit is illustrated by the block diagram and logic of Fig. 9-15. The truth table for the logic diagram is obtained from Table 9-1.

The type of control logic associated with an arithmetic section is generalized in Fig. 9-16. Here the individual commands for add, multiply, divide, and compare are decoded and the necessary control pulses and levels are generated to control the arithmetic section. This association of the control logic with the arithmetic section is an optional one. In Chapter 11 the assumption is made that this control is part of the control section rather than the arithmetic section. Either organization is permissible and used commercially.

In Fig. 9-16, the add and compare commands require the time of a single computer cycle. As a result, the operation flip-flop, which defines the operation time for the command specified, is set and reset within the

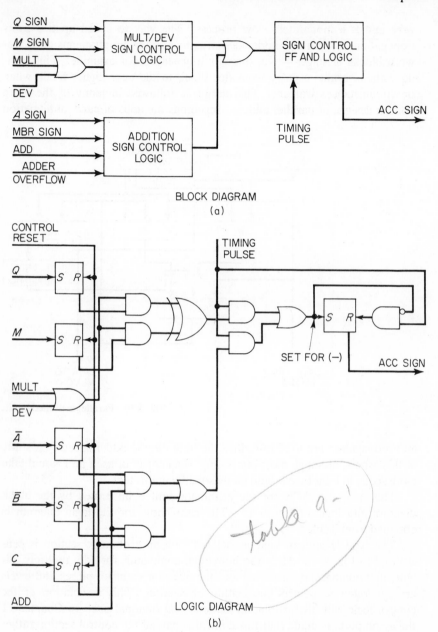

BLOCK DIAGRAM
(a)

LOGIC DIAGRAM
(b)

FIG. 9-15 Block diagram and logic for sign control network.

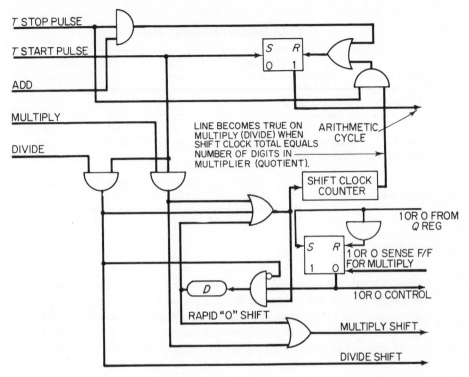

FIG. 9-16   Arithmetic unit control logic—simplified block diagram.

time of a single computer cycle. For multiplying and dividing, however, the process requires several computer cycles. For these, therefore, a counter is employed to ensure that the proper number of cycles will be available for the process. For multiplying, the counter is controlled by pulses that shift the multiplier bit to the logic that detects a "1" or "0." If a "0" is sensed, the shift pulse is immediately gated back to the Q register and the multiplier is again shifted 1 bit to the right. The total count to the counter is the same regardless of the number of "1's" or "0's" detected, but the time it takes to multiply is of course minimized when "0's" are in the multiplier, since no addition is required by a "0" multiplier bit and the count pulse is developed more quickly.

For the division process the same counter will be used to control the operation cycle. For this reason the logic is shared by the two processes. The control method adopted here would fall under the general classification of *decentralized* control, which is mentioned briefly in Chapter 11.

This section is concluded with Table 9-2 listing typical arithmetic processing times of some commercial computers that existed in 1967.

TABLE 9-2

Typical processor arithmetical speeds

Processor	Type	Add./subtr., μsec	Multiply, μsec	Divide, μsec	Memory cycle time, nsec
DDP516	Commercial control	1.92	5.28	10.56	940
Alert	Military	4.00	14.00	32.00	2000
Sigma 7	Commercial	2.26	4.90	12.30	850
Spectra 70/45	Commercial data processor	5.28	65.12	90.81	1440
Litton 304	Military	7.00	20.38	—	1600

RCA

SUMMARY

In this chapter, the operation of the arithmetic section of the computer was the central theme, but only after the fundamental operations of recirculating registers were examined in some detail. Next was defined the number organization with which the arithmetic unit operates. Following the definition of number organization, the actual methods of performing the arithmetic processes themselves received full attention. The serial processes were described first, followed by a brief resumé of the corresponding parallel approaches.

A speedup of the multiplication process occurs in some of the newer processor designs. This innovation uses more than a single bit in the multiplication process. A discussion of multiplication two bits at a time served to illustrate this general technique. The chapter concluded with a block-diagram example of a complete arithmetic section, which was really a combination of previous diagrams. The final table showed what could be expected of processors in terms of operation processing rates.

REVIEW QUESTIONS AND PROBLEMS

9-1. In the serial adder, what is the function of the sign control network (SCN)?

9-2. What is the function of complementer 2 in the serial adder?

9-3. When is it necessary to use double-length registers for the accumulator in the serial multiplier?

9-4. What is the reason for the addition after an improper subtraction in serial division? Is this operation necessary for parallel division?

9-5. If a 10-digit word requires 10 μsec to recirculate in the serial addition loop, estimate the time required to perform the addition of five 10-digit numbers and to return the resultant to the memory.

9-6. Describe in detail the operation of the binary parallel divider.

9-7. Trace the addition step by step of $+10110111$ to -00001011 through an adder circuit. How long should the process take if the system clock pulse rate were 1 MHz?

9-8. Trace the multiplication of the above two binary numbers through a serial multiplier process. Estimate the time of operation for a 2-MHz clock serial system; assume that you can shift without addition when "0's" are in the multiplier.

9-9. What speedup can be achieved by multiplication of two bits at a time?

9-10. Can you estimate approximately the total parts required to construct a binary multiplier? Show your table of parts.

9-11. Estimate the total parts required to construct a complete serial arithmetic unit. Show your table of parts.

9-12. What logic is required to process the *comparison* of two binary numbers in the arithmetic unit? Recommend a system to perform this operation.

THE MEMORY
SECTION 10

The memory section of the data processor, or computer, is that portion which stores both data and the instructions for the program under operation at that time. The transfers of data and instructions to and from the memory to other portions of the data processor are usually one word at a time and at a rate compatible with the processing speeds. The definition just stated refers to what is called the *internal memory* of the computer. It is this type of memory that is discussed in this chapter. *External memory*, the memory not intimately associated with the processor, is discussed in Chapter 13.

Up to the present, the limitations in the processing rates and total storage capability economically feasible in the typical computer have been due to the memory technology employed and its cost. The early machines were serial machines partly because delay-line and serial drum memory storage lent themselves admirably to serial systems. With the advent of the Williams' tube, a memory component with which a parallel transfer of data

auxiliary memory = external memory

excelled, parallel processor computer organizations increased rapidly. The familiar core memories used in 1967 follow basically the parallel organization taken with the Williams' tube. Whereas drum memories were not unusual as *internal* memories in many serial machines, modern usage generally limits their application to external memories. Although some serial machines still use delay lines, they are not the mercury type employed originally in EDVAC, SEAC, etc. The modern, improved types are glass or quartz slabs, in which sonic paths, properly directed, store data by the familiar recirculating loop method. These new delay-line memories are much more stable than their predecessors.

Parallel random-access memories have *ferrite* cores, or some other methods of storing digital *bits* of information in a *stationary* manner. Data are entered or retrieved from these memories one word at a time from 0.5 to 5 μsec. Because of this relatively rapid *access time,* parallel data transfers and parallel organizations are attractive. The older serial *sonic* memories generally required a waiting time for a specific period (sometimes called a *major cycle*) of many word times before an access to the particular word that was desired could be obtained.

Any *internal memory* has three main functions to perform in a digital computer. These functions include:

1. The temporary storage of numbers and instructions directed to and from the input–output
2. The storage of all data and instructions required for the problem being handled by the computer
3. Temporary storage of the intermediate results of any calculation

MEMORY CLASSIFICATIONS

Memory may be classified in many ways. A partial list of these classifications follows:

1. *Location.* This classification was discussed briefly in the chapter introduction. For emphasis, however, a fuller discussion follows at this point. Memories can be intimately associated with the internal logic of the computer, and, therefore, the time involved in processing information from or placing information into them is short (in the order of one-word time or less). Such memories are integral with the computer and are aptly named *fast-access* memories.

Other memory devices are *external* to the processor and require access through the input–output section. Such memories generally transfer data in blocks of many words because to transfer a single word is inefficient from the standpoint of computer timing. Access to the point where the transfer can start takes from a few milliseconds to several seconds depending on whether the external memory is a magnetic drum or a magetic tape transport. Therefore, memories may be classified as to their location—internal or external to the computer or central processor. As pointed out, a companion classification considers access time or the time required to move data (transfer data). A more exact definition is the time interval between the request for transfer of data and the actual completion of the transfer. This is termed *memory cycle time*.

2. *Physical type.* Memory designs may be of many different types; the more popular at present include:

   a. Magnetic drums, disks, and tapes
   b. Magnetic cores, magnetic thin films, and plated wire
   c. Delay lines
   d. Ferroelectric memories
   e. Miscellaneous types
      (1) Cryogenics
      (2) Aperture plate
      (3) Tunnel diode
      (4) LSICs

3. *Type of transfer.* Serial or parallel word transfer is also an important distinction which serves to classify memories.

4. *Survival of data during a power outage.* A memory which serves to maintain information during a *power outage* (power lost or turned off) is said to be nonvolatile. Magnetic drums generally fall into this classification; whereas delay lines are normally *volatile* memories, i.e., all the data stored is lost the instant word circulation ceases.

5. *Usage.* Memories can be classified according to *use*. For example, in some cases the data will never change; a table of logarithms, or trigonometric functions, would thus constitute a permanent memory. In other uses, the memory contents continually must change as the problem solution proceeds to alter the memory. This is an example of a *nonpermanent* or *alterable* memory.

6. *Method of address.* Most computer memories are addressed in a haphazard method determined by the instructions of the program. Such a memory is called a *random-access* memory. Another type of memory is the type designed to flag or determine how many times a repeated word exists in the memory. This type of memory has become known as *an associative* memory. Up to 1967, such a memory had only limited usage, primarily because of the great amount of peripheral electronics required to read the output.

Sequential access — mag tape / slow)

TECHNIQUES EMPLOYED FOR MEMORY

Chap 7 Barlee
210   start @ 212

It may be inferred from the above that digital computer memory techniques are many and varied. All have advantages and disadvantages depending on how the memory is to be used and where the computer is to function (on the ground, in outer space, in submarines, etc.) Some of the more common memory techniques are discussed below. Not included are some obviously trivial types such as flip-flop storage, thyratron storage, capacitor storage, and other types which have special applications as temporary storage registers but are not used to store the extensive amounts of information expected of a computer memory. Only the most commonly used techniques for fabricating computer memories are discussed here.

Delay-Line Storage

In this type of storage, words are continuously circulated in a delay line whose length is an integral number of words when used in a serial system. The delay medium can be columns of liquid mercury (used in the older SEAC, EDVAC, etc.) or more recently magnetostrictive materials in strip or rod form, such as quartz and glass. A transducer is used to excite one end of the line. A sensitive receiver is employed to read (sense) the results of the transmission through the line. Amplifiers are employed at the receiving end to restore the pulse integrity. The restored data are then fed back to the input for further circulation. This circulation continues until new data are placed in storage or existing data are removed from storage. This type of delay line is *volatile*. The newer magnetostrictive and sonic lines appear to have much promise in new applications.

Electrostatic System

This type of medium at one time rivaled the mercury delay line as an internal storage medium. In modern applications, however, it is being replaced by the core type or other similar memories. In the electrostatic system, the information is stored as charged areas on the surface of a cathode-ray tube. These tubes are identical with those employed in cathode-ray oscilloscopes. The best-known version is the Williams' tube type of memory of ORDVAC, SEAC, ILLIAC, etc. The reasons for the loss in popularity of the electrostatic system include:

1. Expensive and extensive circuitry
2. Difficulty in obtaining cathode-ray tubes with a sufficiently uniform phosphor surface

3. Need to rewrite information continually (since the stored charge tended to diffuse and overlap into adjacent cell areas)
4. Fragility of a cathode-ray tube in environments of high acceleration and shock

In addition to the above, these devices are quite bulky in size for the storage capacity obtained. The newer memory systems are more compact in volume and lighter in weight in a bit-to-bit comparison. A Williams tube memory is shown in Fig. 10-1.

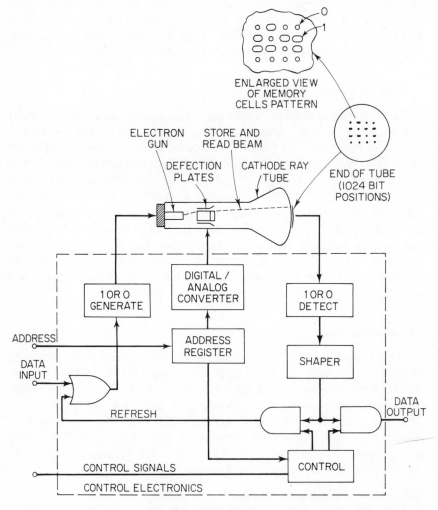

FIG. 10-1 Williams tube memory block diagram. Each Williams tube corresponds to a bit plane in a coincident core memory.

Magnetic Drums, Disks, and Tapes

Basic to these methods, data are stored on a moving magnetic surface by a recording technique similar to that used with a tape recorder. Readback, or recovery, of stored data is accomplished by allowing the small magnetized spots (recorded on the tape by the *recording head*) to pass flux through the gap of a *reading head*. The change in flux caused by the passage of the data (magnetized) spots generates a characteristic current in the coils of the reading head which can be sensed to read the data.

The actual mechanism of the magnetic storage systems vary widely. Tape mechanisms are generally similar to analog tape recorders, except that there are often many parallel channels. Access time to individual words on these devices is usually very slow because, on the average, half of the tape must be searched to find a particular word.

Drums have a faster access time than tapes, and often have 100 or more parallel tracks. Access time is in the order of milliseconds for the average drum. Disk magnetic memory files are, for all intents and purposes, drums laid out on a disk surface, and these also normally have access times in the millisecond region. Disk files are presently marketed with capacities of millions of bits. Magnetic memories of the type discussed, of course, are nonvolatile.

Magnetic Cores

This method of storing information has gained in popularity since its introduction in 1952 and has virtually spelled the doom of the electrostatic memory. In this approach, individual data bits are stored in individual magnetic core elements. The cores vary in size but generally, for modern applications, are about the size of a small Indian bead. Information is stored by saturating a core in one direction for a "1" and in the opposite direction for a "0." Readout is accomplished by reversing the saturation in the "1"-stored cores and sensing the reversal of flux in them. The cores storing "0's" do not change flux polarity; hence, there output is not a detectable signal. A separate sense wire is often used to sense the occurrence or nonoccurrence of the flux change.

Two types of core memory are in wide acceptance. The first type requires the application of the reversing flux as mentioned. It is known as the DRO or *destructive readout* type (all data are reverted to "0's"). The other is called *nondestructive readout* (NDRO) and requires the use of a specially designed core element normally having two holes. (The Biax element is a typical example.) This later type reads by injecting an *interrogate current* through one hole which does not completely reverse the saturation in cores storing "0's" or "1's" in the region of the other hole.

This interrogate current generates a vector flux which instantaneously adds or subtracts to the flux stored. The resulting flux variation is phase sensitive, and the varying current generated by the building up and decaying of the phase flux can be sensed as the storage of a "1" or "0." The principal advantage of this type is that the original flux pattern is not permanently altered by reading; hence, data are not destroyed at any time in the memory, except when a write of new data is required. DRO memories require the rereading of data into the memory after every readout, whereas rewriting is not required after readout in the NDRO memory. Both types of core memories are nonvolatile (provided the system's power-turn-on transients do not cause the circuitry to erroneously alter the data stored— but this provision applies to all nonvolatile storage).

DETAILS OF A DELAY-LINE MEMORY

The delay-line memory is basically a serial memory. Data words are continuously circulated. At discrete times (the beginning of a word time) a word can be started in its transfer in or out of the memory. A major cycle is often defined as the time it takes a particular single bit to recirculate in the memory. A major cycle will be an integral number of individual word times. A memory which stores 10 words will have a major cycle of 10 word times. Appropriate gating is provided to:

1. Permit word entry
2. Permit word circulation or removal
3. Permit word readout

The timing required to open these gates is provided by the computer instructions and is generated by the control section of the computer.

Attenuation of the input pulses in the storage medium is considerable, and, as a consequence, *restoring amplifiers* are required at the receiving end. In many cases, a carrier frequency is required to transmit data efficiently in the medium. As a consequence, the input amplifier is often a modulator, and the receiving amplifier is a demodulator. The functional diagram of a delay memory is shown in Fig. 10-2.

The delay medium in earlier computers was often a column of mercury. These columns, of the approximate length of 18 in., achieved a delay in the order of 450 μsec. At a 1-μsec serial-bit rate this meant that 450 bits could be stored in such a line. Because the delay characteristics varied considerably with temperature, very careful control of the temperature (to the fraction of a degree centigrade) had to be maintained. Even with this difficulty, mercury was chosen as a delay medium because it did not generate the spurious reflections noted in other devices.

Currently, mercury delay lines have given way to *sonic* memories built from either *magnetostrictive* lines or *glass* delay lines. Both of these technologies feature methods of temperature compensation by control of the material characteristics. In the glass lines, the sonic path can be reflected

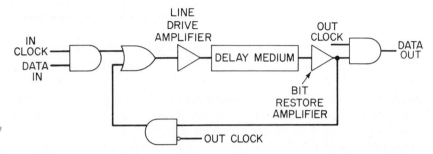

FIG. 10-2   Serial delay line memory.

many times across the slab, each time to a different surface, and directed eventually to an output transducer. This has the effect of telescoping the delay path tremendously over the necessary straight path. This fortunate property of the medium leads to a compact delay device for many applications.

See Bartee 257-262

MAGNETIC DRUMS, DISKS, AND TAPES

The principle of storing digital data on a magnetic surface whether it be a drum, disk, or tape surface remains the same. The recording surface is always a thin magnetic material which exhibits a high magnetic retentivity. The magnetic surface is bonded to a backing material that is nonmagnetic but either electrically conductive or nonconductive. Magnetic-tape storage surfaces used for recording are usually a fine iron oxide material adhering to a plastic surface (acetate or mylar). For drums or disks, the coating is quite often a nickel–cobalt alloy (usually a proprietary secret of the manufacturer) plated to an aluminum or other metallic base.

The principle of writing and reading are generally the same for all three of these rotating memory systems, but the bit-packing density and other details may vary widely. A typical read-write head is shown in Fig. 10-3a. The same head may be used for either reading or writing in much the same way that a single head is used for recording and playback on tape recorders.

The method of writing data into the memory can be considered simply

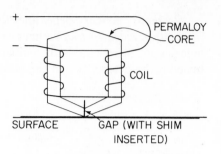

FIG. 10-3a Read–write head.

as turning-on an electromagnet intermittently. The fringing flux about the head gap protrudes down into the highly magnetic coating of the surface. The fringing into the surface occurs because the gap is a high-resistance (high-reluctance) path for the flux. The easier path for the flux is through the surface magnetic coating. Under the gap, the magnetic coating of the surface is saturated and becomes a minute magnet (0.01 in. or less, in length). For one polarity of writing current the magnet is north-south (left to right in Fig. 10-3b). For the opposite polarity, it is south-north (right

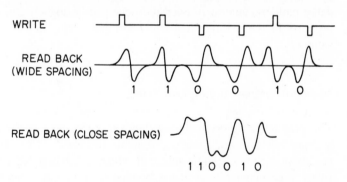

FIG. 10-3b Readback signal versus spacing.

to left). Because each pulse through the head is short (in time), the fact that the surface moves during writing causes little spreading of the recorded pulse.

For readback the process is reversed. Here, the little magnetic domains stored in the magnetic surface material, as they pass the gap, induce a changing flux in the core of the highly permeable material used for the head. The changing flux links the head windings and induces a voltage because of the relationship given in Faraday's well-known law

$$e_0 = N \frac{d\phi}{dt} \times 10^{-8}$$

which says the output voltage is proportional to the number of head turns times the changing flux linking these head turns. Actually $d\phi/dt$ is proportional to the core permeability and the surface velocity; so, this equation could well be rewritten for this application. This voltage is phase sensitive owing to the polarity of the originally recorded magnets.

A great deal of flux spreading occurs during readback, and, as a result, it is difficult to distinguish individual, recorded pulses. Examples of readback related to pulse spacing are shown in Fig. 10-3b. Many types of magnetic memory recording have been used, although these can be considered variations of two distinct families, or types. In the return-to-zero type (RZ), sometimes called the a-c type, "1's" and "0's" are recorded by injecting a current pulse of one polarity into the head for a "1" and a pulse of the opposite polarity for a "0." This type is illustrated in Fig. 10-3b.

A second type of recording is the nonreturn-to-zero (NRZ) type. In this approach an equivalent direct current is passed through the head. The polarity of the direct current is changed whenever the string of "1's" changes to "0's" or a string of "0's" changes to "1's." On readback the head recognizes the transition pulse and employs a flip-flop to change the logic level. The RZ recording usually gives a pulse logic form of data representation, whereas NRZ (see Fig. 10-4) usually gives a level logic

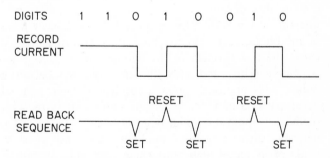

FIG. 10-4 NRZ recording and readback.

representation. Both types of recording have been widely used. The NRZ has the advantage, theoretically, in that twice as high a frequency of recording can be obtained with a given head as can be by using RZ. Return-to-zero recording often results in less power being applied to the head and allows the use of transformer coupling.

A type of RZ recording called *phase recording* was used in the EDVAC drum memory. It had the advantage over the NRZ system of saving components, and it permitted data to be recorded and read back from the drum surface with no loss in timing. This system may very well have been the first serial drum memory in the United States which operated at the 1-MHz clock rate of the computer. A type of recording has evolved which combines the best properties of both NZ and NRZ recording. This is called the *Manchester* (or *Ferranti*) *method* shown in Fig. 10-5. Here the re-

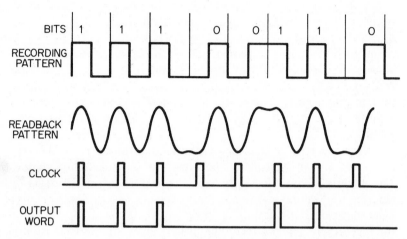

FIG. 10-5 Ferranti recording and readback.

cording flux during the write process is reversed during the "1" or "0" interval. As a result, the magnet being recorded reverses at the center of the bit interval. On readback this reversal is sensed dramatically because the flux reversal in the winding gives a large output signal which is phase sensitive and, after amplification, may be AND-gated with a clock pulse. This approach gives a distinct, reliable logic signal and permits dense packing of the binary information. It is recognized as a standard method, is applicable to all types of binary storage systems using a moving magnetic surface, and is economical in the use of electronic circuitry because of its initial high output and compatibility with a-c coupling.

ORGANIZATION OF DRUM MEMORY

The organization of a drum memory with a serial data transfer is shown in simplified form in Fig. 10-6. Addressing the memory is achieved by:

1. Selecting the proper "head" (or heads)
2. Determining the point to start transfer along the periphery of the drum

Naturally, the memory address register is divided into two sections to accomplish the desired selection. The X portion of the selective word,

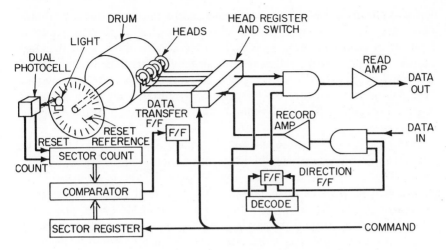

FIG. 10-6 Organization of a drum memory.

when located in the memory address register via a matrix, selects the head. The *Y* portion of the selective word is deposited in the other section of the register, where it remains temporarily. The sectors on the drum periphery are designated by counting sector marks, starting at a zero reference mark. The counter is normally reset to 00. . . at the zero index mark. In a binary counter, whenever the sector mark count is equal to the *Y selective* (i.e., *Y* address) stored in the memory address register, a gate opens in order that a data transfer can occur during the next sector. In this manner, word locations are specified and controlled.

The direction of transfer is determined by the setting of a flip-flop. Data flow into the memory sector location (via the write amplifier during the *write* process) or out through the *read* amplifier (during *readback* process). If the same head is used for both read and write, this flip-flop controls the amplifier switching required.

Another condition for proper performance of a drum memory is its timing with the remainder of the data processing system. Individual bits must closely adhere to a reference time. To achieve this, either the clock for the remainder of the system is obtained from a timing track on the drum or means must be provided to synchronize the drum with the systems clock (or some other reference, such as the frequency of the power line). Both methods are used in practice.

GENERAL ORGANIZATION OF A MEMORY

All types of memories (including the drum memory just discussed) require certain basic components. First of all, there is the memory storage device itself. This, of course, can include all of the types previously covered. Associated with the memory storage device itself are two types of auxiliary or temporary storage registers. The first of these is the memory address register (MAR). This register usually consists of flip-flop stages into which is inserted the word address of data to be extracted or entered. The register is the control that determines location within the memory. It is used to address locations within the memory regardless of the *direction* of data transfer.

This register may be broken up into zones. For instance, word location is sometimes given in terms of X and Y coordinates, especially in a core memory. In a drum memory, the MAR will indicate both the read-recording head to which the data are to be transferred and the sector (distance around the circumference) in which the transfer begins and ends.

In addition, a second register is normally associated with a memory. This is the MBR previously discussed. Its purpose is to store the data temporarily just before they are transferred into the permanent memory storage or just after they are recovered from permanent storage. Quite often it is a serial-to-parallel and parallel-to-serial shift register. In a DRO core memory, this register serves as a temporary memory for the data that are to be read back into memory after a readout. A block diagram

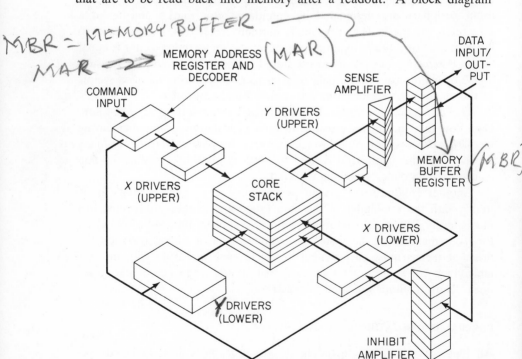

FIG. 10-7   Block diagram of a core memory.

of a core memory organization is shown in Fig. 10-7. The inhibit amplifiers are used during the restoration of data to the memory after a
readout. The sense amplifiers are required to decode the switched signals
out of the cores during the readout process.

CORE MEMORY ORGANIZATION

Three types of core memory organization are in current use. The first
type to be discussed is referred to as *coincident core* or 3D. It features an
individual plane allotted to a particular bit of the word. For instance, bit
3's in all words are stored in plane 3. There are normally four wires
through each core. This organization is popular because the number of
switching circuits is the lowest of the three types of organization for storage
ranging from 512 to 8192 words. A modest number of isolation diodes
are required, two for each X and Y line through the stack. While not
obvious from Figs. 10-8a and 10-8b, the individual X and Y drive lines
thread the corresponding cores on *all* planes, not only those illustrated in
the figures.

A second organization is known as $2\frac{1}{2}$D. For memory sizes within the
range of 512 to 4098 words, it tends to use more electronics than 3D organization does, but the $2\frac{1}{2}$D approach may demonstrate a saving in electronics in sizes for 8192 words and above. Its primary advantage lies in

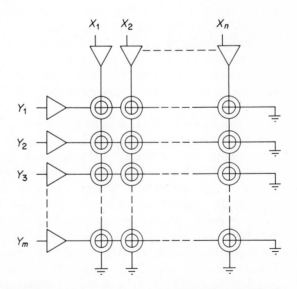

FIG. 10-8a A single memory plane showing the X, Y
drive lines.

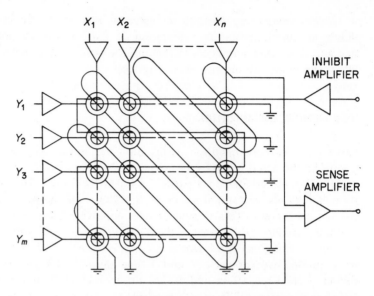

FIG. 10-8b Readout system for a core memory.

the elimination of the inhibit circuit and making a three-wire organization possible. Its operation (read-write) can be somewhat faster than that of 3D because inhibit pulses are not required. In the 3D design, the inhibit pulses must completely bracket the write pulses; hence, the inhibit pulse length determines (to a great extent) the read-write cycle time.

To compare $2\frac{1}{2}$D and 3D organization, the selection and switching are organized similarly, although the number of X and Y switches for the same number of words will vary widely. In the X plane of $2\frac{1}{2}$D, usually many more X lines and X switches will be used. In the Y plane, the switches of the $2\frac{1}{2}$D are organized in the usual 3D manner, except that a separate set of Y switches is used for each bit plane. Because a separate set of switches is available to each bit, distinctive "1" and "0" write fluxes can be generated by programming the X and Y drives without resorting to an inhibit current through the core itself. This greater amount of circuitry in $2\frac{1}{2}$D than in 3D is caused by the necessity for more X amplifiers and for a separate set of Y drivers in each bit plane. These additions are not usually counterbalanced by the elimination of the inhibit drivers for each bit plane. By clever organization of the Y drivers, however, it is possible to drive two planes with a common driver set; one plane is pulsed by a positive current for "1's," whereas its twin is pulsed by a negative current for "1's," and vice versa for "0's." On the readback, the interrogating pulse would also be reversed in the two planes. This results in halving the Y-driver hardware of the $2\frac{1}{2}$D organization previously described.

The third method of memory organization leads to two-wire NDRO design and is called *linear-select* (see Fig. 10-15). All bits of the word that is selected to be written are energized with a word current. The word current normally consists of bipolar cycles which may include more than a single cycle. On each individual bit the proper "1" or "0" current is impressed on the bit wire which threads all bits of this level within the words. The bit current is polarized and brackets in time the word current pulses. Only the word addressed by the word current is influenced by the bit current on the bit lines.

On *readback*, the word lines are supplied with a single unipolar pulse which interrogates that word. The bit lines are now employed as sense lines and connected as inputs to sense amplifiers, one amplifier for each bit plane. The linear-select organization can be used in both DRO and NDRO applications, but its circuitry is expensive. Its chief disadvantage is that two diodes per word are required for isolation. This means, e.g., that, for 4096 words, 8192 diodes are necessary. For small memories, this objection may not be valid. The advantage of the linear-select method lies in the elimination of the inhibit driver of the 3D organization and making possible the use of only two wires through each bit element which reduces core wiring costs.

MAGNETIC-CORE MEMORY DETAILS

The Single Memory Bit

The basic magnetic-core memory in any configuration stores a single bit of data in a single core element. There are as many core elements as there are binary bits to be stored. This memory is a static memory since there are no mechanical moving parts as in the drum memory.

A single core stores a "1" or a "0," as previously indicated in Chapter 6. In review, the core is saturated by exciting it with a sufficient number of ampere turns in either one of two directions ("1" or "0" direction). The current coil here is the driver lines that *thread* through the core center. Examples of bit cores are shown in Fig. 10-9a.

The Memory Plane

A single bit by itself is of no value. Hence, the next logical step is to consider how the individual bits are organized into a complete memory. Normally, the bits are aligned in an array or plane, as illustrated in Figs. 10-8b and 10-9b. The plane illustrated in this figure is an example of a 3D, or *coincident-current core,* memory plane. It is so named because of the method of transferring data to and from a selected bit position.

In Fig. 10-8b, a particular bit core stores a "1" by exciting a given X line (or wire) and a given Y line. The core located at the *intersection* of the particular X and Y lines thus excited is subjected to a magnetizing force H sufficient to saturate the core in the "1" direction. All other cores in these X and Y lines receive only 0.5 H and, hence, are not driven past the hysteresis-curve knee (short of the switching point) in the "1" direction.

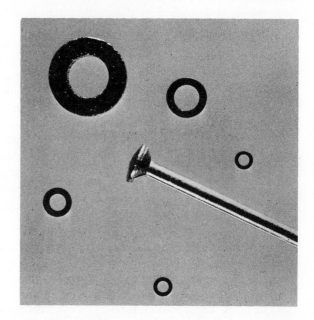

FIG. 10-9a Ferrite cores with common pin (courtesy of International Business Machines Corp.).

A "0" is recorded in the same intersecting position (core) by exciting both the X and Y lines, but in addition the inhibit line (a third wire) is driven in such a manner that it adds a negative 0.5 H. Hence, the core at the XY intersection is not driven in the "1" direction. It remains at "0," or negative saturation, since the total flux applied is $0.5\ H + 0.5\ H - 0.5\ H = 0.5\ H$.

In the 3D organization, the same X lines and Y lines thread the corresponding columns and rows in all bit planes.

The cores on a single plane are all related to a particular binary digit (2^0, 2^1, or 2^2, etc.) for all words. The number of bit cores in this plane of the memory is equal to the number of words in the memory.

For a 10-digit word memory, there will be 10 planes. At a given write time, the corresponding bit core in each plane is addressed and a "1" or

"0" is transferred as indicated for the single plane. In a parallel data transfer, all cores of the selected word are written in at the same instant.

A readout is provided by applying a saturating current, in the "0" direction, to each core bit of the word to be transferred. If the core has a stored "1," it will be switched to "0." The large change in flux generates an output pulse, which is picked up by the sense (output) wire passing

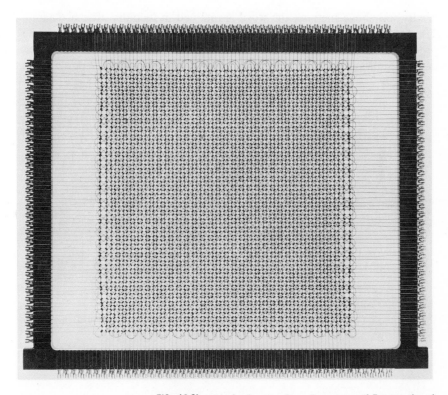

FIG. 10-9b   A wired core plane (courtesy of International Business Machines Corp.).

through the core (see Fig. 10-8b). Quite often the same address register is employed to perform both readin and readout.

Because the readout process flips all cores to "0," the word stored is eliminated from the memory at the instant of readout. For most memories, it is not particularly desirable to destroy the words in the memory during readout. It is generally more desirable to retain the word until the program specifies a new word to replace it. To restore a word in the memory at readout, it is necessary to store the word read out in a temporary buffer register (the MBR previously discussed). The individual sense amplifiers for each plane set the individual flip-flop of the MBR to either "1" or "0" as sensed during the readout. From the MBR the transfer of data is in two directions:

1. Out to the processor, input–output, control, etc.
2. Back into the memory position from which it was transferred during readout

By the above method, the word is retained in memory after a readout. The "0's" in the MBR set the inhibit drivers during the read-in (write) process. A block diagram of the memory transfer portion for the coincident current system is given in Fig. 10-10. This memory, of course, is an

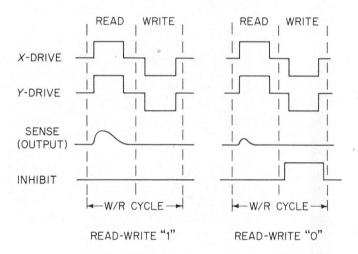

FIG. 10-10 A read–write cycle for a coincident core (3D) memory.

example of a DRO memory and suffers from the usual disadvantage of requiring a write cycle after every readout cycle. Cycle time for such a memory is normally in the range of 2 to 15 μsec. A typical timing diagram is shown in Fig. 10-10.

X and Y Switching (3D)

The actual switching of *read* and *write* currents through a core requires a considerable quantity of logic and circuitry. For the switching of a "1" wire, a very abbreviated example is given in Fig. 10-11. This wire, say

X_1, links the column X_1 in all the planes. There is a separate wire for X_2, X_3, ... , X_n columns also linking the corresponding columns in all planes. In a like manner, there are Y_1, Y_2, Y_3, ... , Y_n wires linking the corresponding rows in all planes.

Basically, a *read* pulse is generated followed by a *write* pulse. This is accomplished by causing a pulse of current to flow from *a* to core to *b* in

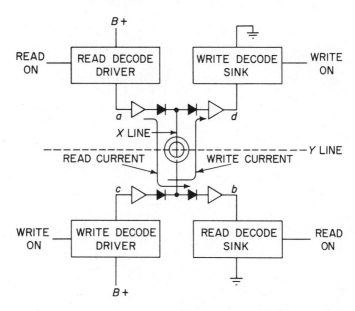

FIG. 10-11   Drive current routing.

Fig. 10-11 for read followed by a current going from *c* to core to *d* for write on both the *X* and *Y* lines simultaneously. The *decode drive* and *decode sink* circuits are effectively low-current switches turned on only during the *read*-current and *write*-current intervals. These switches turn-on, in turn, appropriate high-current line switches, the semiconductor circuits that actually switch the line currents. The line switches are indicated by the open triangles in Fig. 10-11.

The decode drivers and the decode sinks are controlled by a diode matrix which is addressed by the memory address register. A block diagram of a small memory design is shown in Fig. 10-12. Only the *X* lines and circuitry are shown, but the same principle is applied to the *Y* lines. The same switching occurs as in Fig. 10-11. The individual storage flip-flops of the address register are illustrated together with the necessary decode sinks and decode drivers. The blocks marked *T* are usually transformers

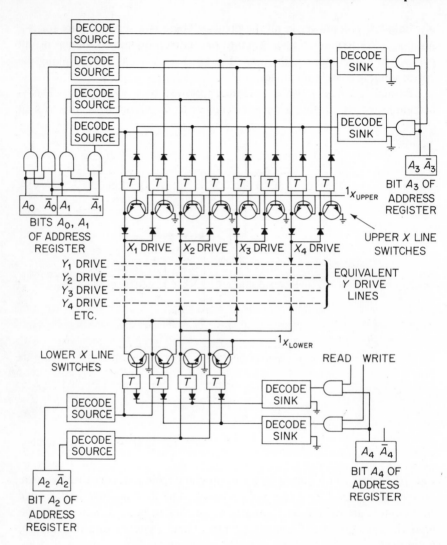

FIG. 10-12 X, Y drive organization for a small 3D memory.

that isolate the actual line-switch transistors from the pulse-generating decode-drive and decode-sink transistors. Diodes are used to isolate the X lines in the same manner as in Fig. 10-11.

NDRO Memory ⟮Nondestructive readout⟯

Quite often considerable savings in computer time can result if the requirement for *write* after a readout is eliminated. To achieve this goal, it is necessary to read out a core by some other means than reversing its saturation for "1" to "0." A special core design (biax) makes it possible to achieve this goal. An example of such a special core is given in Fig. 10-13. This core element has two right-angle holes.

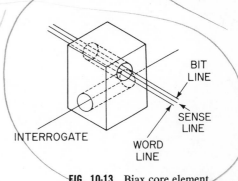

FIG. 10-13   Biax core element.

The cores can be fabricated in a memory in the same way as torridal cores. The X and Y address wires and the sense wire are routed through the same hole. In the second hole is a wire called the *interrogate wire*. During the *read* process, this wire receives a pulse which is of sufficient amplitude to cause the generated flux to react with the flux stored about the first hole. Depending on whether a "1" or a "0" is stored, the induced voltage in the sense wire will have a distinctive phase pattern. This pattern arises from the instantaneous vector addition of flux that occurs coincident with the interrogate pulse. It is this vector addition that is sensed by the sense wire. The flux established by the interrogate pulse was not sufficient to switch the flux into the opposite saturation; therefore, the bit pattern does not have to be regenerated after a readout interrogate cycle.

The *write* process is identical in principle with the 3D method described above. However, a different method of generating the saturation currents may be employed. Figure 10-14 shows typical waveforms for a biax core memory.

Two-Wire Memories

Saving in the wiring of memories occurs if only two wires are used to thread the cores. A biax core memory using this technique is shown in Fig. 10-15. Obviously, the wires must be shared for more than one operation. The external circuitry becomes more complex, and it is necessary to add isolation diodes. On an overall basis, use of the two-wire system may lower the cost of memory plane construction by cutting down on the assembly labor required to thread the memory cores.

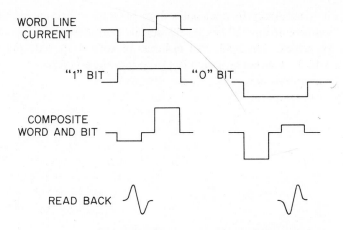

FIG. 10-14 Biax core waveforms (2D memory).

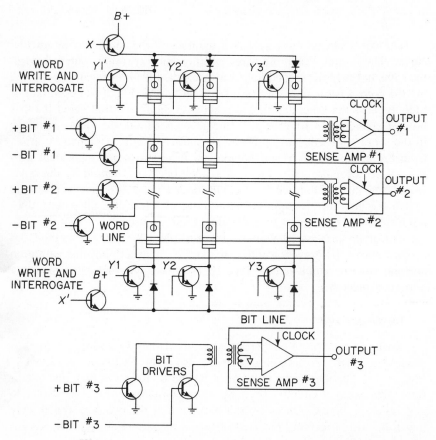

FIG. 10-15 Linear select two-wire memory.

Nondestructive readout

It also has the advantage (because of the shorter lengths of wire thread-
ing the cores) of less inductance and therefore will transfer data more
rapidly than will the 3D design. However, the NDRO signals from the
cores are of lower amplitude; hence, more care has to be exercised in the
design and construction. The design must consider the noise generated by
all cores during the switching cycle and attempt to balance out the effects
of those *not* transferring data. One approach is to use differential sense
amplifiers and design the system in such a way that system noise will
appear at both inputs to the differential sense amplifier at about equal levels.
Because of the ability of good differential amplifiers to reject this particular type of signal (called *common-mode noise*) and still amplify the proper
sensed output signal, they serve as an effective sense amplifier.

With the development of two-wire systems, other modes of storage
than individual cores become possible. One method that is finding favor is
coating a wire with a magnetic material, shown in Fig. 10-16. The core of
this *plated wire* carries the *bit* current.

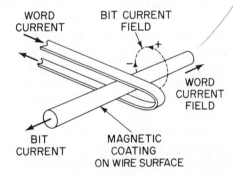

FIG. 10-16   The plated wire approach.

At right angles to the bit wire and coupled as close as possible, a second
wire carries the *word* current. This organization is similar to linear-select
organization and can be used for both DRO and NDRO versions of plated
wire. The magnetic plating itself is annealed to have an *anistrophy* (direction of easy magnetism) circumferential about the wire. The magnetic
field of the *word* winding is at right angles to the easy magnetization direction, but it has been shown theoretically and experimentally that axial fields,
in this orientation, react with the circumferential fields to produce the prescribed *write* or *read* action.

The method of recording and readback is similar to that which occurs
in a biax core. By using excessively large current pulses during interrogation, the data bit will be changed to one polarity, e.g., "0." This action
is similar to that in a DRO memory, and the system would, of course, be

a DRO system requiring a restoring of all "1's" in the word. The interrogating pulse current on the word line is often bidirectional. The sensed outputs occur on the *bit* lines, all outputs simultaneously with the interrogation pulse, and the phase of these outputs determines whether a "1" or "0" was originally stored.

For NDRO, the current magnitude of the interrogating pulse must be closely controlled so that it effectively does not allow the magnetic material to sense a magnetomotive force H greater than indicated by the hysteresis curve knee (or else the data will be destroyed as in DRO).

The development of an optimum plated coating has also delayed the widespread introduction of this system. Such phenomena as the loss of the wire's magnetic properties under storage conditions and the tendency of the stored bits to spread—i.e., the tendency of adjacent bits to merge together—have led to a long and interesting development program. The object, of course, of this program is to obtain a memory system that is cheaper to produce, is reliable, occupies less space, and is faster in readout response than the equivalent core memories. The operational mode is reported to be closer to *thin-film action*. By this statement, it is meant that *magnetic-film domains* switch much more rapidly than cores because cores are not *domain-structured*.† As a result, a thin-film device has the potential of appreciably higher speeds for changing saturation states during the sensing process. This advantage unfortunately is counterbalanced by the much lower switching flux levels and, hence, theoretically lower voltage outputs.

An advantage of the plated-wire geometry over the earlier approach of depositing thin-film dots on a flat surface is that the sensing wire can be strapped over the bit wire more than once, which gives the equivalent effect of a multiturn transformer on the interrogation pulse line. It gives a tighter, more efficient energy coupling.

OTHER MEMORY TECHNIQUES

In attempts to reduce the cost of assembling a memory plane and to increase access speeds, many techniques are presently being investigated by various engineering organizations. A possible answer uses a magnetic material deposited as a thin film on a flat surface. Conductors are also deposited and insulated from each other and the magnetic material. This

---

† *Domain structure* is the ordered structure occurring in thin magnetic films, where within small areas all crystals line up in a single direction. In adjacent areas, the crystals will align themselves in some other direction. The boundaries between the areas are sharply defined. The application of a magnetic force produces the effect that all domains tend to align themselves in the direction of that force.

technique appears to be successful for some specialized applications and generally promises a low-cost manufacturing method when the technological problems are solved; for large memories it is probably not economical because more complex electronic circuitry is required to recover the stored data effectively.

Other approaches include aperture plates, where the memory material is a sheet perforated with holes and the wires are strung between and about the holes. In development pioneered by the Bell Telephone Laboratories, the memory material is slotted and the wires are laid in right angle slots. This particular memory has the general appearance of a waffle and, for its intended application, is a good solution.

Other techniques such as cryogenic elements and tunnel diodes have been proposed and used to a limited extent, but their use has not been as widespread, nor does it promise to be, as the magnetic types discussed earlier in this chapter.

Another type of memory, however, should be included for the sake of completeness. This is called the *unalterable* or *permanent* type. One form is the *rope core* memory consisting of a string of large toroids pulsed sequentially by a pulse train. Each stored word is output in series on its own output line. The individual word line will either pass through or around each toroid; therefore, when each toroid is pulsed in sequence, the polarity of the pulse in the particular word wire represents the individual bits polarity in the stored word. Many word wires can be accommodated by the single string of toroids. The system is illustrated diagrammatically in Fig. 10-17.

Because of its bulk, however, the rope core method is superseded by permanent LSIC memories. In these memories, individual memory cells are

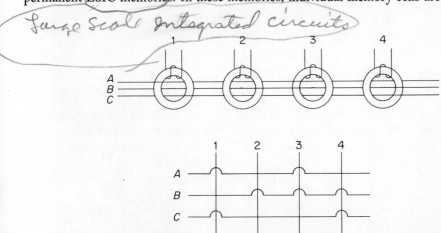

FIG. 10-17 Rope-core permanent store.

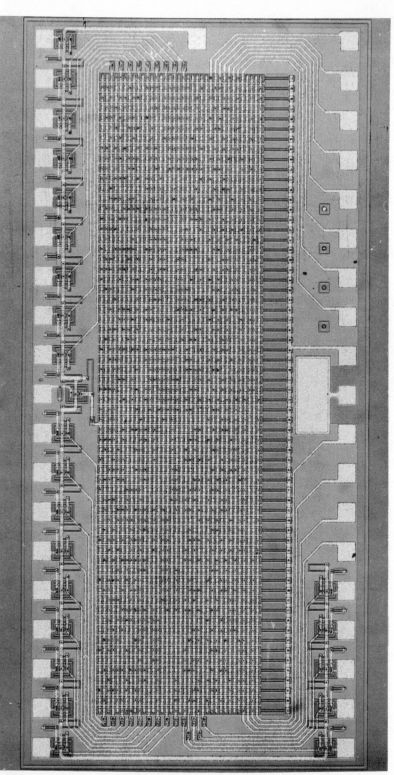

FIG. 10-18a

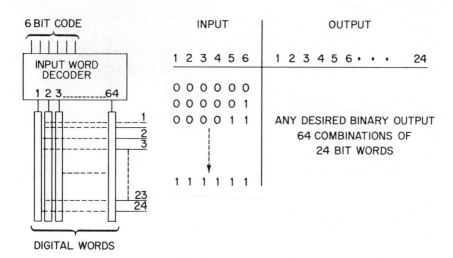

FIG. 10-18b LSIC permanent word store—digital word translator. (Photograph on facing page courtesy of Honeywell Inc., Florida Division.)

formed on an LSIC chip. By addressing a particular word, the stored bit pattern can be read from the chip. A different set of words requires a new pattern, which is obtained by processing with a different set of *chip masks.*† With computer-controlled design methods now in effect, the initial economic barrier has been overcome. A view of a typical LSIC permanent word store is given in Fig. 10-18a and b.

SUMMARY

This chapter has summarized several approaches to the design of an internal memory. Topics discussed included memory classification and techniques employed for memory. In some detail, delay-line, rotating-magnetic, and magnetic-core memory organizations and techniques were discussed. Various magnetic recording methods are examined including the RZ, NRZ, and Ferranti types. The organization of 3D, $2\frac{1}{2}$D, and linear-select core memories are compared. Also explored were DRO and NDRO memories and their distinct properties. The chapter concluded with a brief discussion of nonalterable memories such as rope core and LSIC.

†*Chip mask*—the pattern controlling the formation of active devices in LSIC chip manufacture.

answer these questions

REVIEW QUESTIONS AND PROBLEMS

10-1. Name the function performed by the memory section of the computer.

10-2. Name several volatile memory types. What types are nonvolatile?

10-3. What are the characteristics of a Williams tube memory?

10-4. What is the delay required for a serial memory to store ten 30-digit words if the digit rate is 1 MHz?

10-5. How many tracks are required on a magnetic drum if the bit spacing is 80 per inch, the word length is 40 bits, the drum is 4 in. in diameter, and 4000 words are to be stored?

10-6. What is the function of the memory address register? What is the function of the memory buffer register (MBR)?

10-7. What is the function of the four windings through any core of a coincident core (3D) memory?

10-8. What advantages are attributed to NRZ recording?

10-9. What is the primary advantage of a NDRO core memory? What are the disadvantages?

10-10. What is being done to reduce the cost of memories on a per bit basis?

10-11. Sketch the organization of a 2½D memory with the following characteristics

Given:
 1. 8 each *X* drivers.
 2. 4 each *Y* drivers per plane.
 3. 8 each planes.

Find:
 1. The total number of words in this memory.
 2. The number of flip-flops in the MAR.
 3. The number of flip-flops in the MBR.
 4. The total number of *X* and *Y* drivers.
 5. The total number of cores required.

10-12. Can you name some possible uses of a nonalterable memory? What advantages do LSIC's promise over the rope core design?

Page 232

PROGRAMMING AND THE CONTROL SECTION   11

This chapter discusses briefly some of the fundamentals of programming, but the details of this subject are left to other texts in the field. Various types of machine instructions are mentioned and immediately followed by brief examples of how a one-address simple program might be organized. The remainder of the chapter discusses the general operation of a one-address control section and a short explanation of a timing chart.

PROGRAMMING FUNDAMENTALS

While this book is devoted entirely to describing how a computer operates, and serves as an introduction to fundamentals of computer design, very little has been said about programming. This subject cannot be ignored, however, since the operation of the control section is strictly dependent on the program and organization of individual instruction words.

The program of any computer is the sequence of instructions loaded into its internal memory prior to operation. The computer interprets each of the instructions in turn and thereby executes the program. In all but the simplest of machines, the sequence of instructions may be varied by inserting a new and different program. The term programming generally refers to the entire complex process of (1) breaking down a problem into those elementary steps which the computer can perform; (2) writing the proper steps in the necessary sequence; (3) converting the program, as written, into one of the languages that the machine understands; and (4) testing the results with a simple set of data. In other words, it is the process of directing the machine through a desired process or set of calculations.

A computer basically operates from coded information. The data are coded; the instructions are coded. The instructions, when coded in a form intelligible to control-section components, are called *machine instructions*. It is this form of programming instruction that will be explored further in this chapter.

The programmer may or may not work with instructions in machine instruction form. In the early days of computers, all programs were coded directly in machine instructions, and, as a result, the programmer (or coders) knew what each code meant and what each bit stood for in the instruction. Today it is the fashion to write program sequences in a special computer language employing English words and familiar symbols and to allow the computers themselves to translate these word statements into machine instruction sequences. Such computer processes are highly sophisticated and require extensive translation programs of their own. Computers capable of using machine langauges must have sufficiently large memories and a proper instruction repertory to be able to handle translation programs. Names of these program-oriented languages include FOR-TRAN, ALGOL, ARGUS, JOVIAL, etc. The process of converting a *source* program to an *object* program (machine instructions) is called *compiling* or *assembling.* A program requires a compiler when one machine instruction is generated by one source (program-oriented language) instruction. An assembler, however, can generate several object instructions from a single "source" statement (if the statement is composed properly in the source langauge).

By using program-oriented languages, it is possible to train laymen (completely ignorant of how a computer functions) to program a computer effectively. In addition, programmers trained in a particular program-oriented language, such as FORTRAN, should be able to use any computer designed to assemble programs written in FORTRAN form. Complete compatibility between two different machines, however, both using the same program-oriented language is *not* always possible—even though this would seem to be logical. Machine differences and idiosyncrasies account for the incompatibilities, when they occur.

TYPES OF MACHINE INSTRUCTIONS

Machine instructions fall into many classifications. The most common distinction is between those that have an address and those that do not. Here, this classification will be broken down further and variations within the usual classification will be discussed.

Memory Transfer

These classes of instructions have an *operation code* which identifies the *exact instruction* and an *address* (to and from memory to another device). They are used to *transfer* data to and from the *memory* and the *accumulator,* between the memory, i.e., and other *registers* associated with the *processor* or the *input–output.*

Input–Output

These instructions have an *operation code* and an *address.* The operation code identifies the operation to be performed and the *address* of the device which is to be controlled. Instructions in this class may also be used to control buffered channels. Transfer instructions between the input–output and the memory could also be classified as a *memory transfer.*

Arithmetic

These instructions include the *processing* instruction. They have an operation code and an address. Their address usually refers to a memory address but may also be a register address.

Manipulation and Shift

These instructions are used to shift words within and between registers. They contain an operation code, and often the address portion will be used to indicate the required number of shifts. These instructions can be used to mask out portions of words, move characters within words, combine characters into words, or break words into characters, etc.

Control

These instructions can be used to change the progress of the program. They include *jump* or *skip* instructions, and other instructions which change the present instruction. Included in this grouping would be *interrupt servicing* instructions.

Logic

This instruction performs Boolean operations such as AND, OR, and EXCLUSIVE-OR, on a pair of stored words, one in the memory and one in the accumulator.

Table 11-1 lists a few sample instructions that one might find in a

TABLE 11-1

Sample instructions[a]

Instruction	Function	Operation symbol
1. LDMNNN	Load the word following this instruction on the tape into the memory address NNN.	$T \rightarrow M$
2. SKEMXX	Control instruction, cause I/O (input–output) device XX to perform function M. (M could be coded to cause device to start, stop, read, print, test for error, etc.)	XX *action*
3. TRMNNN	Clear register M. Transfer contents of memory address NNN to register M.	$M \rightarrow M_r$
4. ADDNNN	Add contents of memory address NNN to that in accumulator. Put results in accumulator.	$M + A \rightarrow A$
5. MLMNNN	Multiply contents of M register by number in memory address NNN, and put result in accumulator.	$M_r \times M \rightarrow A$
6. TFMNNN	Transfer contents of accumulator to memory address NNN.	$A \rightarrow M$
7. TOTNNN	Transfer contents of memory address NNN to I/O output bus.	$M \rightarrow I/O$
8. TITNNN	Transfer contents of I/O input bus to memory address NNN.	$I/O \rightarrow M$
9. HLT	Halt machine (no address required).	H
10. RTMNNN	Return instruction counter to fetch instruction from memory address NNN.	$IC \rightarrow X$
11. CPRNNN	Compare contents of accumulator with contents of memory address NNN. If comparison, *less than*, continue with next instruction counter address. If comparison *equal*, replace instruction counter contents with index register. Execute the new instruction counter address. (This is a typical "jump" instruction.)	$A = M \begin{vmatrix} < \rightarrow IC \\ = \text{Jump IR} \end{vmatrix}$

[a] These are just a few examples of instructions that one might find in an instruction repertory.

processor instruction repertory. Practical computers have been built with less than 15 instructions. Usually, however, somewhere between 30 and 100 kinds of instructions will be required.

SAMPLE PROGRAM

To demonstrate the operation of a simple program, assume the existence of several simple one-address instructions. These instructions consist of an operation code represented by a three letter *mnemonic* code and a three-digit address. This is the way the programmer, who works with *machine instructions,* will write his program. Also assume that, during the coding process (preparing a paper tape or deck of cards for inserting the program into the computer), the proper binary code for the *machine instruction* will be generated. The form of the instruction word is

XXXNNN

X = alphabetic character

N = octal address digit

The X characters represent a code which the programmer employs to identify the instruction intended. This alphabet code will be converted to a binary "1's" and "0's" code at the time the instruction is inserted. For example ADD might translate into binary 13 (1101). The N characters are often written in octal form because of the ease in converting octal code to binary code.

As an example, assume that the instruction exists as given in Table 11-1. This is just a partial list with sufficient listed instructions to continue the example. Assume also that it is desired to calculate $y = 5X + 2$, for $x = 1, 2, 3,$ and 4 only. This, of course, is a trivial example, hardly justifying a computer but serves to illustrate the basic problem.

The operator writes a program as illustrated in Table 11-2. This program first loads the data and instructions into known memory locations. On the operator's pressing a *start* button, the computer sequences and executes the simple program.

In Table 11-2, the alternate instructions punched in the tape (identified by an asterisk), are *bootstrap* instructions. Each bootstrap instruction is followed by a *data* word (which can be an operational instruction or data), and this word is inserted into the memory according to the address in the bootstrap instruction. The data load process is *halted* when the complete program has been loaded. Depressing the *start* button in the console initiates the program (step XX).

[NOTE: The first 25 instructions are only *load* instructions. The LDM instructions appear only on the tape and are *not* transferred to the memory.

TABLE 11-2

Sample program using no jump instructions

A. *Load instructions:*

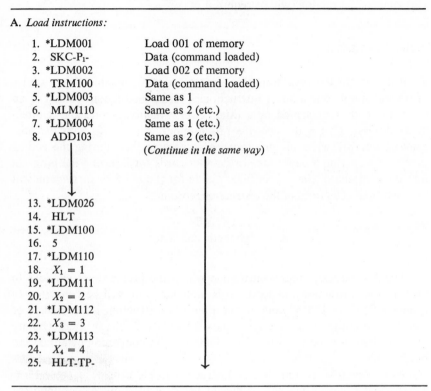

1.	*LDM001	Load 001 of memory
2.	SKC-P$_1$-	Data (command loaded)
3.	*LDM002	Load 002 of memory
4.	TRM100	Data (command loaded)
5.	*LDM003	Same as 1
6.	MLM110	Same as 2 (etc.)
7.	*LDM004	Same as 1 (etc.)
8.	ADD103	Same as 2 (etc.)
		(*Continue in the same way*)

13.	*LDM026
14.	HLT
15.	*LDM100
16.	5
17.	*LDM110
18.	$X_1 = 1$
19.	*LDM111
20.	$X_2 = 2$
21.	*LDM112
22.	$X_3 = 3$
23.	*LDM113
24.	$X_4 = 4$
25.	HLT-TP-

B. *Process instructions:*

Number	Setting of instruction counter	Instruction	Process stop
XX. Start	000		
26.	001	SKC-P$_1$-	Turn on printer
27.	002	TRM100	$5 \rightarrow$ M register
28.	003	MLM110	$5 \times X_1$
29.	004	ADD103	$5X_1 + 2$
30.	005	TEM104	$5X_1 + 2 \rightarrow$ M
31.	006	SKC-P$_2$-	Transfer I/O (printer)
32.	007	TOT104	$M \rightarrow$ I/O
33.	008	TRM100	$5 \rightarrow$ M register
34.	009	MLM111	$5 \times X_2$
35.	010	ADD103	$5X_2 + 2$
36.	011	TFM104	$5X_2 + 2 \rightarrow$ M
37.	012	SKC-P$_2$-	Transfer I/O (printer)
38.	013	TOT104	$M \rightarrow$ I/O
39.	014	TRM100	$5 \rightarrow$ M register

TABLE 11-2 (Continued)

Number	Setting of instruction counter	Instruction	Process stop
40.	015	MLM112	$5 \times X_3$
41.	016	ADD103	$5X_3 + 2$
42.	017	TFM104	$5X_3 + 2 \to M$
43.	018	SKC-P₂-	Transfer I/O printer
44.	019	TOT104	$M \to I/O$
45.	020	TRM100	$5 \to M$ register
46.	021	MLM113	$5 \times X_4$
47.	022	ADD103	$5X_4 + 2$
48.	023	TFM104	$5X_4 + 2 \to M$
49.	024	SKC-P₂-	Transfer I/O printer
50.	025	TOT104	$M \to I/O$
51.	026	HLT	Halt operation until XX start

The remaining 26 instructions actually sequence the program. These later instructions are transferred to the memory and actually process calculations.]

The reader may note a great deal of repetition in this program. It cycles through the same sequence of instructions *four* times, with the only exception that the MLM instruction address changes from 110 to 111 to 112 and finally to 113. As a consequence, he might ask if there is a more efficient way to handle this general problem of repeated instruction cycles.

The better way, of course, is to make use of the jump instruction CRM, shown in Table 11-3. In this approach, the value of X is increased by the necessary increment (e.g., a value of 1) by adding a process step that adds a 1 to the previous value of X. To provide a cutoff of computer operation, it is also necessary to compare the value of X with a final value. Until X reaches this final value, as detected by performing the comparison called for in the CPR instruction, the process continues. If we were to compare X with 5 located in memory position 104, the values of y for X from 1 to 4 would be computed as before. When $X = 5$, the CPR instruction would sense a comparison and at this point would cause the jump. What happens here is that the instruction counter is loaded with a new address 013, probably from an index register. This address, when serviced, contains the *halt* instruction.

The advantage of this program method is, of course, that fewer total instructions must be written into the program; hence, less memory space is devoted to storing program instructions. In addition, the program can be changed easily to handle any values of X by changing one word in the memory, i.e., the contents of 104. Also, the size of the X increment is changed by changing the 001 stored in 102 to a new increment size.

TABLE 11-3

Sample program using a jump instruction[a]

Process instruction	Start of instruction counter	Instruction	Process stop
XX. Start	000		
1.	001	SKC-P$_1$-	
2.	002	TRM100	5 → M register
3.	003	TRA102	1 → A
4.	004	ADD103	A add M = X_1
5.	005	CPR104	Compare with 104 ⎡ If $X < 104$ contents,
6.	006	TFM103	A → M ⎱ continue with step 6. If $X = 104$ contents,
7.	007	MLM103	$5X_1$ ⎣ do step 16A.
8.	008	ADD105	$5X_1 + 2$
9.	009	TFM106	$5X_1 + 2 →$ M
10.	010	SKC-P$_2$-	Transfer I/O (printer)
11.	011	TOT106	M → I/O
12.	012	RTM002	R → 002
15A.	005	CPR104	Compare with 104 ⎰ $X = 104$ contents,
16A.		Load TRD013	Load TRD013 ⎱ therefore do step 16A.
	013	HLT	Halt operation until XX

[a] The process for loading is similar to that in Table 11-1; hence, the loading process is not repeated here.

This simple example proves the desirability of studying construction of the instruction repertory. By the addition of two instructions (to the previous group used in Table 11-2), the list of progress steps was reduced from 26 to 13. In addition, this minor instruction modification provided a much more flexible method of changing the program to handle a greater range of X values, as well as a means of changing the increment steps.

A second way to show a comparison between the two approaches is to refer to Fig. 11-1. Here *flow charts* of the corresponding programs are graphed in a descriptive manner. The elementary sample programs demonstrated would, of course, represent a small portion of a total progarm. Such samples could be a *subprogram* (or *subroutine*). The term *subroutine* refers to a small distinctive segment of an entire program which can be filed and incorporated at appropriate times into other major and longer programs. Consequently, most major programs are written by combining these segments, or subroutines, together into a total program. Jump instructions are used to advantage to move back and forth from a main program into necessary subprograms. By using standard (error-free and

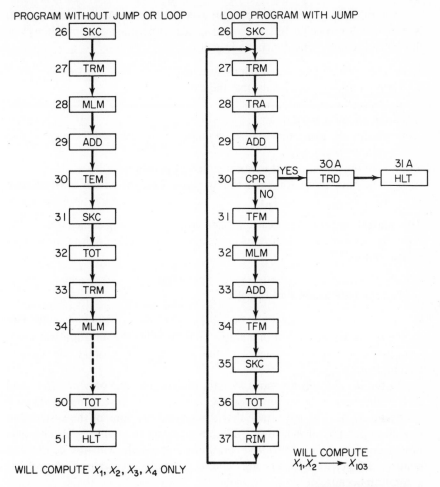

FIG. 11-1 Flow charts.

tested) subprograms, it is possible to make full use of previous work when devising a new program.

THE CONTROL SECTION

The *control section* of the computer controls and programs the operation in an orderly fashion. It decodes the instruction words and provides the proper timing sequences and signals at the proper intervals throughout the computer system.

It is difficult to generalize computer control sections since each system is designed for specific functions and needs. For most systems, however, the control section provides such services as:

1. A central clock (for synchronous systems)
2. Timing impulses, or signals, that indicate
   a. the start of a word time
   b. the end of a word time
   c. groups of word times (e.g., a pulse every five word times)—also called a *major cycle*
   d. a timing pulse to start major computer operations
   e. a distinct pulse for each timing pulse interval within a word time $(T_1, T_2, T_3, \ldots, T_n)$

The control section, on occasion, also provides warning indications if the error checks indicate a failure of the program, a function failure, or a component failure.

Centralized and Decentralized Control

In a *centralized* control system, all clocking signals, timing signals, and timing levels are generated in a single section. This organization was common in earlier computers and had the advantage of positive, direct, and uncomplicated control.

In the *decentralized* control system, the control unit only *monitors* and *directs* the several subsections of the computer in an executive manner. This method has the advantage that the several portions of the system can operate separately at their own optimum and particular speeds. It also permits a degree of *simultaneous* operation not possible with the centralized control. Modern computers are tending toward decentralized control organization because of these advantages.

Instruction Structure

The instruction structures of computers vary, depending on the number of individual instruction and address bits included in a single machine instruction word. The characteristic speed and modes of a computer depend greatly on the structure of instruction organization that is employed. Types of structures are listed in Table 11-4 along with their advantages and disadvantages. Instruction structures generally divide into one-address, two-address, three-address, and four-address configurations.

The instruction structure is not necessarily constant in a given computer. It varies, depending on whether the instruction is intended for *internal* use in the computer or to address input–output devices. Practice

TABLE 11-4

Types of instruction structures and their advantages

Structure	*Advantages*	*Disadvantages*
One-address instruction	1. Uncomplicated decoding 2. Relatively simple hardware	1. An instruction order required for every operation 2. Overall computer speed slower
Two-address instruction	1. Some possible speed up from parallel operation, such as two words moving at the same time	1. More hardware than for one-address instruction
Three-address instruction	1. Fewer instructions through use of three addresses	1. More hardware than for one and two addresses, but more versatile (e.g., third address serving as location for next instruction)
Four-address instruction	1. The most flexible of the four types, containing three data addresses and a fourth address for next instruction's location	1. Same as above

varies with individual data processors. Examples of the breakdown for a one-address instruction and a three-address instruction are given in Figs. 11-2 and 11-3. In some processors, one or more instructions may be

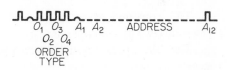

FIG. 11-2   Organization of a one-address instruction.

grouped in a single computer word. For instance, in Fig. 11-3, three one-address types are grouped in a single word. The computer selects which of the three are to be obeyed and in what sequence.

FIG. 11-3   Organization of an instruction word containing three one-address instructions.

Instruction Decoding

The decoding of a one-address instruction is shown in Fig. 11-4. The operation code portion and the address portion of the instruction are transferred from the MBR, and the separate portions are routed to and decoded within the two separate decoding matrices.

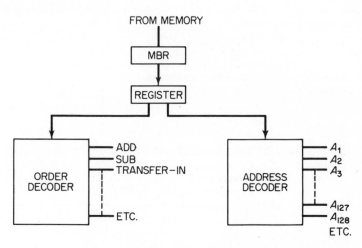

FIG. 11-4   Decoding a one-address instruction.

One-Address Instruction System (Cycle of Operations)

The execution of an instruction in a one-address system logically divides into two general operations.

The first operation called *program time* refers to the following three steps:

1. Fetch the instruction address (usually from the instruction counter).
2. Transfer the instruction word from the MBR to the operation decoder, and address decoder.
3. Decode the instruction (both operation and address). This operation generally takes the same amount of elapsed time regardless of the command being executed.

The second operation called *operation time* is that period devoted to the execution of the instruction. The length of time required for this operation is a variable. To illustrate the method and clarify the philosophy, the total operations steps combined to perform a complete addition of two numbers are listed in Table 11-5. The block diagram of the process for executing an order is given in Fig. 11-5. The operation flow steps are listed in the figure as well as in Table 11-5.

TABLE 11-5

Instruction operations required to perform a complete addition[a]

Operation 1	a. Fetch instruction address, and transfer instruction.
	b. Move instruction 1 from memory via MBR and then to the operation decoder and address decoder.
	c. Decode operation code and address.
	d. Transfer word 1 to accumulator.
Operation 2	a. Fetch instruction address, and transfer instruction.
	b. Move instruction 2 from memory via MBR and then to the operation decoder and address decoder.
	c. Decode operation code and address.
	d. Transfer word 2 (aligned with word 1) through the adder.
Operation 3	a. Fetch instruction address, and transfer instruction order.
	b. Move instruction 3 from memory via MBR and then to the operation decoder and address decoder.
	c. Decode operation code and address.
	d. Transfer word in accumulator to memory address 4, etc.

[a] Steps a, b, and c in each operation are accomplished during *program time*. Step d is accomplished during *operation time*. This type of operation could be performed by the adder in Fig. 9-3.

The operation sequence of the instruction counter may be changed by inserting (into the instruction counter) a complete new setting by the jump instruction technique. These jump instructions are often stored in particular portions of the memory or in special index registers. The object is to transfer the contents of the index register into the instruction counter. The instruction register's original contents may be stored temporarily in a third register for future reference; i.e., the original contents are stored so that they may be recalled and the computer programs returned to the point where the normal routine left off.

Often, the index register is used in other ways to modify an instruction. For instance, rather than transfer the contents, the procedure often is to *add* the contents of the index register to the contents of the instruction counter. This generally means that the instruction counter and index register contents together are run through an adder and the result then put in the instruction counter. Index registers are also used in count modes (as was implied in the earlier section on programming).

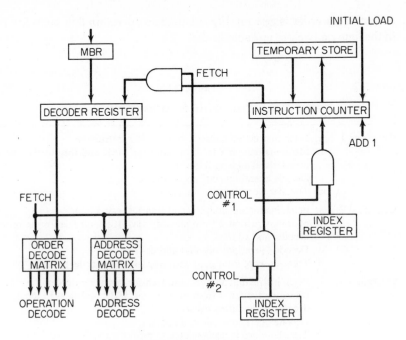

Typical Operation Flow

1. Fetch—find address of first command in Instruction Counter

2. Move—the first command from the MBR as specified by Instruction Counter to Decode Register

3. Decode command No. 1

4. Transfer data and add 1 to the Instruction Counter

5. Fetch—find address of second command in Instruction Counter

6. Move—the second command from the MBR as specified by Instruction Counter to Decode Register

7. Decode command No. 2

8. Transfer data or perform operation and add 1 to the Instruction Counter

9. Etc.

FIG. 11-5 Operations for processing a one-address instruction.

By means of the index register technique, it is possible to jump from the normal instruction set to a completely different one. On the command of a second jump instruction the program can return the instruction counter to its former contents and proceed with the normal routine. Jump instructions are generally caused by the occurrence of a specified result during a calculation, e.g., if contents of the A register go from positive to negative during an accumulation. If a jump is to occur, it is built into the instruction repertory of a particular computer. If the jump condition is detected (whatever the criteria), the normal operation of the machine is halted and a command is generated calling for the change to the jump routine.

By using either the instruction counter or index register (or both), the normal instruction is replaced with a new instruction. The simplest approach is to change the contents of the instruction counter by use of the index register and then proceed in a normal manner with the new instruction counter contents specifying the next command.

Control Elements and Techniques

Some of the basic control elements are shown in block-diagram functional form (Figs. 11-6 and 11-7).

FIG. 11-6 Clock generator.

Clock Generator. Figure 11-6 illustrates the clock generator, which provides a continuous stream of precision frequency timing pulses. This device establishes the basic timing of the computer. The basic frequency is usually established by a precision frequency oscillator (often crystal controlled) or by a track on a precision speed-regulated magnetic drum. These pulses are distributed to many places and are closely controlled for pulse shape, i.e., the rise and fall time, width, etc.

Time-Pulse Distributor. This device, shown in Fig. 11-7, generates individual timing pulses $T_0, T_1, T_2, \ldots, T_n$. The counter controls a matrix which sequentially selects gates T_1 through T_n, as shown by the figure.

Order-Decoder Matrix. This is a straightforward matrix operated by the order decoder. The outputs are lines which provide an initiating pulse or signal to command transfers such as add, multiply, and subtract. This device, in general, furnishes a control level to gates throughout the computer. There is a line for every instruction.

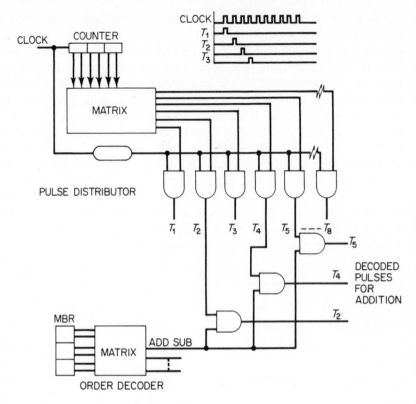

FIG. 11-7   Time pulse distributor and instruction routing.

Timing Charts and Control Logic

Another method of presenting the relative timing that occurs during the execution of a program is to use a timing chart, as shown in Figs. 11-8 and 11-10. Each event is indicated in its relative time slot. For convenience, the program time and operation time are also drawn on the chart. Figure 11-8 indicates the time required to perform the transfer-and-add operations shown in Fig. 11-9, with an adder of the type shown in Fig. 9-3.

A timing chart, together with a list of events, allows the designer to block out the logic for the control of these events. Such a logic diagram is shown in Fig. 11-9 for the transfer-add process.

Figure 11-10 is an abbreviated timing chart for the multiplication process. Note that, once the actual multiplying begins, the system remains in the operation-time phase until the multiplication is complete. To accomplish the sequencing required, one method uses a counter to count the multiplier bit shift pulses to the register containing the multiplier. This has been assumed and is shown in Fig. 11-11. For a multiply process in an eight-word system, the multiply counter would count to eight-word times, or the shift and add process would repeat itself eight times for the completion of the multiplication process. In the multiplication operation the OT-PT † flip-flop is not allowed to toggle at each word time, as for addition or transfer. The multiplication command, in conjunction with the multiplication-process counter (eight-word counter), will generate an inhi-

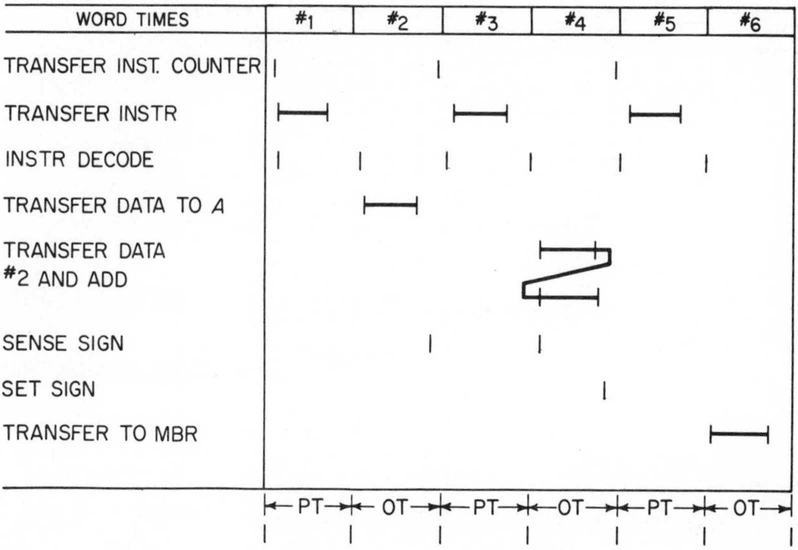

WORD TIMES	#1	#2	#3	#4	#5	#6
TRANSFER INST. COUNTER						
TRANSFER INSTR						
INSTR DECODE						
TRANSFER DATA TO *A*						
TRANSFER DATA #2 AND ADD						
SENSE SIGN						
SET SIGN						
TRANSFER TO MBR						

|←— PT —→|←— OT —→|←— PT —→|←— OT —→|←— PT —→|←— OT —→|

FIG. 11-8 Timing chart for transfer-add operation.

bition to the OT-PT flip-flop to prevent it from toggling word counts until the multiplication is complete. This is the method for extending the operation time over the time duration of the multiplication operation.

Figure 11-8 shows the *general* timing required for the transfer and add process. Although data of eight bits are shown, a single computer word will usually be ten bits in time duration. The two additional bit times are required as *timing intervals,* parallel transfers, etc. These events must be performed between the start and the completion of an addition cycle.

[NOTE: The "dump" of the contents of the instruction counter into both the operation decoder and the address decoder takes place in one bit time. What does this tell about the type of transfer specified for the instruction counter to the decoders?]

Figure 11-9 shows in simplified form how the various signals are com-

† OT-PT, *operation time—program time.*

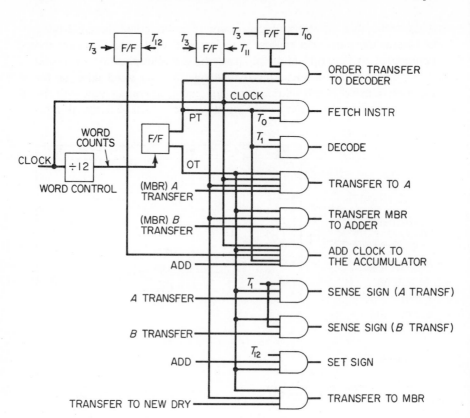

FIG. 11-9 Signal control for transfer-add operation.

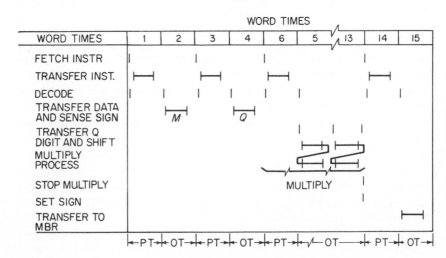

FIG. 11-10 Timing chart for transfer-multiply operation.

bined with gates, flip-flops, etc., to derive the actual logic for the transfer-add command portion of the control. In this figure at time T_0 the instruction counter is shown to be transferred to the decoder. At T_1, the instruction is decoded, and the transfer of the instruction from the MBR begins at T_3. This continues until T_{10}. If a seven-bit instruction is assumed, T_{11} and

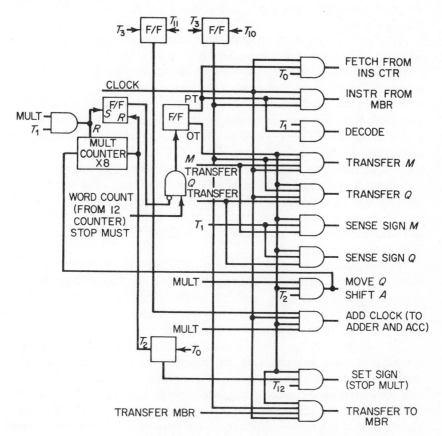

FIG. 11-11   Control gating for transfer-multiply process.

T_{12} are blank. This completes the first word time, which as can be seen requires 12 bit times.

At T_1 of the second word time, which is also an operation-time interval, the command from the MBR is decoded. At T_3, word A starts transferring to the accumulator. (If the data word is eight bits long, this transfer is completed at T_{11}.) At T_2, its sign is sensed. Next comes a program-time interval. At T_0, the instruction counter is transferred, and at T_1 it is decoded. At T_3, the second command for the MBR is started in its transfer to the decoders. Again, T_{11} and T_{12} are blank (if no timing takes place).

At T_1 of the next operation time, this last command is decoded, and the addition process starts with the sensing at T_2 of this sign bit. Immediately after sensing T_2, the complementers are set in the adder. At T_3 through T_{11}, both the word in the accumulator and the data in the MBR are passed through the adder. At T_{12}, the carry is sensed which sets the sign for the sum.

At T_0 during the next program time, the instruction counter is transferred and the process for *transfer back to memory* is initiated.

The same types of diagrams can be drawn for the transfer-multiply process. The difference, of course, lies in the extension of the operation time during the repetitive process of additions required for the multiplication process. In this case, we inhibit the word pulses from repeatedly setting and resetting the OT-PT flip-flop. When multiplication is specified by command, the flip-flop is frozen in the OT position until the required number of additions (or, rather, multiplicand shifts) is sensed. During this interval, the multiplication process is completed. For an eight-bit multiplicand, the interval will be eight word times in the worst case. It can be shorter if the logic permits a multiplier shift for an "O" to occur in less than one word time or, of course, if multiple shifts on repeated "O's" in a word time are allowed.

A counter may be used, as shown in Fig. 11-11, to count the word shifts (move Q). After eight counts, the OT-PT flip-flop permits the next program-time interval to be initiated, which signals the completion of the multiplication process. Again, Fig. 11-11 illustrates the control logic in simplified form for the sequence of instructions.

The complete design of the control section continues with the careful mapping of each instruction of the repertory in the manner described briefly for the two examples given above. The final step combines the individual command-control gating into a single package that will specify the control for the entire computer. This step is, of course, one that takes a great deal of knowledge, experience, and perseverance. The use of logic reduction techniques should prove very helpful in combining individual diagrams (such as those shown in Figs. 11-9 and 11-11) into a *composite diagram* specifying the complete control logic. In a sense, this is the culminating effort in the engineering design of any computer.

THE OPERATION OF A THREE-ADDRESS SYSTEM

One-address systems are not the only possible organization for a computer. Figure 11-12 shows a hypothetical three-address system. Here, the opera-

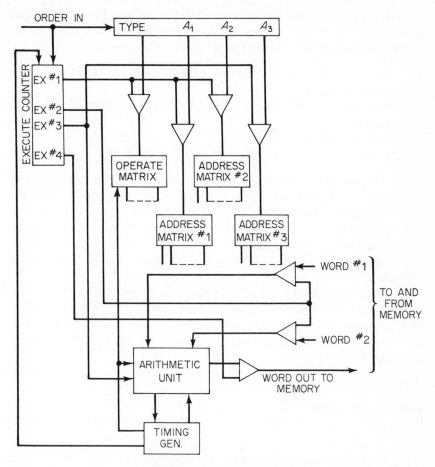

FIG. 11-12 Three-address instruction operation illustrating the use of the execute counter.

tion is decoded at the same time as address 1 and 2. A third matrix is shown to decode address 3, but, since this is accomplished during another timing period (*execute* 3),† a practical system would probably time-share either matrix 1 or 2.

For the operation of the three-address system given in Fig. 11-12, it is assumed that the three addresses are:

1. The memory address of word *A*
2. The memory address of word *B*
3. The memory address into which the results are to be inserted

† *Execute* is a term employed to indicate the start of a major control interval.

The operation proceeds as provided for by the four-step execute counter. This counter advances to the next step at the completion of the task in progress. The tasks corresponding to the four steps are:

1. Move the instruction into the operation decoder and address decoder, and decode the order.
2. Move words *A* and *B* from the memory into the arithmetic unit simultaneously.
3. Perform the operation.
4. Move the results of the operation back to the memory.

The three-address system will use a little more hardware, but, since two two words are moved in parallel, it results in faster operation. The use of an instruction counter is not as popular here as in the one-address system, but it is possible. Often the third-address in the instruction serves as a location address for the next *command* rather than as an address of where to deposit the results. Systems have been constructed, however, for both uses.

When it is felt that both the next instruction address should be specified and the address to which the results of the computation will be transferred, then the alternative is to go to a four-address system. The EDVAC computer installed at Ballistics Research Laboratories† in 1950 was a four-address machine.

MICROPROGRAMMING

A totally different method of organizing a control section is to use a technique known as *microprogramming*. In this approach each instruction to be executed by the main program is partitioned into its several basic operations. Each instruction is thereby executed by performing the required basic operations in sequence. The sequence is controlled by *microinstructions*‡ which are normally stored in a rapid-access *read-only micromemory* (sometimes called a *control* memory). By this means the instruction repertory of the computer can be modified by changing only the micromemory. The microprogramming approach, therefore, leads to a control section whose design is flexible. Its chief fault appears to be its slower than usual instruction-processing time. Use of an I-C read-only memory for storing microinstructions may in time overcome this disadvantage.

---

† Ballistics Research Laboratories, U.S. Army Proving Grounds, Aberdeen, Maryland.

‡ *Microinstructions* are the commands stored in a read-only memory for executing a microprogram.

SUMMARY

This chapter has discussed a few of the basics of programming, including a discussion of source programs, object programs, and machine instructions. Types of machine instructions were defined, including such classifications as Memory Transfer, Input–Output, Manipulation of Shift, and Control. A sample program, including sample instructions, was presented and examples were given of how a very simple program could be composed both with and without *jump* instructions.

The fundamentals of a one-address central section was discussed from the point of view of centralized versus decentralized control, instruction structure, instruction decoding, and the cycle of operation for a one-address control system. This was followed by a section demonstrating the logic techniques for generating control signals. Two examples were given, one having the timing for a hypothetical transfer-add instruction and the second a corresponding timing for a transfer-multiply instruction. The chapter concluded with a brief treatment of a three-address control sequence, and a discussion of microprogramming.

REVIEW QUESTIONS AND PROBLEMS

11-1. What is meant by the term *programming?*

11-2. Distinguish between a source program and an object program.

11-3. Write a sample program, developing the instructions required to compute. Use jump instructions where possible.

$$0.5x^2 + 2x + 7 \qquad \text{for values of } x = +1 \text{ to } +25$$

11-4. Draw the flow chart for Problem 11-3, above.

11-5. What functions are provided by the control section?

11-6. What is meant by centralized control? By decentralized control?

11-7. Describe the execution of a one-address order.

11-8. What is the function of the instruction counter? The decoder register? The memory address register (MAR)?

11-9. What is the function of the execute counter in a multiple-order address system?

11-10. Describe the operation of the time pulse distributor and the order decoder.

Read over again

THE INPUT–OUTPUT SECTION 12

The input–output section is that portion of the computer which serves as an interface between the peripheral equipment and the computer proper. The input–output also includes the interface between the controls, the keyboard (if one is employed), and the displays. In this chapter, the logic section which controls the switching functions is referred to as the input–output section as distinguished from other peripheral devices which are sometimes designated input–output devices or peripheral equipment.

INTRODUCTION

The basic input–output function of a computer includes:

1. The data transfer operation between a high-speed computer and the slower data processors external to it;

2. The preparation of data in the proper code or the provision of a code
transformation for communication with other devices

Basically, the input-output section interconnects *internally* with the
memory section under control of the control section, as discussed in the
preceding chapter. The general design of the input–output section varies
widely, depending on what peripheral devices are used. For the simplest
computer, the peripheral device for which interfacing is desired may be a
simple, single, *digital typewriter,* such as a Flexowriter. For a more complex computer installation, interface with several peripheral devices may
be required with the exact information flowing in or out under supervision
of the computer's control section. Several channels may be supplying data
simultaneously, or one channel may have a priority status to interrupt other
channels of information flow. This *priority-interrupt* feature is programmed in many computers today. After such a priority-interrupt signal,
the interrupted channels will resume normal operation when the priority
condition has been satisfied. Because numerous options are possible, the
input–output section is determined both by the computer's usage and by
the peripheral devices employed. The simplified block diagram of a typical
input–output section is shown in Fig. 12-1.

Ground-Based and Mobile (Airborne) Computers

The general-purpose computer for ground-based operations has numerous possible interface devices. Some of these devices, listed in Table 12-1,
are generally designed to provide data to and from human operators.
There are, of course, exceptions. For instance, the digital-to-analog
(D/A) and analog-to-digital (A/D) *converters* (included in Table 12-2)
might be used for special applications in ground systems, whereas their
use in airborne applications (Table 12-2) is quite normal. Other exceptions include connections to communication links and to other computers.

In many control, airborne, or missileborne applications, where human
monitoring is *not* performed directly as it is in a computation laboratory,
inputs and outputs are frequently obtained from or supplied to analog
devices, as shown in Table 12-2. Accelerometer or gyro inputs are examples of analog inputs. Output to an analog autopilot would be an example of an analog output necessarily supplied by an airborne computer.

Human monitoring can also exist in many mobile applications. In
others, however, telemetering is used for information describing system
performance. A list of some likely and more common interfaces is given
in Table 12-2 for a missileborne or an airborne application.

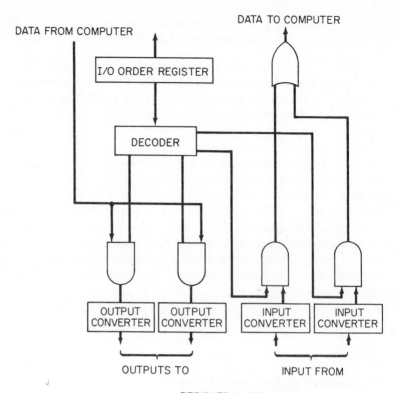

FIG. 12-1 A generalized input–output section.

TABLE 12-1

Ground-based interface devices

Device	Input or output
1. Paper tape reader	Input
2. Magnetic tape	Input–output
3. Flexowriter (digital typewriter)	Input–output
4. Card reader	Input
5. Card punch	Output
6. Paper-tape punch	Output
7. Printer	Output
8. Keyboard	Input
9. Page scanner	Input
10. Decimal display	Output
11. Data communication terminal	Input–output

TABLE 12-2

Airborne interface devices

Device	Input–output
1. Accelerometer inputs	A/D input or digital input
2. Gyro inputs	A/D input
3. Sensors	A/D input
4. Star trackers	Digital input
5. Doppler navigator	Digital input
6. Shaft-position sensors	Digital input
7. Autopilot controls	D/A outputs
8. Discrete control signals	Input–output: normally a level voltage
9. Shaft position controls	D/A outputs
10. Navigation display	D/A or digital output
11. Telemetry	Digital output
12. Data communication link	Digital input–output

Off-Line and On-Line Operation

Common methods of data storage such as paper tapes and Hollerith cards (IBM cards), are often prepared outside the computer. Once prepared, these tapes and cards may be placed in a tape or card reader, respectively, for actual data-flow input to the computer.

Another and possibly more important example is the use of *magnetic tape* for inserting (or extracting) information into (or from) the input–output section. The tapes can be prepared in peripheral equipment (not a physical part of the computer itself) and can also be read on equipment external and separate from the computer. Such operations as *preparing* a magnetic tape for insertion into the computer and the operation of *reading* a magnetic tape obtained from a computer output are examples of *off-line operations* utilizing off-line devices or equipment. The process of actually reading in the tape to the computer's internal memory and the process of the computer's actually *writing* onto the tape from the internal memory are examples of *on-line* operation.

On-line operations are controlled by the computer and require computer time to perform. If the on-line operation is a slow one, the computer is tied up until the completion of the operation. Since it is preferable that the computer should be completely free from involvement, off-line operations are much preferred for some of the routine data-transfer operations required to support a computer complex.

BASIC METHODS OF INPUT-OUTPUT

The basic well-known problem associated with the input–output of any computer is the fact that the input–output requirements are not always known or completely anticipated at the time the computer is designed. As a result, a flexible approach is taken that permits exact peripheral equipment line-up to be determined at a later time with the understanding that variations in peripheral line-up will *not* require basic logic or organizational changes in the computer (nor in any interfacing control units).

Input–output schemes differ widely between manufacturers. These vary from systems which supply tightly specified input and output buses to those with which all the associated peripheral modules must be designed to fit the application. Other systems exist which have a large amount of *buffering capability.* For these systems, the peripheral equipment operates fairly independently of the internal control of the computer and is reasonably standardized, it thus requires little (if any) specialized development for new systems. From the organizational standpoint, computer input–output methods generally fall into four classifications: (1) bus; (2) centralized; (3) buffered; and (4) complex interface.

The Input–Output Bus

This method is the simplest from the standpoint of the computer and is basic to all the other methods. In this case, the peripheral units may be located remote from the computer. All communication, both data and commands, is accomplished on a digital basis. A digital word is transmitted in either character or full-word format and in either parallel or serial form. Each peripheral device has its own command and address decoder. Generally, a command must contain, as a minimum, the following information:

1. Command to be executed
2. Peripheral device addressed
3. Memory address to which the transfer is to be executed
4. Direction of transfer (if a bidirectional) device

Response lines are also required to indicate to the computer the status of the peripheral equipment at the time it is interrogated. The advantage of this system is that the interface with the computer is straightforward and the peripheral device lineup does not have to be determined in advance of the input–output design. It does require, however, that each peripheral device should conform to the chosen bus format, contain its own command decoder, and be capable of being addressed separately.

The peripheral equipment designers must be supplied with a specification at an early date and must agree on the system interface. Generally, each data word transferred is preceded directly by a command word. Figure 12-2 is a block diagram of this method.

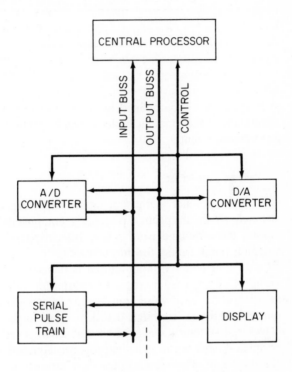

FIG. 12-2   Decentralized input–output.

The Centralized Input–Output

For this approach, peripheral devices (such as A/D, D/A, synchro-to-digital converters, incremental pulse counters, digital shaft positioners, etc.) are effectively built into the input–output section of the computer or, more practically, into an adjacent unit. The basic input–output basic control unit contains a command decoder which services all standardized peripheral modules. The specific peripheral module lineup is selected for the application. Figure 12-3 shows this organization in block-diagram form.

The centralized input–output organization has the advantage that only a single command decoder for the system is necessary. Consequently, the cost of the total system is probably reduced. Also, it yields some added advantage in placing the peripheral modules under the same control as the computer. The disadvantage of this approach is, of course, that the com-

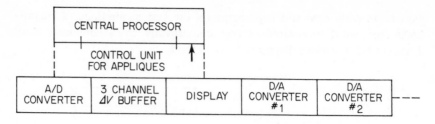

FIG. 12-3 Centralized input–output.

plete system must be defined in advance of implementation. The use and adaptation of the modular building-block design, however, eases this problem to some extent.

Buffered Input–Output

A third popular method of input–output organization is with *buffered channels* to the respective peripheral equipments. With buffered input–output, the command word selects the peripheral device, the starting and stopping point within the memory, the direction of data flow, etc. The advantage of buffered input–output is that only one command (in a single group of commands) is required to transfer data (rather than a separate instruction for each word transferred). Once started, the buffered input–output completes its assigned task without further prodding. Quite often a buffered system is designed so that external interruptions from external peripheral devices can halt the program sequence and request service from the computer. This servicing can be performed on a priority basis; i.e., the high priority programs are serviced ahead to those with less priority.

The buffered input–output interface is especially adaptable to military

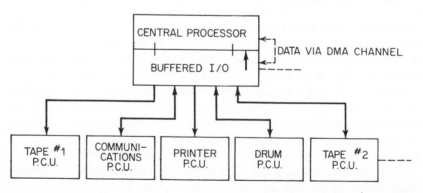

FIG. 12-4 Buffered input–output.

and commercial types of peripheral units, such as printers, magnetic tape transports, disk files, communication modems, etc. A block diagram of this method is presented in Fig. 12-4.

Complex Input–Output Interfaces

The probability exists that the advantages of all three of the previous types of interfaces may be required at the same time. This may occur, of course, when the computer is added to a system already in existence or when the peripheral devices are already specified and cannot be easily replaced or modified. Such a complex input–output interface is shown in Fig. 12-5. However, it is evident that this system is generally built up of modules of the other systems discussed and, as a result, should be relatively easy to fabricate providing the proper "homework" is done in advance; i.e., a set of basic building-blocks must be established. The individual blocks may be modified in a given situation but the establishment of a standard series obviates the necessity of starting from the beginning each time a new system is defined.

SIMPLE DATA TRANSFERS

Data transfers in and out of a processor may be in either serial or parallel format. It is not unusual for a serial machine to have a parallel interface (serial-parallel interface). For instance, a serial machine using 24-bit words may transfer a single output word to a buffer register (usually a shift register) and the output of this register would be the 24 register bits all sampled at once, i.e., in parallel. For input purposes, the process can be reversed, i.e., a parallel 24-bit input word (after loading the register) may be serialized in the same buffer and, at the proper time, reinserted back in the serial data stream. A simple example of this type of transfer scheme applied to an output is a numerical display. Here, a shift register would be serially loaded with the word to be displayed. If there were six decimal numbers, then the word shifted to the register would be coded as six successive BCD characters. This would, of course, require a 24-bit register. Since the display requires a decimal indication, it is necessary to convert here from a BCD to a decimal code. Each four bits in the register contain a BCD character. These four bits, using a simple BCD decimal matrix, can convert the four BCD bits to ten distinct decimal lines. Such a required matrix was previously described in Chapter 7. The 10 decimal lines then can each light 1 of 10 decimal indicator digits, respectively.

Therefore, in addition to the 24-bit registers, 6 separate matrices and

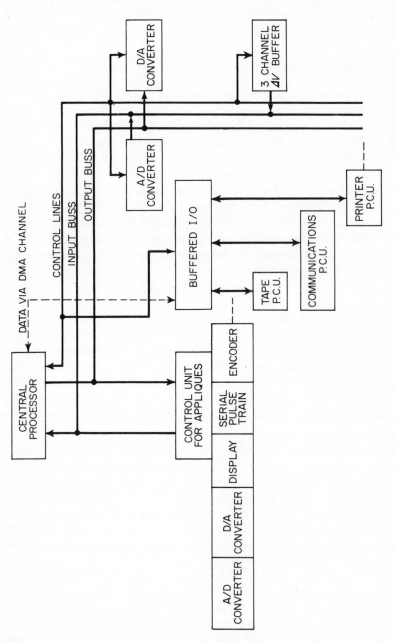

FIG. 12-5 Complex input–output.

6 digit displays (each capable of displaying 0 to 9) would be necessary to accomplish the complete display function. This same scheme might well be adaptable to a six-line character printer also, if the printer required only a decimal code.

A reverse process to the above (parallel-serial interface) would be the input from decimal code switches. Here the 10-level switch positions would be converted to BCD format and then the input for each character (0 to 9) would be fed to four register bits. Each switch would have its own four positions in the register. All switches would be positioned first and then at a pushbutton operator command, the computer would serialize the register contents and transfer them to memory. Again, a 24-bit register would handle six decimal code switches of the type described.

A second simple transfer scheme is the *serial-serial* method. Here a word is loaded serially into a shift-register buffer by a computer clock pulse and output subsequently is by a second clock pulse (generated by the device that accepts the buffer contents). This type of transfer can be used for both input and output transfers by merely interchanging clock pulses and switching the register inputs and outputs.

A more common transfer than the above, however, occurs when the computer uses a relatively long word length and desires to communicate with a character-coded device such as a teletypewriter or a paper or magnetic-tape unit. The desirable approach is to load several characters into a single word or, in the opposite manner, take a single word and divide it into characters. A 24-bit word, e.g., can be divided into six BCD characters, four 6-bit alphanumeric characters, or three 8-bit alphanumeric characters, depending on the character code employed. Depending on the transfer direction, this process is called *packing* or *unpacking*. A relatively simple means of accomplishing this is shown by the logic of Fig. 12-6. In the register, four 6-bit characters can be packed or, in the reverse direction, can be unpacked. The bits are intermingled so that a single clock bit can accomplish the required shift between successive character transfers. At the end of four shifts, the packing or unpacking process terminates. Therefore, the transfer ratio (if this term may be used here) is four character transfers per single computer transfer.

INPUT–OUTPUT ORGANIZATION

The details of how the input–output section of a computer performs may best be illustrated by the following relatively simple examples. Suppose it is necessary to interface with:

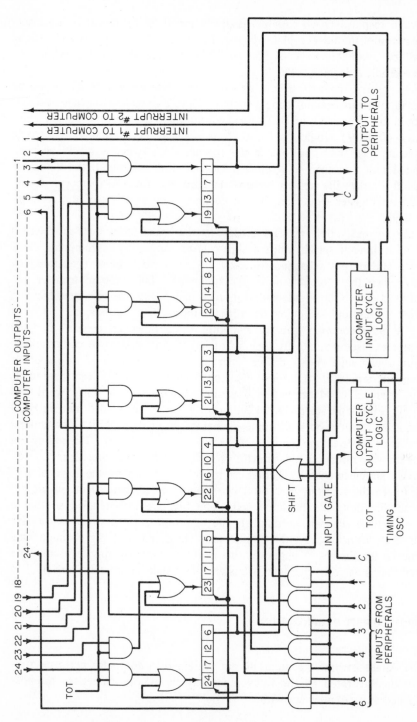

FIG. 12-6 A character–word buffer.

1. Two separate parallel output channels of 24 bits
2. One parallel input channel of 24 bits
3. Two output D/A converters (12 bits parallel)
4. One input D/A converter (12 bits parallel)
5. A computer-controlled typewriter [used as a keyboard and a printer (6-bit parallel code)]

Direct Input–Output Interface

Assume that the computer has a built-in register which stores the word for output. At the time of output transfer, an output strobe pulse is generated and carried to the external logic to indicate that the word in the register can now be accepted by the external device (i.e., the individual word bits are available now on the output lines). The strobe pulses serve two purposes: (1) to identify the output word as data; and (2) to provide a gating signal.

For input transfer, the reverse process can be assumed. That is, an input strobe pulse is generated to indicate when the data on the input lines are ready as an input to the computer register. In both cases, the transfer to and from the computer via the register is a parallel format, and the direction of data movement is indicated by which of the two strobes (input or output) is generated.

The above outlines the basic plan, but there is a reasonable amount of preparation to be done before the physical transfer of data takes place. For instance, there is (1) the problem of routing the data to and from the specified external device only; (2) the problem of ensuring that both the external device and the computer are ready for a transfer; (3) the decision on location of storage in the memory; (4) the question, *where from* in the memory; and (5) the question, *to or from what registers* in the computer is the transfer to be effected. These are all legitimate operations that must be specified precisely.

All these problems are solved by an orderly exchange of commands, strobes, and responses, starting at the beginning of the process. For the sake of simplicity, assume a 24-bit output transfer is to be effected. The first operation involves a *device-acquiring command* (identified in the repertory as a *CON command*) which serves to connect the desired output peripheral-device channel to the computer. This command is divided into two portions: One portion, say six bits, identifies it as the CON command; the second portion, perhaps nine bits, specifies the address code which identifies the peripheral channel. This command is transferred out via the output register to the input–output unit. It is identified as a command (not data) by a strobe pulse, called the CON strobe, generated when the command is located in the transfer register and ready for interpretation. The CON command is recognized by a decoder in the input–output. When the CON strobe occurs, the address is decoded, which sets up a flip-flop in the input–output to route the data. The data appear subsequently on the output lines after routing through the correct set of output gates.

The input–output will return the CON strobe to the computer on a *response* line, which in effect releases the original CON strobe. This action permits the computer to proceed with the next step of the transfer process.

The next step can be the generation and forwarding to the input–output of an *acknowledge* pulse which lets the input–output know the response has been received, and the transfer will proceed now as planned. This *acknowledge* pulse is really a second strobe announcing the completion of the transfer. It is not always supplied.

The channel is now locked to the computer, and the transfer will be acceptable to both devices. The actual transfer of data begins by the initiation of the *data-transfer command* (identified as TOT), which in essence addresses the memory cell from which the data are to be recovered. The TOT command does not appear in the transfer register. The fact that the data are transferred from memory to the transfer register is made known to the input–output by the appearance of the TOT pulse, at which time the data are gated through the channel specified by the CON command. A response is generated by the input–output, and an acknowledgment is generated by the computer, which signifies the completion of the transfer process. The absence of a response setting at the CON or TOT strobe time informs the computer that the transfer process is not proceeding satisfactorily; after a programmed wait, the computer sequence may be to "skip to the next command" or "take other action," as the program demands. The acknowledgment strobe can be used in the input–output for resetting logic flip-flops, etc.

The input transfer follows much the same itinerary, but an *input-transfer command* (identified as TIN) with its distinctive strobe is used instead of TOT and its strobe.

With this background, it is now possible to complete the discussion of the interface proposed and illustrated in Fig. 12-7.

Essentially, eight channels are required. Except for the bits involved in the data words, they are all basically either input or output channels. It is assumed that, in the peripheral devices, there is a flip-flop which, in its set position, allows the TOT or TIN strobe to be returned as a valid response. If this flip-flop is reset, the response will be blocked. The computer, not receiving the expected response after a programmed wait, will proceed to the next command. A flip-flop located in the decoder can also be used in the same way to gate back (or not gate back) a re-

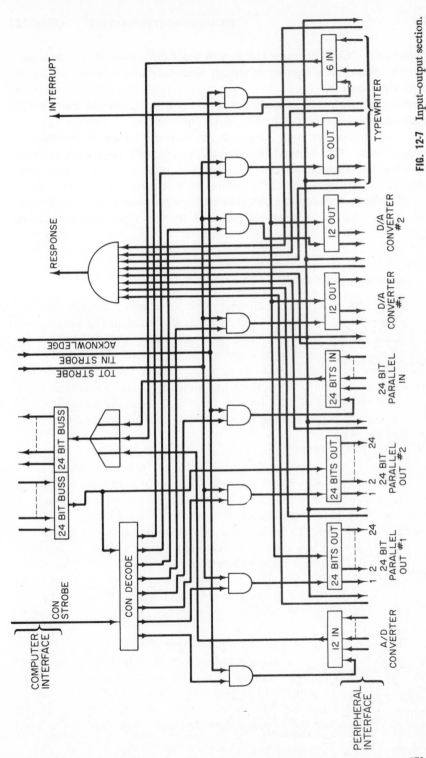

FIG. 12-7 Input–output section.

sponse to the CON strobe. The fact that a CON strobe response is not generated indicates a transfer is already underway or a malfunction exists in the input–output.

Although, in many systems, the program will periodically call up the required input–output commands, a second method of control requires peripheral equipment itself to signal the computer when it is ready to transfer data. This method involves the peripheral's raising an external incoming line (sometimes called a *flag*) indicating its desire. The computer observes this signal (or interrupt, as it is generally called) and, at the computer's convenience, switches to a routine which services the device. This type of exchange is indicated for the typewriter connection in Fig. 12-7.

Buffered Input–Output Channel

A buffered input–output channel provides a more flexible interface mode than the direct input–output interface discussed in the last section. It has the happy facility of loading or unloading a peripheral device without requiring an individual command to transfer each individual word. The buffered input–output may be designed to have several channels, i.e., it can service several peripheral devices simultaneously. Of course, there must be a staggering of data transfer times, otherwise the memory would be in a chaotic condition not knowing what data to accept or transmit or where to put it.

A single-channel buffered input–output unit illustrates simply the functioning of this type of interface. First of all, it is commanded to be operational by a computer instruction. Next a command word is stored in a register within the buffered channel; this becomes the first position in the memory to or from which data are to be transferred. A second command word is sent to the buffered input–output and stored in a second register. This word is a number indicating, e.g., the number of words to be transferred. The first register, hereafter, will be called the *present-address register* (PAR); the second register will be called the *word-count register* (WCR). In one of the two command words, there will be one bit which will indicate the direction of transfer, i.e., either in or out of memory.

The usual way for a buffered input–output channel to operate is for the peripheral device to signal the buffered input–output by means of an interrupt that it is ready to transfer data. This *interrupt* causes the proper strobes to generate, which will in turn move data to the buffered input–output. The direction of flow depends upon identification, by the bit mentioned above, of the required flow direction. The fact that a word

transfer occurs is recorded by counting down "1" in the WCR and counting up "1" in the PAR. The "1" count to the PAR changes the address
in the register to the next higher number. This register is used by the
computer to *address* the memory. During buffered input–output transac-
tions, the memory address associated with that particular buffered channel
is taken from PAR rather than from a program-command address. The
significance of the WCR is that the end of the transfer is indicated by this
counter's decrement to zero.

For multichannel buffered input–output units, each individual channel
will have its own PAR and WCR. These must be loaded separately by
words transmitted via the direct input–output channel. A block diagram
of a buffered input–output with two channels and above-mentioned registers is shown in Fig. 12-8.

A problem develops when more than a single peripheral device has

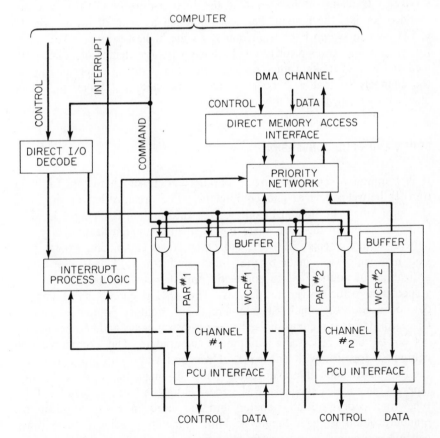

FIG. 12-8 Buffered input–output block diagram.

access to the memory. This occurs when two or more peripherals desire access at the same instant. It is usually solved by assigning each channel a priority rating. The channel with the highest priority will predominate (*priority preempt*) and, when it demands service, it will block out whatever channel of lower priority is then operating.

The priority preempt, will of course happen at controlled times, e.g., at the time a word of lower priority has completed its word transfer, not in the middle of a word transfer.

The various interrupts from the individual peripheral channels are stored individually in a *channel interrupt flip-flop* (CIFF). The priority network scans these flip-flops and selects the one with the highest priority to service. At the completion of the highest priority transfer, the priority network looks for the next-highest priority CIFF demanding service and allows this channel to transfer. The process continues until all CIFFs are serviced. If it should happen that the highest-priority CIFF again demanded service, the system, before completing its scan of lower priority CIFFs, would switch back immediately to the highest-priority CIFF. For this reason, the lower-priority CIFFs have a poorer chance of being serviced and careful thought must be given to the assignment of peripherals to the channels so that a fast-service peripheral does not block the other channels by being assigned too high a priority.

CODES AND CODE CONVERSION

It is common practice to provide parallel coding of characters for data transfer between devices and equipments. The organization of the ASC II code (American Standard Code for the Information Exchange) is given in Table 12-3. In the past, there has been little standardization of codes between interconnected military and commercial equipment, except possibly between devices made by the same manufacturer. This lack of standardization, of course, led to confusion and the obvious need to provide a special code for conversion devices. The ASC II code is an attempt to develop a code on which all commercial and military equipment can be standardized. It is a compromise between several codes and earlier endeavors to tie data processing equipment, computers, and communication equipment together with one code. These codes apply to interconnecting cables and to such interchangeable items as magnetic tapes and paper tapes. Other codes such as IBM codes, Honeywell codes, Baudot Teletypewriter codes are all popular and are used in many applications. Standardization is the ultimate goal but difficult to achieve since much existing equipment based on different codes is already established in the field.

TABLE 12-3

The American Standard Code (ASC II) for information interchange[a,b]

	000	001	010	011	100	101	110	111
0000	NULL	DC_0	⁺o	0		P		
0001	SOM	DC_1	!	1	A	Q		
0010	EOA	DC_2	"	2	B	R		
0011	EOM	DC_3	#	3	C	S		
0100	EOT	DC_4 (stop)	$	4	D	T		
0101	WRU	ERR	%	5	E	U	Reserved	
0110	RU	SYNC	8	6	F	V	for	
0111	BELL	LEM	' (apos.)	7	G	W	future	
1000	FE_0	S_0	(	8	H	X	standard-	
1001	HT_{SK}	S_1	)	9	I	Y	ization	
1010	LF	S_2	*	:	J	Z		
1011	V_{TAB}	S_3	+	;	K	ǀ		
1100	FF	S_4	, (comma)	<	L	\		ACK
1101	CR	S_5	–	=	M	ǀ		①
1110	SO	S_6	.	>	N	↑		ESC
1111	SI	S_7	/	?	O	←		DEL

[a] *Example:*

| 100 | 0001 | = A

b₇ . . . . b₁

[b] *Abbreviations:*

NULL	Null/idle	SO	Shift out
SOM	Start of message	SI	Shift in
EOA	End of address	DC_0–DC_4	Device controls (DC_0 reserved
EOM	End of message		for data link escape)
EOT	End of transmission	ERR	Error
WRU	Who are you?	SYNC	Synchonous idle
RU	Are you. . . ?	LEM	Logical end of media
BELL	Audible signal	S_0–S_7	Information separators
FE_0	Format effector	⁺o	Word separator (space)
HT	Horizontal tabulation	↑	Exponentiation
SK	Skip (punched card)	←	Replaced by
LF	Line feed	ACK	Acknowledge
V_{TAB}	Vertical tabulation	①	Unassigned control
FF	Form feed	ESC	Escape
CR	Carriage return	DEL	Delete-idle

Code Conversion

A code conversion where only bits are interchanged is simple to perform with Boolean logic, as shown in Fig. 12-9. The general procedure is to write a Boolean function for each level of the code and derive the logic, as illustrated in Fig. 12-9.

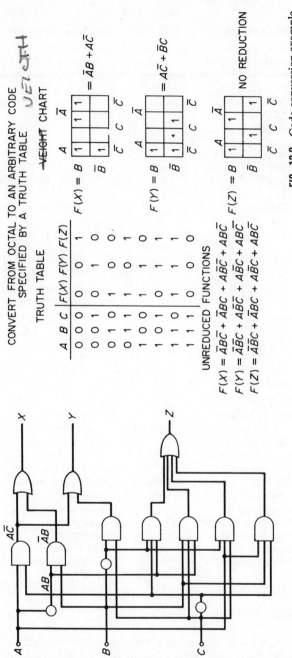

CONVERT FROM OCTAL TO AN ARBITRARY CODE
SPECIFIED BY A TRUTH TABLE

TRUTH TABLE

A B C	F(X)	F(Y)	F(Z)
0 0 0	0	0	1
0 0 1	0	1	0
0 1 0	1	0	0
0 1 1	1	0	1
1 0 0	1	1	0
1 0 1	0	1	1
1 1 0	1	1	1
1 1 1	1	0	0

UNREDUCED FUNCTIONS

$F(X) = \bar{A}B\bar{C} + \bar{A}BC + AB\bar{C} + AB\bar{C}$
$F(Y) = \bar{A}\bar{B}C + A\bar{B}\bar{C} + A\bar{B}C + ABC$
$F(Z) = \bar{A}\bar{B}\bar{C} + \bar{A}BC + A\bar{B}C + ABC$

WEIGHT CHART

$F(X) = B$ $= \bar{A}B + A\bar{C}$

$F(Y) = B$ $= A\bar{C} + \bar{B}C$

$F(Z) = B$ NO REDUCTION

FIG. 12-9 Code conversion example.

BCD TO BINARY AND BINARY TO BCD CONVERSION

This discussion concerns an auxiliary function that is occasionally performed by the input–output section. BCD to binary and binary to BCD conversions may be performed by computer programming but may also be performed by a moderately complex logic device described below. Use of the logic device would be preferable where relatively too much computing time would be devoted to performing conversions.

The basic process consists of transferring the word to be transformed into a shift register and then circulating this word around the loop with the LSD placed in the MSD end. The combination of shifts and complementations necessary to perform the desired conversions will be briefly described. Block diagrams of the conversion systems are given in Fig. 12-10.

To perform the binary to BCD conversion of Fig. 12-10a, the circulated word is shifted with the MSD end first. The word is shifted one bit and a test is made. If the number in the right-hand four bit slots is less than 5, add 0. If it is 5 or greater, add 3. The first four slots are tested during the first four bit shifts. During the subsequent four bit shifts, the four right-hand bit slots are tested as before, and so are the next four bit slots. The successive sequences in Fig. 12-11 show the process, step-by-step. The converter device is implemented by logic which complements the individual bit stages according to a predetermined truth table specifying the proper result for each check condition.

The BCD to binary conversion shown in Fig. 12-10b is similar, but the shift is in the *opposite* direction (left to right). If the result is 7 or greater after a shift, 3 is subtracted from the left-hand set of four bit positions. After four shifts, the first group of four and the second group of four are tested and the proper subtraction made. The process continues in this manner until completion. The precise steps of the process are shown in Fig. 12-12.

PARITY-CHECKING AND ERROR-CORRECTION CODES

Although the majority of data storage devices (such as magnetic tapes) and the majority of data transfer methods (such as printed cards or paper tape) are inherently reliable in their operation, still, errors can and do appear once in a great while. These errors often appear as a dropped bit or an added bit within a character. One method to protect against error is to record a *parity bit* along with the character when the character is stored or transmitted. When the character is retrieved or received, it is

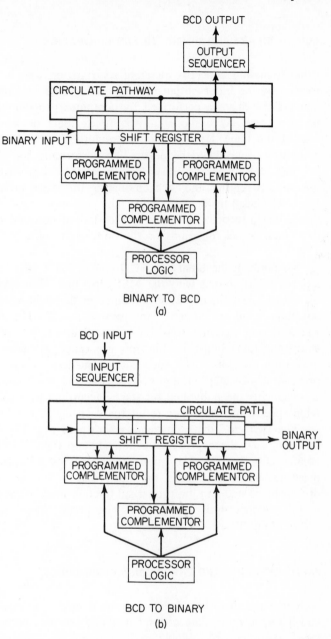

FIG. 12-10 Converter block diagram.

automatically checked to see if the parity condition is correct. If parity does *not* check, a *parity-error-detecting circuit* (such as the one suggested in Chapter 7, Fig. 7-20) senses the failure of the parity test and triggers an alarm indicating to the operator such a failure has occurred. In some devices, the character so flagged may be retransmitted automatically.

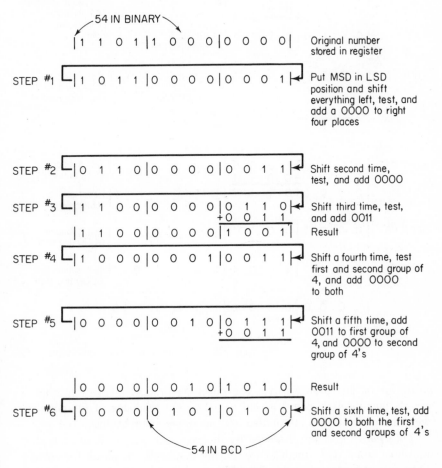

FIG. 12-11   Binary to BCD code conversion.

As an illustration of a parity bit, consider the section of paper tape shown in Fig. 12-13. Whenever the coded character has an even number of bits, no hole is punched in the parity column. If the coded character has an odd number of bits, the parity column will have a hole punched in it, which makes the total number of holes across the tape, including the parity-bit hole, even. This method is referred to as *adding an even*

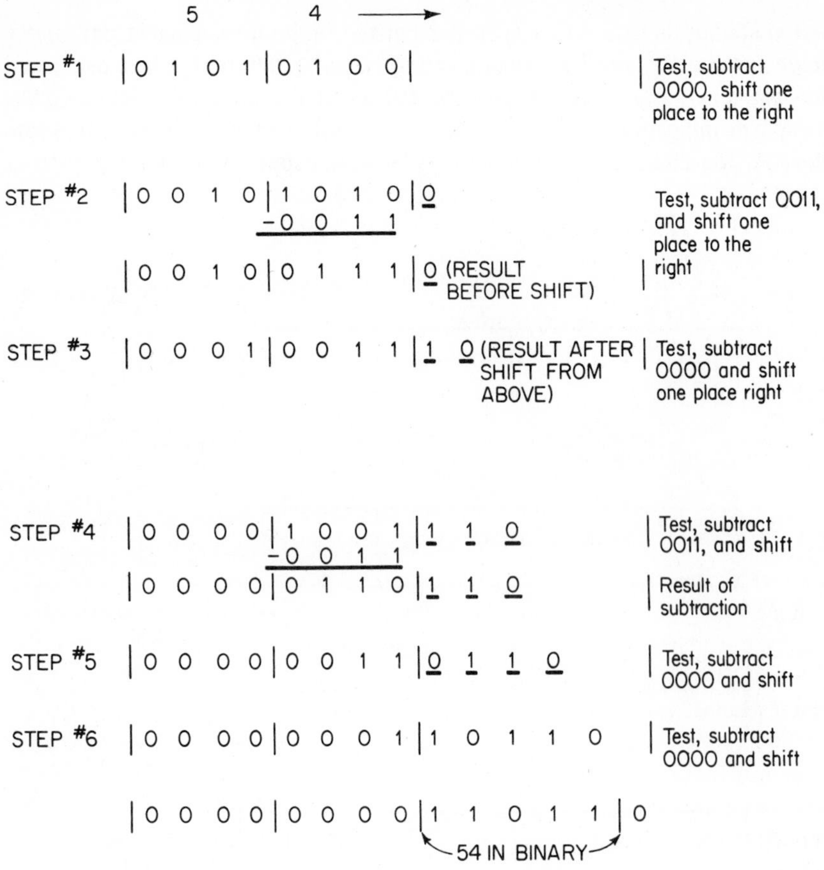

5   4 ——————▶

STEP #1 | 0 1 0 1 | 0 1 0 0 | | Test, subtract
                                                         0000, shift one
                                                         place to the right

STEP #2 | 0 0 1 0 | 1 0 1 0 | 0̲   Test, subtract 0011,
                      − 0 0 1 1   and shift one
           ──────────────   place to the
           | 0 0 1 0 | 0 1 1 1 | 0̲ (RESULT | right
                                       ⁻ BEFORE SHIFT)

STEP #3 | 0 0 0 1 | 0 0 1 1 | 1̲   0̲ (RESULT AFTER | Test, subtract
                                            SHIFT FROM   0000 and shift
                                            ABOVE)   one place right

STEP #4 | 0 0 0 0 | 1 0 0 1 | 1̲ 1̲ 0̲ | Test, subtract
                      − 0 0 1 1   0011, and shift
           | 0 0 0 0 | 0 1 1 0 | 1̲ 1̲ 0̲ | Result of
                                                           subtraction

STEP #5 | 0 0 0 0 | 0 0 1 1 | 0̲ 1̲ 1̲ 0̲ | Test, subtract
                                                           0000 and shift

STEP #6 | 0 0 0 0 | 0 0 0 1 | 1 0 1 1 0 | Test, subtract
                                                           0000 and shift

           | 0 0 0 0 | 0 0 0 0 | 1 1 0 1 1 | 0
                                       ╰── 54 IN BINARY ──╯

FIG. 12-12 BCD to binary code conversion.

parity bit or just *even parity*. The checking process involves testing to
see whether the hole count is odd or even. On readback, if the count is
even, the parity test is affirmative and no *single* error has occurred.

Odd parity may be produced by the generation of a bit to make the
total hole count *odd*. In this case, during readback, the check for correct
parity would be a total count of holes that are *odd* in number. The process

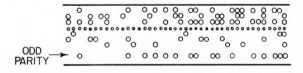

ODD
PARITY ——▶

FIG. 12-13 Paper tape with parity bit.

just described is defined as *horizontal parity* since the check is on a *particular character line*. A *vertical parity* can be obtained by considering the hole count in a lengthwise direction along a particular column. This same type of parity generation and check occurs in a serial transmission of data. Here an individual toggle flip-flop, set before the first bit transfers, is tested at the end of the word transfer to see whether its final position is *set* or *reset*. During parity generation, the position of this flip-flop determines whether a parity bit is added to the serial pulse train. At the receiving end a second flip-flop's position is checked to see if its position is properly *odd* or *even* depending on the type of parity used.

Parity generation and sensing can be either the horizontal or vertical type, or both types may be employed simultaneously.

Error-Correcting Codes

Although use of a single parity bit can sense an error of a *single* bit, it is useless for multiple-bit errors (two or more). Also, other more complex arrangements of extra bits not only can be used to *detect* errors but, in some cases, can *correct* an error. Such *error-correcting codes* have been proposed and are in actual use. Although most are quite complex, only a simple example of an error-correction code, the Hamming code, will be demonstrated here.

The Hamming code is employed to detect and correct errors in transmission of binary data. Any error will appear as an error in the *parity bit position* of the word, i.e., the parity bits will be different at the receiving end from those at the transmission end. The change in the parity bits dictates which bit of the word is in error. The code works as follows:

A parity bit *pattern* is assembled, and the necessary parity bits are transmitted with the word. For instance, a seven-bit word will require a pattern of three parity bits. This pattern is illustrated by

$$\underbrace{X_1X_2X_3X_4X_5X_6X_7}_{\text{word bits}} \qquad \underbrace{P_1P_2P_3}_{\text{parity bits}}$$

The parity bits are derived from the following word bits. Assume the *even* parity condition will be used. The pattern for the parity bits is then assumed to be

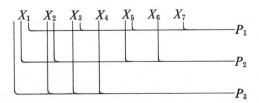

As an example, assume the word is

$$0\ 1\ 1\ 0\ 1\ 1\ 1\ P_3\ P_2\ P_1$$

Write the even parity bits for the above, using the pattern agreed upon,

P_1 (will be even parity if $X_1\ X_3\ X_5\ X_7 = 0\ 1\ 1\ 1$) = 1
P_2 (will be even parity if $X_1\ X_2\ X_5\ X_6 = 0\ 1\ 1\ 1$) = 1
P_3 (will be even parity if $X_1\ X_2\ X_3\ X_4 = 0\ 1\ 1\ 0$) = 0

The graphing of the above is

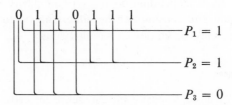

The word transmitted is

$$0\ 1\ 1\ 0\ 1\ 1\ 1\ \underbrace{1\ 1\ 0}_{\substack{\text{parity}\\\text{bits}}}$$

Suppose the parity bit at the receiving end comes out 010. This is incorrect for the word transmitted; in fact, it indicates that there must be an error in bit X_7. This is discovered by comparing the parity transmitted, 110, with the parity tested, 010, and noting that a change only in P_1 could be caused by X_7's being of the incorrect polarity. Note further that there being no change in P_2 and P_3 removes the chance of errors in the other bits X_1 to X_6. Therefore, the result of this test indicates that X_7, received as a "0," should be changed to a "1." This change then corrects the error in transmission.

[NOTE: With three parity bits, the error will be coded; hence, a comparison of the parity transmitted with the parity received establishes which of the transmitted bits must be in error.]

The practice and theory of error-bit checking is quite involved and the reader, therefore, is referred to specialized textbooks for a more detailed treatment.

ANALOG-TO-DIGITAL AND DIGITAL-TO-ANALOG CONVERTERS

Shaft Encoder

A shaft encoder consists of a disk, divided into a binary segment code beginning at a starting or reference point on the circle. Coded "1's" and

"0's" are represented by conducting or nonconducting segments, wrapped around in a circle. Such a device with seven tracks (which can identify a location of one part in 128) is shown in Fig. 12-14. The individual segments complete an electrical contact via an individual track brush when

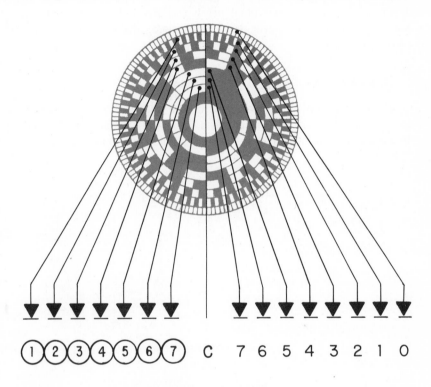

BRUSH POSITIONS

FIG. 12-14 Shaft encoder disk.

the "1" segment is under the brush. There is an open circuited contact when a "0" segment is under the brush. The completed electrical path runs via the track brush through the metal of the disk to a central brush contact on the device's shaft. To prevent ambiguity at the crossover points (1 to 0 on a track or vice versa), two common methods are employed:

1. The disk uses Grey code rather than pure binary. This code prevents ambiguity of no more than one digit since Grey code changes only one digit per digit regardless of the number of code bits involved.
2. A V-brush connection is used. Of two brushes on a track, the brush selected for contact is the one at a distance from any code crossover

point. The brushes are arranged in a V pattern, and therefore, the term *V brush* has been given to the arrangement.

Both the V-brush method and the Grey-code method are used with about the same penalty of extra gating elements required for both. As shown in Fig. 12-14, individual brush contacts are brought out through isolation diodes. The particular shaft-encoder disk shown is one using a V-brush scheme.

Servo Analog-to-Digital and Digital-to-Analog Converters

Low-speed converters make use of the shaft encoder combined with an electromechanical servomechanism. An A/D (analog-to-digital) type of converter is shown in Fig. 12-15. A follow-up analog servo employs

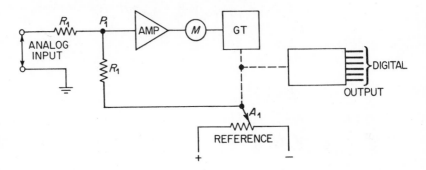

FIG. 12-15 Electromechanical A/D converter.

an encoder in the output shaft to give a digital representation of the analog voltage input. The system is designed, as any other servomechanism, with the motor rotating in such a direction as to cause the output of potentiometer A_1 to balance (sum out) the input analog voltage at the amplifier input's summing point P_1. The code read on the encoder brushes driven by the servomotor is a digital indication of the original analog voltage at e_i.

A shaft encoder is also a vital component in the opposite conversion process, that of going from digital to analog (D/A converter) representation. A typical D/A converter appears in Fig. 12-16. Here, the digital input register is compared with the digital feedback from the encoder by a comparator. A digital unbalance causes the comparator to provide analog voltage steps in a direction that will reduce the digital differences between the register and the encoder. When the two numbers balance, rotation of

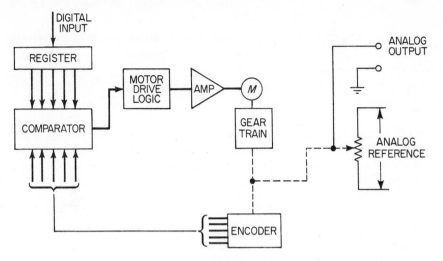

FIG. 12-16   Electromechanical D/A converter.

the motor and shaft ceases. An analog potentiometer on the output shaft gives the desired analog signal output.

All-Electronic A/D Converters

Electromechanical techniques are not the only solution to A/D conversion. One frequently used type of all-electronic A/D converter is shown in Fig. 12-17. The principle used here relies on the design of a sensitive

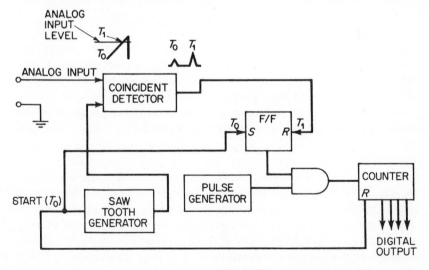

FIG. 12-17   All-electronic A/D converter.

voltage-level comparator and an accurately linear sawtooth waveform triggered at regular intervals. A measurement is made of the time it takes the linear sawtooth to rise from the initial T_0 level to a level equal to the analog voltage level determined by the comparator. The time is measured by totaling the clock pulses gated between T_0 and the time of intersection, T_1 in an ordinary binary counter. Since the count of pulses is proportional to the rise distance the sawtooth rises, the counter output is the digital representation of the input voltage level. This technique yields accuracies in the region of 0.5 per cent, the accuracy depending primarily on sawtooth linearity and on a measurement resolution within plus or minus one count of the correct count on the counter.

Use of Summing Networks in A/D and D/A Conversions

In this chapter, the use of electromechanical servos was previously discussed as a method of performing either A/D or D/A conversions. Although these devices are adequate in systems where the slow response time (in the order of seconds) is not a disadvantage, they are not sufficiently rapid for many modern instrument applications (where conversions may be desired at perhaps 100,000 times per second). The accuracies or precision expected of electromechanical servosystems is limited primarily by the precision of the analog system components such as potentiometer linearities, reference voltage tolerances, and encoder resolution (number of bits). This limitation also exists in the all-electronic systems discussed below, but, in this case, precision is limited to summing-resistor accuracies, the reference voltage stabilities, the number of bits in the digital readout (the last is also influential in the electromechanical systems case), all of which can be more precisely controlled. All-electronic switching and decision making takes place in microseconds (or fractions thereof) and the analog accuracies can be easily held to 0.1 per cent and, with some expense, to 0.01 per cent.

An all-electronic A/D converter that makes use of summing techniques is shown in Fig. 12-18. In this particular approach, the analog input voltage is balanced at a summing point P, against the sum of opposing voltages that appears on the summing-collector resistors (connected via transistor switches to the reference voltage source of polarity opposite to the signal). (Actually a balance of currents is achieved.) The technique is to subtract the largest reference current first and note if the comparator output shows a zero or reverses polarity. If its output sign does not reverse, the summed current remains connected and a "1" is placed in the register's first position. A second component of summed current (one-half the first) is subtracted in turn and the same process followed. If the comparator changes sign, the particular comparison current is not used, a "0" is entered in the second position of the register, and the next lower step in subtraction is attempted. The process is completed when all values have been attempted. The sum remaining in the register at the end of the process is a measurement of the analog input in digital form.

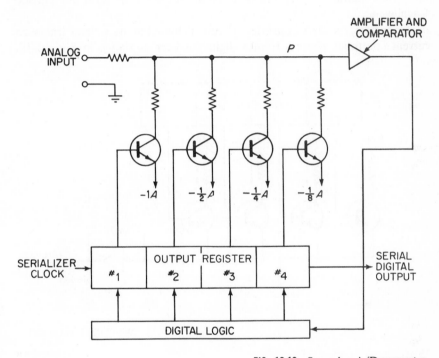

FIG. 12-18   Summing A/D converter.

The basic advantage of this approach is the relatively high operating speed of this device. Switching reference currents, in turn, into the circuit registers is done at 1-μsec intervals. Thus, a 10-digit conversion is accomplished in 10 μsec. By using a parallel rather than serial approach, the time could be even more drastically reduced.

A second advantage of this general approach is that all bulky electro-mechanical components are eliminated. The summing A/D converter can be built with microminiature techniques, including the manufacture of summing resistors by thin-film technology.

Although, for the version discussed above, it was assumed that reference voltages would be switched in and tested in a prescribed sequence, a somewhat slower but comparable technique is to make the output register an electronic counter which merely counts until the correct sum of voltages (or currents) from the references equals the junction input signal. An electronic comparator (or level detector) indicates when the reference voltages switched sequentially by the counter are equal to the original signal. Such a device is simpler logically than the sequential switching of binary references but is slower in its processing capability since the counting is done in a serial binary sequence until the comparison is achieved.

Conversely, a D/A converter is formed by summing several transistor current controlled sources from a digital register as shown in Fig. 12-19.

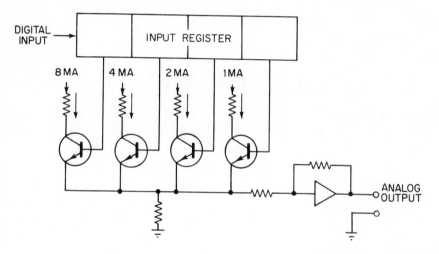

FIG. 12-19   Summing D/A converter.

The number in the register turns on switches whenever a "1" appears. The sum of the currents generated is an analog measure of the digital register input.

Although not shown in these figures, the above devices may be designed to convert both positive and negative inputs (dual-polarity) for A/D operations at the expense of a slight increase in complexity. For those particular applications requiring dual-polarity capability, the polarity of the input signal must first be sensed so that the proper polarity reference can be chosen. This applies to either the A/D or D/A device if it is to have a bipolar capability.

Decoder Networks

Resistor networks are employed in both A/D and D/A converters, as already pointed out. There are many varieties. In some applications *weighted* voltages are summed at a typical operational amplifier summing point. This system was suggested in the discussion of the electromechanical D/A converter. The more usual practice, however, is either to employ a fixed voltage (or current) source and switch weighted resistors or to switch the legs of a ladder network between a reference voltage and ground. For the ladder approach, depending only on the make-up of the binary number, a particular leg will be switched to ground if a "0" or to the reference voltage if a "1."

For a relatively low accuracy system or if there are only a few levels to decode, the single weighted-resistor network of Fig. 12-20a will accomplish the task. The output voltage results from the total current flow through the load resistor R_L and is equal to $i_T R_L$, where i_T is the sum of currents through R_1, R_2, and R_3 in the figure. The voltage contributed in each leg is equal to

$$V_o = \frac{E_R R_L}{R_L + R_L(2^n - 1)} = \frac{E_R}{2^n} \tag{12-1}$$

where n = number of summing resistors; E_R = reference voltage; and V_o = output voltage of the decoder. A truth table of Fig. 12-20b with voltage levels demonstrates the process precisely.

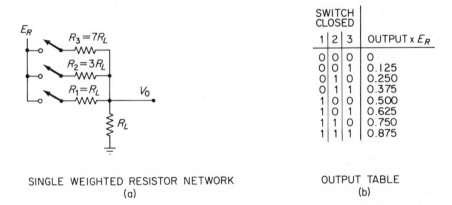

SINGLE WEIGHTED RESISTOR NETWORK
(a)

SWITCH CLOSED			
1	2	3	OUTPUT x E_R
0	0	0	0
0	0	1	0.125
0	1	0	0.250
0	1	1	0.375
1	0	0	0.500
1	0	1	0.625
1	1	0	0.750
1	1	1	0.875

OUTPUT TABLE
(b)

FIG. 12-20 An example of a weighted resistor D/A decoder.

Although Fig. 12-20 is a straightforward approach, it suffers from the necessity of scaling the resistors proportionately and accurately. Further, since, for any practical converter, the variation of the resistor values is $(2^n - 1)/1$, it is difficult to obtain semiconductor switches whose resistance value, when closed, is a sufficiently small part of the forward voltage drop that its effect on total accuracy can be ignored. The switch of the lowest-resistance circuit (the highest current increment) is the most critical and, in a sense, sets the total accuracy limits.

A second approach is to use the ladder network of Fig. 12-21. In this case, the maximum ratio of resistance is 2/1. The total ladder may be made as long as necessary within the allowable accuracy of the components. The output voltage can be calculated from the equation

$$V_o = \frac{E_R}{2}\left(\frac{1}{2^n} + \frac{1}{2^{n-1}} + \cdots + \frac{1}{2^0}\right) \tag{12-2}$$

As an illustrative example, by using the network shown in Fig. 12-21 having three binary switches, the output for 011 would be

$$V_o = \frac{E_R}{2}\left(0 + \frac{1}{2^1} + \frac{1}{2^0}\right) = \frac{E_R}{2}\left(\frac{1}{2} + 1\right) = \frac{3}{4}E_R \tag{12-3}$$

Figure 12-21 lists the truth table of connections and the output voltages for each combination of these switches. These voltages were all com-

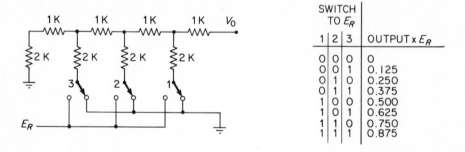

SWITCH TO E_R			
1	2	3	OUTPUT x E_R
0	0	0	0
0	0	1	0.125
0	1	0	0.250
0	1	1	0.375
1	0	0	0.500
1	0	1	0.625
1	1	0	0.750
1	1	1	0.875

FIG. 12-21   An example of a ladder network D/A decoder.

puted in the same manner as the example above. When the switch is open, the equation term is "0" and, when closed, the $1/2^n$ term adds to the voltage output.

Multiple Converter Systems

In any practical system using A/D and D/A converters, the normal mechanization involves either or both numerous analog channel inputs and digital channel outputs. As a result, in the interest of efficiency and lowest possible cost, there is an advantage in combining analog channels before input to the A/D converter, which in turn, transfers to the digital processor. When possible, each analog signal is first standardized, i.e., put into a form that is within a standard range. For instance, the signal voltage could well be adjusted (amplified or attenuated) to a range of 0 to +5 volts. If the original signal is alternating current, it will also be converted to direct current. A device normally termed a *signal conditioner* performs this standardization function. A second consideration for multiple conversions is the rate at which the individual analog input signal varies. If the rate is relatively slow (a few cycles per second or less, e.g.), the computer usually finds little need to monitor the signal continuously. In fact, the A/D converter itself operates in periodic cycles. For instance, it periodically standardizes and converts an input to the computer as a digital number representative of the analog signal amplitude sampled. Because of these factors, an A/D converter samples the analog input at discrete intervals. The sample interval is a function of the variation rate of the analog signal and need be no faster than necessary to reconstruct from the data sample a sufficiently accurate indication of the variation of the original sample. A sampling figure of having merit and some theoretical foundation is the rule, "sample at a rate at least twice that of the highest expected frequency variation."

Because A/D converters normally sample at rates higher than the highest frequency of interest of any given analog input, it is normal practice to share a single A/D converter with a number of analog channels. A device called a *multiplexer* switches several input channels in turn to the A/D converter. The rate of switching the samples is adjusted to be consistent with the need of adequate sample periods for each channel and, in addition, allows the A/D converter sufficient time to perform its data conversion. The computer, by commanding the switching sequence of the multiplexer and the rate of input of a digital number from the converter for each conversion process, inherently controls the system's functioning.

On the opposite side of the coin, the D/A output follows a similar sequence, but the process here is not quite a mirror image of the A/D function. In the D/A case, a digital output word from the computer is converted to an analog signal, and this signal stored temporarily is an analog level storage device. Here a *demultiplexing* process makes it possible to share a single D/A converter with several analog output channels. Usually the D/A output is switched sequentially by computer command to the appropriate channel storage (sample-holding) device. The D/A converter output is transferred during the switch-closed interval to this particular sample-holding circuit. During the next interval, the D/A output will be stored elsewhere in one of the other channel's sample-holding circuits. Periodically, the first channel storage will be reserviced. The sampling interval must be at a sufficient rate that, between samples, the sample-holding circuit's voltage level remains within the error specification. A block diagram of the entire process is given in Fig. 12-22. Again, the individual

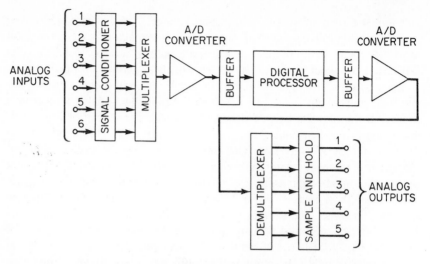

FIG. 12-22   Multiplexing and demultiplexing converters.

sample-holding circuits may also be expected to provide an output signal-conditioning function which corresponds in reverse to the input signal-conditioner's function.

SUMMARY

This chapter has introduced the reader to the input–output section of the processor. The input–ouput section was defined as the logic section that forms the communication link between the processor and the peripheral devices. The topics discussed included airborne, and ground-based computers, off-line and on-line operation, and expected airborne and ground-based peripherals. The basic methods of input–output organization followed and a comparison was made among the bus, centralized, and buffered-channel approaches. This discussion was expanded in later sections where the direct input–output interface was explored in detail. This was followed by a discussion of a buffered input–output channel. Short sections covered code conversion, the ASC II code and BCD to binary conversion processes. Also discussed were parity-check and error-correcting codes. The chapter concluded with a section briefly describing the process of A/D and D/A conversion. Both electromechanical and all-electronic devices were introduced, including a survey of weighted-resistor and ladder-network decoders. Finally, an explanation was given of the advantages of multiplexing and demultiplexing systems.

REVIEW QUESTIONS AND PROBLEMS

12-1. What are the differences between the input–output sections of a ground-based commercial computer and an airborne computer?

12-2. In your own words, define on-line and off-line operation.

12-3. What are the functions of an input–output section?

12-4. What is meant by peripheral equipment?

12-5. Why is a buffer register often used in a general input–output section?

12-6. Draw the logic to convert from the following three-bit code *A* to three-bit code *B*:

Code A	Code B
000	~~101~~ |||
001	110
010	101
011	100
100	011
101	010
110	001
111	000

12-7. Describe three methods of converting an analog voltage to a digital voltage.

12-8. What is the resolution of a D/A converter that employs 10 weighted resistors? What would be the advantage of constructing this decoder with a ladder network.

12-9. Compose a section of paper tape with the following message, using an odd parity bit:

WORLD WAR I ENDED IN 1918.

12-10. Organize an input–output section that will operate the following peripherals:

a. Paper tape reader.
b. Paper tape punch.
c. Two magnetic-tape units. Use a buffered input–output.
d. Five A/D inputs under computer control.
e. Three D/A outputs under computer control.

PERIPHERAL
EQUIPMENT

13

This chapter briefly describes a few of the types of peripheral equipment often associated with data processors. Only the more common ones will be described, and these will not be covered in any great depth because of the wealth of data available in other texts and in the commercial literature.

Many devices that interface with computers have a limited use and should be considered in the classification of special devices. In this classification would be such items as inertial platforms, star trackers, and machine-tool controls. These are not discussed at all, and the student is referred to other appropriate sources for details of such specialized equipment.

This chapter does, however, discuss some of the more commonly used equipment for loading computer programs, such as the paper-tape reader, punched-card reader, and incremental magnetic-tape reader–recorder. It also discusses typical bulk storage devices, including continuous-run magnetic-tape machines and disk files. Incremental and continuous-run magnetic-tape units actually fall into both the classifications of data loading and bulk storage devices.

Output equipment covered includes paper-tape punches, card punches, and printers. Again, the magnetic-tape machines are also included in the output device classification.

Typewriters and typewriterlike devices are also interesting peripheral input–output devices which are used to print out results and the typewriter keyboard can be used for data input. More often, however, the digital typewriter is used by the operator for *control monitoring* rather than program loading. The operator can insert individual instructions or call up diagnostic programs with the console typewriter, if he wishes, in most of the large systems.

Quite often a paper-tape punch and a paper-tape reader will be included as part of the digital typewriter assembly. For low-cost systems, this device becomes the central input–output communication device for the computer, since it incorporates the functions of reading tape, punching tape, and printout. Also, the keyboard permits an input communication mode. More highly developed systems normally have a separate tape reader, tape punch, printer, and keyboard. This arrangement allows the use of individual higher-performance devices at the rather obvious penalty of higher system cost.

MECHANICAL METHODS

Mechanical devices used for peripheral equipment include the paper-tape reading devices, paper-tape punching devices, card-reading devices, card-punching devices, and printers of various types as mentioned in the last section. These devices are among the earliest used in the data processing field, having among their ancestors the earliest teletype and standard punched-card office equipment. The first printers were modified typewriters, teletype printers, or even modified adding machines. Early in the 1950's, high-speed printers, designed especially for computer peripheral applications, made their appearance. This section will first consider paper-tape equipment, i.e., both *readers* and *punches*.

Paper-Tape Readers and Punches

Paper-tape readers are devices often employed to load coded data into a data processor. The data are coded on the paper tape in the form of punched-hole combinations. Codes vary according to the system. Normally a single row across the tape represents a character. Codes employed vary from the teletype Baudot code (five-character code) to the newer codes such as ASC II (eight-bit code). The normal paper tape is 1 in. wide. It contains sufficient horizontal channels to represent the code and an additional hole channel for the feed sprocket. The standard character spacing is 10 characters per linear inch.

The code character is sensed by reading the combinations of holes and no holes. Sensing devices may be electromechanical such as the wire brush (Fig. 13-1a), mechanical such as the star-wheel switch (Fig. 13-1b) often

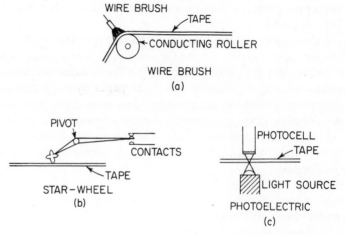

FIG. 13-1 Methods of reading paper tape.

used in low-speed units, or optical using photo electric cells, more often used on the more expensive and faster models (Fig. 13-1c). Mechanical units read up to 150 characters per second, while the photoelectric models are capable of reading up to 500 characters per second.

The tape is read by pulling it past a row of reading heads at the sensing station. There is a separate sensor for each code column. Sometimes the sprocket hole is sensed to ensure a reading at the center of the data holes. In any event, the tape is pulled through the reading station by a sprocket wheel. Normally associated with the unit are a supply reel and a take-up reel, although some systems do without reels and fanfold the tape. On the reel models there is normally a dual set of tension arms between the reading station and the respective reels to control tape slack.

Paper-tape units normally contain toggle switches for control of tape direction, unit on-off, etc. For computer installations, these units can also be controlled automatically by the computer. A peripheral control unit

(PCU) is normally used to match the computer and the paper-tape reader interfaces.

Paper-Tape Punches

A variety of separate paper-tape punches are available on the commercial market. The majority of these function at speeds (manufactured by Tally Corporation), of 40 to 150 characters per second. Teletypewriters, such as the Teletype Model 35 (manufacted by Teletype Corporation), may come equipped with integral tape handling devices (built-in punch and reader). These units operate in conjunction with the typewriter and will both punch and read tape at approximately 10 characters per second. We shall not be concerned with this particular class of paper-tape devices.

In the usual method of punching a paper tape, the individual column punch hammers are driven through the paper by the action of an eccentric cam which pushes the shaft upward and so imparts motion to the punch pin. The punch pin punches the actual hole in the paper.

The complete rotation of the eccentric cam causes a single punch cycle. An *interposer* (a sort of wedge) is positioned between the shaft and the electromagnet, where a hole is to be punched. Where no hole is to be punched, the interposer is left in its original state. It is the interposer, when positioned, that permits the shaft motion to be linked with the punch pins of that particular channel. Without the setting of the interposer, no punch is accomplished. Once the punch action ceases, the tape advance mechanism advances the tape one character space to await the next character punch action.

In addition to code punches, a separate punch is required to punch the sprocket hole. This hole is punched regardless of whether a character requires a punch hole or not. In addition, a seventh channel may be provided to punch the parity bit when it is required by the character code. Typically, an associated electronic control unit will be included as part of the system; therefore, it is merely necessary to present a "1" on those data input lines that require a hole punch. The stepping forward to the next position is accomplished after the punch by internal timing circuitry which activates the tape-advance solenoid. Some units, in addition, provide a parity-check error signal which prevents a punch if the parity signal indicates a failure or invalid punch code.

All units from a typical product line will operate from the same PCU. Basically, all that appears to be needed to drive the punch units are data lines and a sprocket line pulsed at a minimum of +6 volts for a period of 10 μsec wherever a hole is to be punched. The typical current supplied would be 12 mA for each channel punch activation for the period. The actual data magnet drive power, advance pulse drive power, and punch power are internally developed in the associated control unit. There often is no *ready signal* available from the punch, but there usually is a trigger return that indicates the start of the actual punch interval. This pulse, delayed properly, could be used to set a flip-flop in the PCU from which a ready signal to the computer could be derived if desired.

Card Equipment

Card reading and punching is a process very similar to that of paper tape. Both the reading and the punching processes are identical with paper tape. The card's physical shape and codes are different, however, from a typical tape, as shown by Fig. 13-2.

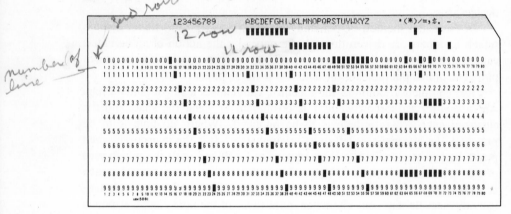

(a)

(b)

FIG. 13-2 (a) Punchcard (courtesy of International Business Machines Corp.). (b) Paper tape being read.

Cards are read by moving them lengthwise (in a direction parallel to the 12 rows) past a reading head. Likewise cards are punched by moving them in a similar manner past a punching head. Reading can be accomplished either mechanically with star wheels and wire brushes or photoelectrically, just as for paper tape.

Cards to be processed in either reading or punching mode are stacked in a loading hopper, often in quantities up to 500. The cards are then fed individually past the reading or punching heads at a rate often exceeding 400 cards per minute and stored in a second or output hopper.

Two card-reading modes are feasible, alphanumeric and binary. In the alphanumeric mode, the Hollerith code divides the card into 80 columns, each containing the code for one character. When reading Hollerith-coded cards, the data-processing unit reads the columns serially and feeds the code through a built-in alphanumeric decoder which produces a six-bit (or other code) coded character. In order for this code to be compatible with a 24-bit interface, another packing operation normally takes place at the computer interface. The alphanumeric system permits a maximum of only 80 characters on a card.

In the binary system of coding cards, each of the 80 card columns contains two 6-bit characters. The reader in this system scans each column twice: First it extracts the lowermost six bits of the first column (rows 12, 11, 10, 1, 2, 3) and sends them to the interface; then it extracts the uppermost six bits of the first column (rows 9, 8, 7, 6, 5, 4) and sends them to the interface. This action is repeated for columns 2, 3, etc., through column 80. No decoding is necessary at the card reader to convert the code from 12 bits to 6, as was true for the alphanumeric system. The binary code allows twice as many (160) characters on a card as the alphanumeric system.

Although a longitudinal movement of a card to this point has been assumed, one version of a card punch processes the card by moving it with the long side leading. The following processing description refers to this particular method.

Here the card-punching operation is divided into four cycles—feeding, punching, checking, and stacking—which are described as follows:

Feeding. After the *power on, reset,* and *start* switches have been depressed, a card will feed into the ready station and will be held there by a lever.

Punching. Upon receipt of a feed and punch command, a card-movement mechanism passes the card, twelfth row first, face down, under the line of 80 punches, stopping the card momentarily under each of the 12 rows. At the proper column positions, determined by the punch code received from the computer, the card is punched. When a card in the ready position starts the movement for punching, a second card is fed into the ready station.

Checking. During the third cycle, the card is fed through a set of post-punch check brushes and checked for errors.

Stacking. The card is placed on the output stack.

After the start button on the card punch has been depressed, the unit is under the control of the computer program. Then, a "card punch select" signal from the computer program can start the card punch in the operation just described.

Computer "punch-character-code" transfer is accomplished in serial fashion, one row at a time. For example, the coding of the 80 digits in row 12 is done by shifting the code in, column by column, until the last column contains either a "punch" or a "no punch" signal. This requires 80 shifts prior to the punch scan for that row. This process is repeated each time a new row is positioned under the punches until all 12 rows have been punched.

Printers

The first printers used with computers were probably the teletype units. These were quickly followed by typewriters modified to operate by computer-coded signals. The advantages of these particular devices were, of course, their availability, the ability to provide more than a single printed copy, their low cost, and the ability to print all alphanumeric symbols. In addition, the keyboards served as a computer input device. The printout speeds of these printers vary approximately from 10 to 40 characters per second. A typical 40 character per second unit is shown in Fig. 13-3. Although this appears to be a typewriter, it is not really. It is a true digital drum printer and works on the hammer-impact principle shown in Fig. 13-4.

For this popular printing method, used by several manufacturers, the printing drum consists of individual character cylinders fastened together to form a drum. There are as many cylinders as there are columns to print. On each cylinder one can find as many as 63 individual characters. The individual cylinders are lined up so that all the *A*'s are in line, all the *B*'s, all the *C*'s, etc. For each column of the printer there is an individual hammer. The paper page stops in one position long enough for the cylinder drum to make a complete revolution. As the character desired for printing appears in each column, the hammer strikes the paper, causing the character that is under the hammer at the time to be printed.

[NOTE: A single character (e.g., *E*) is printed in every column that requires an *E* at the same instant of time. This is typical of an in-line printer with a drum-hammer mechanism.]

Normally for this type of printer, the complete character row is stored within some internal buffer in the printer electronics. The stored character code is matched with a code wheel linked and rotating with the drum. When there is a match between the character stored in a particular column and one in the code wheel, that character is printed in that column. Before the paper page moves again, the code wheel will have provided for an

FIG. 13-3 Digital printer (courtesy SCM Corporation, Kleinschmidt Div.).

attempted match with every possible character, resulting in the selected character in each column being printed for the complete row. After the complete cycle of the drum, the paper page is advanced one line to await the next printing cycle.

This method is used in the 40 character per second unit illustrated and also in mechanical in-line printers that operate at higher speeds. Up to 20 lines per second are normal for some of the higher-speed units.

Nonmechanical methods using photographic light-sensitive and heat-sensitive paper are also available. With these up to a million characters

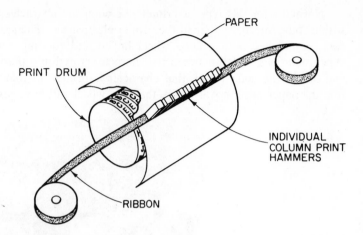

FIG. 13-4   Printer method employed.

printed per second have been reported. Because of the expense and generally poor quality of printing, these printers are only used when high speed or high volume of data for short periods of time are required.

MAGNETIC TAPE EQUIPMENT

Magnetic tape equipment is widely used as auxiliary memory and as data transfer devices. Ground-based data processor installations often use batteries of such equipment and find it useful for storing computer programs and the intermediate and final results of data processing operations.

Because the equipment of International Business Machines Corporation dominated the industry initially, the standards employed in their series 729 became the popular standard of the industry. These standards are for such things as tape speeds, character spacing (density), character codes; the format of data, the spacing intervals between files and records of data, the size of the reels, and many other things are normally specified according to IBM standards. The general items covered by IBM specifications are listed partially in Table 13-1. Tape units come generally in two varieties, incremental and continuous run. The characteristics of each type of unit are discussed in the following paragraphs of this section.

Incremental Magnetic Tape (IMT) Devices

This class of device was developed originally as data-storage equipment only, but later models have both a storage (designated *write*) and a

TABLE 13-1

IBM standard seven-channel magnetic-tape formats and specifications

1. Number of tracks	7 (6 data, 1 check bit)
2. Character density	200, 556, 800 bits per inch
3. Data format	Binary or character
4. Type of recording	NRIZ[a] (Ferranti) two-gap heads (write-read)
5. Tape speed	75 or 112.5 in. per second; rewind, 500 in. per second
6. Error check	Vertical: odd parity for each character
	Horizontal: odd parity for record of each track. Check of character (LRCC[b]) recorded in EOR gap
7. Groupings	Record: group of words ending in $\frac{3}{4}$-in.-wide gap (EOR)
	File: group of records ending in $3\frac{1}{2}$-in.-wide gap and/or *tape mark* character (EOF).
8. End-of-tape mark	$\frac{3}{16}$- by 1-in. aluminum strip, 10 ft from tape end, sensed to stop unit
9. Tape-capstan start–stop time	Less than 3 msec

[a] NRLZ—Designation for Ferranti or Manchester recording code.

[b] LRCO—Designation of parity check character-recorded in End of Record (EOR) gap.

reading capability. One unit recently marketed provides for reading operation only, but this device would be considered data-loading equipment rather than a true memory unit. All types of units, however, generally use $\frac{1}{2}$-in. magnetic tape and record in an IBM seven-bit character format with standard *end-of-file* (EOF) and *end-of-record* (EOR) intervals provided between files and records. As an optional feature, either odd or even parity may be recorded for each character and longitudinal parity may be recorded in the EOR interval. Tape prepared on the write-only models can be read on any seven-bit IBM-compatible continuous-run magnetic-tape transport. A typical unit is illustrated in Fig. 13-5.

The characteristic of all IMT (incremental tape) recorders is that they record a character on demand and then stop. This permits data arriving at a variable rate to be recorded evenly spaced on the tape. Stepping motors are used for both reel and capstan drives; therefore, the entire drive mechanism for the tape is usually much simpler than the on continuous-run machines. The tape-movement rate at best is only a few inches per second.

Writing rates are within the range of 100 to 500 characters per second. Character spacing is generally 200 or 556 characters per inch.

Units which perform both reading and writing are available from some manufacturers. In the reading mode, there are two methods of operation. An individual unit will read in either or both modes, as the design permits.

FIG. 13-5 Incremental tape unit (courtesy of The Kennedy Company, Pasadena, California).

1. *Continuous reading mode.* In this mode of operation, the stepping motor steps at its maximum slew rate, perhaps 1000 steps per second. Reading is similar to that in a continuous-run machine. The distance needed to start or stop, i.e., the distance the tape will move between the time a command is given and the time when the tape fully complies, typically amounts to a distance of five characters.
2. *Incremental reading mode.* In the incremental reading mode, the tape steps in an incremental manner just as it does for writing. The reading rate is often much less than for continuous reading, being typically in the order of 150 characters per second. The tape will, however, stop positively or start positively within a single character space.

In many respects the use of the IMT unit overlaps that of the paper tape unit. The character reading and writing rates of the two types of equipment are similar. The advantage of IMT lies in its ability to record at a much denser character spacing than paper tape. Also, the recorded tapes can be read directly on IBM-compatible magnetic-tape transports as already mentioned. The read-write versions of incremental magnetic tape equipment, in addition to acting as a supplemental memory, could conceivably also double as a computer program-loading device and thereby eliminate the need for a separate paper-tape reader.

Continuous-Run Magnetic Tape

Continuous-run magnetic-tape (CRMT) units generally include all those which do not operate in an incremental manner. Normally they operate at much higher character rates and transfer data in blocks or files consisting of a large number of characters. Because the seven-track IBM format is the most widely used in the industry, the units of interest usually employ this style. Nine-track ASC II coded units are also readily available if required. Because of the wide variation possible in its use on a mobile computer, a single continuous-run magnetic-tape unit will not cover the spectrum of possible uses effectively. For instance, in application when economy is a prime consideration (and weight, volume, or compliance with the usual military specifications on ruggedness and electromagnetic interference are not specifically required), a high-quality commercial unit, such as that shown in Fig. 13-6, will probably satisfy the requirements. On the other hand, when compactness and military specifications are important and the price restrictions can be relaxed somewhat, a militarized version is required. Either classification uses the IBM format, will stop and start within the $\frac{3}{4}$-in. EOR interval, and will use essentially the same peripheral control unit, although some changes in data-line voltage levels may be required.

When extreme compactness and low power are desired, possibly neither of the above unit types will suffice and a special unit may be required. An example of such a requirement would be a space vehicle manned or unmanned. Even though the IBM format generally can be adhered to, because of power limitations, the start and stop times will increase to about 1 sec. This statement assumes operational speeds of 30 to 60 in. per second are to be maintained. In many applications, the restriction in start and stop time may not be important. When it is important, special manipulations such as repositioning the tape initially to the last EOR interval or slowing it down would be logical considerations.

Another important consideration for units that will operate in an outer-space environment is the problem of obtaining a unit that is *space qualified*. The normal aircraft unit is not usually qualified for a spaceborne operation. If space use is required, the qualification testing can be long and expensive and may be the major consideration in the choice of a unit. Also, very high reliability and especially low error rate in data transmission can be among the more important system requirements. A spaceborne unit is likely to be sealed, which would make it difficult if not impossible to change tapes during a manned flight. For this reason, the use of tapes loaded in cartridges has gained wide support.

Most manufacturers include with the mechanical transport unit a substantial portion of the necessary electronics and often a power supply. The electronics most often supplied include the read and write amplifiers; parity generation and detection electronics; skew electronics, which permit an alignment of reading and recording signals from the individual heads; control electronics for starting, stopping, rewinding, and detecting end-of-tapes and certain errors; tape-capstan speed controls; reel speed controls;

etc. The electronics necessary for interfacing with the computer, including command decoders, buffered registers, and the conversion of computer logic control signals to signals required by the tape-unit electronics are in-

FIG. 13-6 Continuous-run magnetic-tape equipment (courtesy of Honeywell Inc., EDP Division).

cluded in a specially built PCU (peripheral control unit). The PCU is not normally supplied by the tape-unit manufacturer.

Continuous-run magnetic-tape units can be operated in reasonably sophisticated ways, and, as a result, the PCU or software must provide capabilities not normally required of other peripheral devices.

Automatic searching for a data record on the tape or searching to alter a record on the tape is an example of the type of sophistication implied. The searches mentioned may be required of a tape moving either forward or in reverse. This capability either is built into the PCU as additional hardware or is accomplished by programming steps or subroutines. Since special tracks are not usually supplied for tape data addresses, specific data are located by the reading of tape-recorded identifying characters, usually recorded just previous to each stored data record.

Although a continuous-run unit can transfer data between itself and the computer via the direct input–output channel, it would appear that use of a buffered channel is preferable because buffered channels are particularly efficient for transferring data at rates adjustable and controllable by the peripheral device. In addition, transfers normally occur in blocks rather than as individual characters or words. Buffered channels are designed to expedite block transfers.

With a direct input–output transfer, not only are single commands required to transfer each word but the programmer must be careful to time his instruction decoding sequences so that the interface transfer rate is compatible with the tape equipment's operational rate. This particular problem, on the other hand, is not a factor when using an incremental tape unit.

The following are mechanical features of tape transports which affect their operation and deserve serious consideration when choosing a transport:

The Tape Drive. Capstans which use vacuum or air to grip the tape are normally preferred to the mechanical "pinch" roller type, because less wear is imposed on the tape. This factor is, of course, more critical at high tape speeds.

Tape Slack. Tape slack is provided between the capstan and reels to achieve the high acceleration and deceleration necessary to permit narrow record gaps. Vacuum columns with photoelectric cell sensing are generally preferred for gentleness in tape handling. Both the response and damping achieved by vacuum methods is normally superior to that achieved by mechanical tension arms and servos. For relatively slow start and stop machines, tape slack may be unnecessary. For machines operating at high altitude, a vacuum-column design may be impossible; thus, the approach must be abandoned altogether for this particular environment.

Concentric or Coaxial Reels. Most tape transports use concentric reels which are usually easier to load. Coaxial reels are employed in some machines to conserve panel space. A special gearing arrangement is used to control the tape tension between the reels and the capstan. Normally, the coaxial arrangement is not used for high-speed computer-control transports.

Of primary interest, of course, is the ability to store and retrieve data without introducing errors. In the average tape-data system, this is handled by the addition of a parity bit for each character and the storage of a longitudinal parity character at the end of each record. Upon playback (read) these introduced parity characters are checked and an alarm raised if a parity error is detected. Usually the circuitry required for recording parity is included within the peripheral unit's electronics, although this may be an option. Parity circuitry would, of course, be a functional part of a PCU.

When a parity check alone is deemed insufficient, more stringent methods may be adopted to ensure the accuracy of data during storage and transfer. One method, adopted for the Gemini mass-storage system, was to use redundant tracks. Clock, date, and parity were all recorded with the same data on each of three separate tracks. *Logic voting* was then used during the reading process. (*Logic voting* is a reliability technique whereby three parallel logic circuits are used. The decision as to the correct output of the combined logic is based on a vote principle. If two of the three circuits indicate a "1" output, and the third a "0" output, "1" is the assigned output. Reliability is improved because there is less likelihood of two circuits rather than one failing at a given time.)

A method proposed by Leach Corporation for the LEM recorder when used to check digital data was to make use of Hamming or similar error-checking codes. These check bits could be stored as separate characters. Normally, either of the last two techniques reduces the probability of error to an acceptable level.

In machines employing parity check, the detection of an error will call for a rereading of the entire record block where the error was detected. In more highly developed installations, this will be accomplished automatically.

CATHODE-RAY-TUBE DISPLAYS

Cathode-ray-tube (CRT) displays are rapidly becoming a popular method of displaying the contents of computer memories. They are also used for displaying figures and drawings that can be programmed by the computer. In addition, aircraft traffic-control radar and military command and control systems combine radar-system oscilloscope displays with pertinent data stored in the computer memory.

The Two Basic Types

The display systems discussed here use CRTs and are limited to those two general types which appear to be of most interest for interface with a computer. The first type of display considered is the interrogator version which handles only alphanumeric data. Figure 13-7 shows a sample of this class. These units, in effect, are replacements for electronic typewriters and can be used where no permanent record need be prepared. Data already in

FIG. 13-7 A typical alphanumeric display (courtesy of Sanders Associates, Inc.).

the computer may be called up for display by the CRT. The data-editing capabilities of the device may then be called on to modify the data displayed. Characters can be deleted and new ones inserted. Also complete lines of paragraphs can be modified or replaced in the same general way. Normally, a complete page of data may be typed via an associated keyboard, viewed for errors, and then inserted into the computer by a separate "data-enter" key. These display devices are used as remote terminals for both retrieval and insertion of memory data. They can be attached to typical telephone-line data modem† such as the Bell System's Model 201, or directly to the computer by a specialized PCU.

The second type of CRT display is one which has a *vectoring* capability, and may or may not possess the alphanumeric interrogating capability of the type just described. The most useful type of CRT display for demonstrating the full capability of the computer will most certainly combine both the interrogation and the vectoring capabilities. A block diagram of a typical system of the most general type is given in Fig. 13-8.

† See Glossary (page 396).

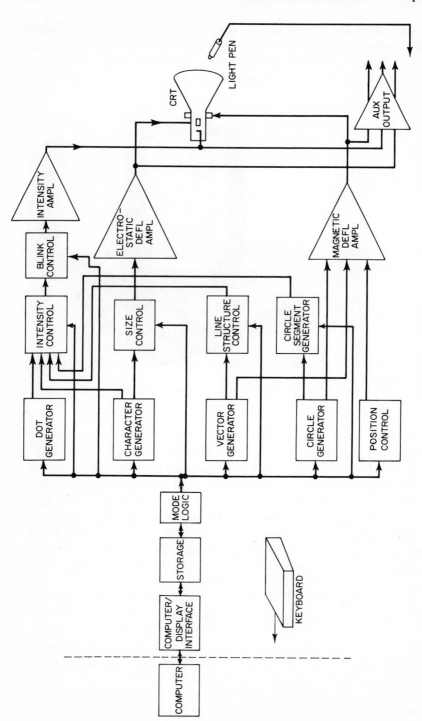

FIG. 13-8 Generalized computer-controlled display block diagram.

The vectoring capability permits line drawings to be reproduced on the scope. This permits a form of scope drafting with corrections and additions performed with a light pen directly on the oscilloscope face. This is desirable in military tactical displays to show targets, their direction, position, etc. Combining this with the use of alphanumeric (or alphameric) symbols makes it possible to designate and identify line vectors and targets.

Systems still more recently developed allow, in addition, the display of background data, in the form of either a superimposed television picture or a projection of photographic images on the back of the CRT. The latter system uses a specialized CRT which features a window through which the desired image is projected.

Component Parts

The component units that are assembled to form the complete display system consist typically of the following:

A CRT display and control unit consists of the scope, the controls for the scope, and the scope electronic devices, such as deflection amplifiers and D/A converters.

Coupler units normally contain the logic decoders which position the scope's electron beam, select the characters to be displayed, and provide the interface with the computer. Some CRTs will make use of both electrostatic and electromagnetic deflection simultaneously. The electromagnetic deflection positions the beam, whereas the electrostatic deflection writes the character once the beam is positioned.

Character generators on command generate a specific alphanumeric character or symbol. There are several possible ways to generate characters, including the use of Lissajous patterns, dot matrices, stroke generators, and special character-generating tubes (e.g., Charactrons†).

Vector generators will draw a straight line on the scope, the length and direction dependent in the starting location and ending location included within the instruction format which specifies the vector.

A light pen or light gun picks up light from a narrow selected area of the scope when pressed against its surface. It may be employed to select a point on the scope for a location request or to indicate to the system that an instruction entered refers to the point selected by the pen.

A keyboard, along with select buttons on the console and a light pen, in combination or alone, becomes the main communication link with the

---

† *Charactron:* Trade name of tubes produced by Stromberg Carlson Division, General Dynamics Corporation.

display. The probability is that the keyboard will be alphanumeric in nature but may also contain special symbols for specific applications.

Although the above items are typical components for a display system, many of them can be considered as options in any particular system. On the other hand, some display systems will contain many more features than those listed. Some of these features may include:

1. A multicolor display CRT
2. The addition of background information in the form of backscreen photo-image projection or the use of television techniques, as previously mentioned

TABLE 13-2

Typical display command-word structures

Output words

Format 1. (Use to position beam initially.)

0	α	X	Y
0 1	3 4	13 14	23

Format 2. (Use to draw characters.)

1	
0 1	23

Each bit calls for a particular stroke form to be generated; therefore, alphanumerics and other characters can be drawn. The 0 bit identifies a format 1 or a format 2 word.

In α of a format 1 word, the actual bit-character code is interpreted as follows:

    0 Position beam to X-Y, normal character size; do not display point.
    1 Position beam to X-Y, double character size; do not display point.
    2 Position beam to X-Y, quadruple character size; do not display point.
    3 Display a point at X-Y.
    4 Display an intensified point at X-Y.
  X-Y are the position coordinates.

Input word (Indicates coordinate of light pen)

0		X	Y
0	3 4	13 14	23

3. The capability of making an instantaneous recording of a display at a particular time; and
4. The generation of special symbols such as circles, dashed lines, and symbols that flicker.

An example of a command structure for a typical display system is summarized in Table 13-2.

DISK FILE

Magnetic-tape bulk storage suffers from defects which may, under certain circumstances, limit its use as a bulk storage device in a particular system. First, it is bulky for small quantities of data. Second, if *random* storage of records is assumed, to acquire access to a particular record requires many seconds on the average.

If a great deal of data must be stored and a relatively rapid access maintained, the use of a magnetic-drum or disk file should be considered because access is usually in the order of milliseconds.

Mechanically, of course, disk files and drums differ extensively from magnetic tapes. The disk file is in continual motion whether data is being transferred or not. Data is transferred to or from the disk surface via magnetic heads; but, in this case, the heads generally float a few microinches off the surface rather than ride in contact with the surface, as is the usual case for magnetic tape.

The difference between a drum and a disk file lies in the mechanical configuration. A drum is a rotating cylinder with individual reading-recording heads mounted so as to write or read parallel paths (tracks) around the circumference of the rotating surface. There is generally a head (or head set) for each track. The minimum track spacing is in the order of 50 milli-inches. A disk file, however, has a flat surface, more like a phonograph record. Separate track heads for each track may be provided, but there is a type of disk for which a single head (or head set) is movable to the desired reading area. In the disks considered here, it is assumed that the heads are fixed and one is required for each track. Disk-file resolution is limited to what can be recorded on the innermost track. Often, head groupings may be provided on *both* sides of the disk. A typical commercial disk file appears in Fig. 13-9.

The problem of switching appears to be identical for either the drum or the disk. In all cases, a reference (index) starting point is defined, and all recording is referenced initially to this point. A single recording head senses the location of this index point. In addition to the index point described, other index marks are provided at regular intervals about the circumference. These points are known as *sector marks* and permit a designation of circumference distance from the index point. In addition, a third track of reference marks is usually provided. This track provides the timing for identification of individual bits within the sectors and is aptly named the *clock track*. The usual track head is employed for both reading

FIG. 13-9 A typical commercial disk file (courtesy Libra-scope Group, General Precision Inc.).

and writing and is electronically switched to *read,* to *write,* or to *neither read nor write,* as required.

Data can be acquired in serial (one track at a time) or in parallel (many tracks at a time), depending on the system's design. Combination serial and parallel systems are not uncommon.

In some systems the bit clock is transferred to the computer and is used as the computer clock. In other systems, the disk (or drum) is synchronized to the computer's internally generated clock; and in still other systems the computer and disk (or drum) systems are entirely asynchronous with each other.

The electronics normally furnished with the disk (or drum) include the read-write heads, the read-write amplifiers, and the solid state switches to switch the individual or groups of heads. Quite often a power supply may also be included. A PCU is not usually included in the electronics described, and this must be furnished to match the particular computer to be employed. The function of this PCU is similar to those discussed before, i.e., it decodes commands addressed to the disk unit, stores the address for the desired head, and selects the sector at which the transfer operation is to begin. Other functions in addition to these, of course, include buffering the data transfer, providing the proper electrical levels and timing, and providing a parity generation and check as required by the system.

Characteristics on which to base the selection of a disk file include:

1. The word capacity of the disk
2. The access time to reach a particular data word on file
3. The environmental capability
4. Reliability and maintenance features
5. Method of synchronization
6. Data transfer rate
7. Mechanical characteristics (size, weight, and volume)
8. Reliability of data storage and retrieval
9. PCU complexity
10. Unit and system cost

Summary of Bulk-Storage Peripheral Units

Three types of peripheral bulk-storage units were considered. These three consist of incremental magnetic tape, continuous-run magnetic tape, and a disk file. The detailed characteristics of the respective devices were considered, and a brief summary of relative and typical characteristics are given in Table 13-3.

COMMUNICATION LINKS

It is becoming increasingly necessary to transmit and receive data over communication links or telephone lines. The problem often encountered is to put the data in such a form that a normal voice telephone line of 3000 cps bandwidth can transmit the data reliably. Usually, a device called a *modem*

TABLE 13-3

Typical characteristics of bulk storage methods

	Incremental tape	*Continuous run tape*	*Disk file*
Words stored	0.72×10^6	2.88×10^6	0.25×10^6
Transfer rate (words/sec)	75	15,000	40,000
Random access time (average)	48 min	192 sec	8 msec
Slew rate	5 in./sec	75 in./sec	
Cost/bit	$0.0003/bit	$0.00016/bit	$0.0034/bit
Cost/unit (average)	$6,000/unit	$15,000/unit	$20,000/unit
Power, watts	300	1000	1180
Weight, lb	70	200	90
Volume, ft³	2.6	3.0	11.5
PCU–I-C flat-pack count estimate	73–123	135	272
Use (other than mass storage)	Load or unload memory	Load or unload memory	

is employed to: (1) convert digital data in serial bit-stream form to a dual-frequency tone (one frequency represents "1" the other "0" and the data is transmitted as tones); and (2) reconvert data received from the line as a dual-tone to a serial bit stream of "1's" and "0's."

The computer employs a PCU at the interface with the modem. The

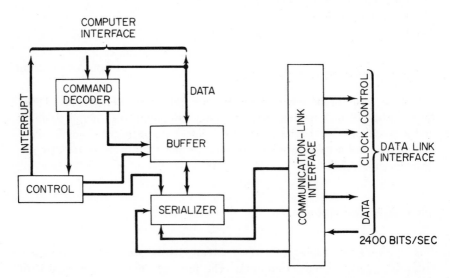

FIG. 13-10 A computer data-link interconnection.

PCU's function is to transfer data from the input–output bus of the computer (probably in parallel form) to or from a register in the PCU. The register, on the other hand, transfers data to and from the modem at a rate suitable for serial transmission or reception. A typical transfer rate to and from telephone-line modems is 2400 bits per second. A block diagram of this interconnection is shown by Fig. 13-10.

PERIPHERAL CONTROL UNITS

Discussion

The general function of a PCU is to provide the necessary interface between the peripheral device and the computer input–output. The PCU provides a decoding of computer commands relating specifically to the particular peripheral device; also, it develops the necessary control voltage levels and timing for operation of the peripheral-device controls. For instance, a relay that starts or stops the device must be turned on and off. Applying power to the read or write amplifiers, selection of one of two speeds forward, etc., are all examples of typical controls operated by the PCU. Other services rendered by the PCU may include the following:

1. Convert the word format of the computer data to the character format for data in the peripheral device. If the peripheral device provides data input to the computer, the reverse conversion (character to word) may be necessary.
2. Provide circuitry to generate the proper drive voltages to supply output data lines and provide noise protection on input data lines.
3. Provide special control signals and timing for its own internal operation during data manipulation and transfer.
4. As an option, provide the addition of a parity bit to outgoing computer data and check parity of incoming computer data.
5. Provide possibly for combining several incoming data channels into a single input channel before connection with the computer input bus.
6. Accept error indications from the peripheral device, and generate a computer interruption to advise the computer of the error.
7. In some instances, when required, provide addressing control to the peripheral device.
8. Control more than a single peripheral unit when so designed.

Although a portion of the electronics required to control a peripheral device is furnished by the manufacturer, that required at the interface with a particular computer is often neglected. This is understandable, since

peripheral manufacturers often do not know in advance who their computer customers will be, and computer interfacing requirements are generally nonstandard throughout the industry.

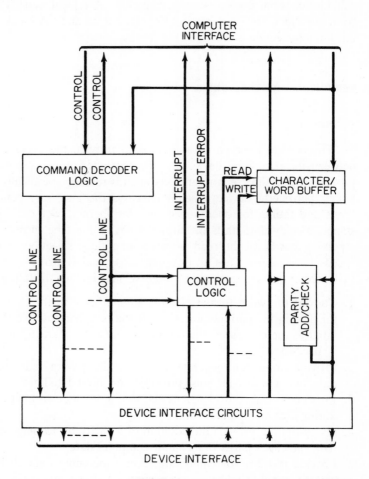

FIG. 13-11   Block diagram—generalized PCU.

A generalized block diagram of a PCU is given in Fig. 13-11. The two
nominal arrangements for the interface of a PCU with the computer are
diagrammed in Fig. 13-12.

The typical PCU receives its control commands from the direct input–
output bus. In the simpler devices, the data flow in or out will also be
from the direct input–output bus. Such devices as paper-tape punches,
paper-tape readers, card punches, card readers, low-speed printers, incremental tapes, and keyboards would probably connect to the computer in

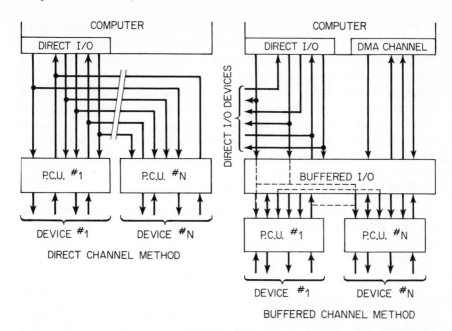

FIG. 13-12 Input–output systems—interconnections.

this way. For the high-speed devices, the control commands are still forwarded to the PCU by the direct input–output bus, but the data flow would most likely be through a buffered input–output channel. The method, as pointed out in the last chapter, permits data transfers without individual commands for each word transferred. Such peripheral devices as continuous-run magnetic tapes, disk files, and CRT displays would probably use this particular method.

The functions of the various subblocks in the block diagram of the basic PCU (Fig. 13-11) are briefly summarized below.

Command Decoder

This subsection of a data processing system decodes the commands to the PCU, allows the PCU to generate control levels to the peripheral device, and sets the PCU in the mode to transfer data. It generates all the necessary control pulses to the computer or to the peripheral device.

Character-Word Buffer

This subblock is required in some systems to sectionalize the words of the computer into characters for the peripheral device. The function would be required on transfers from the computer to the peripheral unit. In the reverse transfer, the character-word buffer would assemble characters from the peripheral into a group, and transfer this group into the computer as a single word. This mode of operation is called *packing*. Many systems do not require such a buffer since the computer and peripheral may both use the same word length. The advantage to the computer user of having such a device in the system is that the number of computer transfer commands will be reduced, since the computer transfer operation is on a word rather than a character basis.

Control

This is the circuitry provided in order that the character-word buffer will function automatically.

Interface Circuits

This subsection includes all the line drivers, and output lines to the peripherals and the noise-rejection circuits (if used) on input lines from the peripherals. The line drivers are employed to match the relatively high-impedance logic circuit to low-impedance cables and output lines. Line drivers are often required to change or increase voltage levels. The noise-rejection circuits will contain filters to reject unwanted line noise and may also have level-changing capabilities as needed.

Parity Check and Generating Circuits

Many peripheral devices have their own parity generation and parity check circuits but this practice is by no means universal. Where there is a need for parity circuits and these are not provided in the peripheral unit, the PCU may be required to supply these functions.

Miscellaneous Circuits

Many specialized functions may be included in a PCU when required. As an example, the PCU for a disk file in most cases will provide addressing registers for the storage of data addresses in the disk file. On other occasions, it may be required to combine incoming data from several devices in the input bus. In this case, a large OR gate on the computer input bus is likely. Such logic could well be part of the PCU.

A TYPICAL CONTINUOUS-RUN MAGNETIC-TAPE PCU

A typical PCU that would operate a magnetic tape system is illustrated by the block diagram of Fig. 13-13. The list of controls is given in Table 13-4.

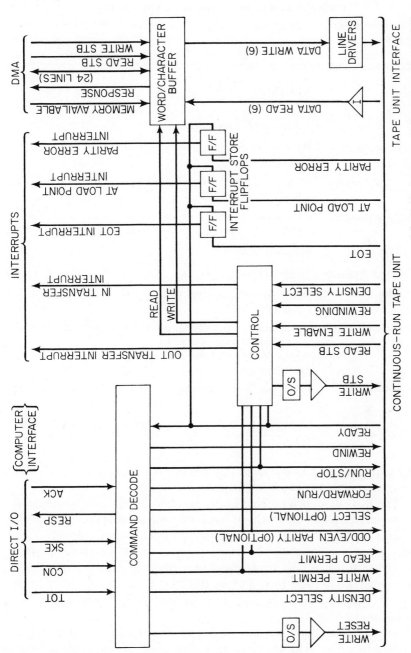

FIG. 13-13 Typical continuous-run tape PCU.

TABLE 13-4

List of controls and continuous-run magnetic tape

Input controls and signals	Function	Interface
1. Write data	Date to be recorded. This is a level logic. 7 lines.	0 V or −4.5 V during data interval, −4.5 V true.
2. Write strobe	Negative going strobe. 0.8 μsec after edge of data interval.	Pulse, 1–3 μsec, 0 to −4.5 V.
3. Write reset	Write longitudinal parity-check character.	Pulse, 1–3 μsec, 0 to −3.5 V.
4. Density select	In the true position, selects high density recording.	Level, −4.5 V true and 0 V false.
5. Write permit	Permits writing when write enable ring is in place.	Level, −4.5 V true. Only applied when tape has stopped.
6. Read permit	Permits reading.	Level, −4.5 V true, 0 V false.
7. Odd/even parity	Selects odd parity when true.	Level, −4.5 V true, 0 V false.
8. Select	Selects particular unit and puts it in ready status.	Level, −4.5 V true, 0 V false.
9. Forward/reverse	Selects forward direction when *true* and reverse direction when *false*. Must be set 1 sec before *run/stop*.	Level, −4.5 V true, 0 V false.
10. Run/stop	Causes unit to *run* when true and *stop* when false.	Level, −4.5 V true, 0 V false.
11. Rewind	Caused unit to rewind when true.	Level, −3.5 V true, 0 V false.

The timing diagram is shown in Fig. 13-14. An approximate parts count by function is supplied by Table 13-5.

The PCU described in those figures and tables is the minimum required for a continuous-run tape unit. It has been assumed that search operations in either forward, reverse, or bidirectional modes are accomplished by computer programming alone. In actual practice, storage registers might be added which would hold for comparison a word or character on which to base a search. In some PCU designs, this is done, but, in the one proposed here, it appeared to be beyond the *minimum* design necessary for unit operation.

The data interface transfer, shown in Fig. 13-13, is via a buffered input–output unit. The use of such a buffered unit is reasonable in view of

TABLE 13-4 (Continued)

Output signals and alarms	Function	Interface
1. Read data	Data read from the tape. 7 lines.	0 V true, > 2.5 V false.
2. Read clock	A clock simultaneous with data on read data lines. About $\frac{1}{2}$ normal data interval duration.	0 V true, > 2.5 V false.
3. Read parity error	A pulse is provided simultaneously with read data when parity check fails.	0 V true, > 2.5 V false.
4. Ready	Indicates transport is in remote state and ready.	Level, -0 V false, > 3 V true.
5. End of tape	Senses end of tape tab.	Level, 0 V true, > 2.5 V false.
6. At load point	Senses beginning of tape.	Level, 0 V true, > 2.5 V false.
7. Rewinding	Senses the unit is rewinding.	Level, 0 V true, > 2.5 V false.
8. Density select	Senses high-density selected.	Level, 0 V true, > 2.5 V false.
9. Write enable	Senses write-enable ring in place.	Level, 0 V true, > 2.5 V false.

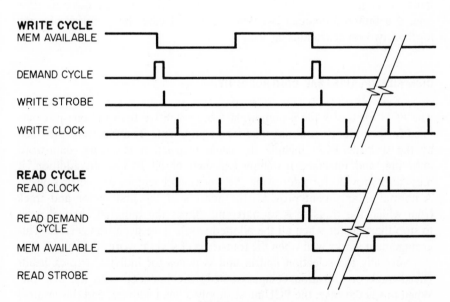

FIG. 13-14 Continuous-run tape PCU data timing.

TABLE 13-5

Continuous-run tape PCU parts count

	4 ea. dual input NANDs	2 ea. four input NANDs	1 ea. eight input NANDs	FF[a]	O/S[b]	Power drivers	Dual EX-OR	Misc.	Total function
Command decode	6	5	2	10	2	5			30
Control	6			7	4				17
Character-word buffer	20	18		24		2			64
Interface					·	15			15
Miscellaneous	1			3	2	2			8
TYPE TOTAL	33	23	2	44	8	24			134

[a] Flip-flop.

[b] One-shot multivibrator

the characteristics of a continuous-run tape. First, it allows of groups of words to be transferred with a minimum number of commands. Second, the program no longer needs to time precisely the interjection of the transfer commands into the program. Because computer word-transfer rates must be aligned closely with the magnetic-tape unit's character-transfer rate, if a buffered channel is employed, it will ease the problem of tying together two asynchronous devices.

DISK FILE (PERIPHERAL CONTROL UNIT)

The PCU for a disk file is somewhat more extensive than the one just outlined for continuous-run magnetic-tape equipment. The functions provided by the disk-file PCU include the usual instruction decoding, data-word buffering, and interface matching expected of all PCUs. In addition, it must also provide for addressing the tracks and sectors on the disk itself. A normal arrangement provides the address of the first sector and track from which the transfer is to start and allows the buffered channel itself to stop the transfer when all the allotted words have been transferred. This arrangement works well when the transfer is of several words duration.

Normally the selection matrix and switches for individual track heads (head-track organization being assumed) are included with the disk file. When this is the case, the PCU must supply a head address, and this address is stored either in the device or the PCU for the duration of the transfer. The address for the sector is also stored in a separate register and, for the sake of discussion, it will be assumed that this particular register is in the PCU.

The normal way for a transfer to begin is for the processor to place in the disk address registers an instruction word which contains the track address, the sector address, and a single bit which indicates the direction of transfer (on or off the disk). The specific head involved can be selected immediately, but data may not be transferred until the proper sector is in position. To locate the proper sector, one technique uses a counter which is reset by an index mark once each disk revolution. This index mark identifies the *first* sector, sector 1. As the disk spins, a new sector mark is detected as each sector passes. These sector marks are totaled in the counter. The counter contents, therefore, is a *record of the actual position of the disk,* to the nearest sector. When the sector count matches the address in the sector address register, the logic is arranged so that, at the beginning of the next sector (at the sector mark), the transfer begins. The reader will note that the address for the transfer sector is in reality the address of the sector immediately preceding the desired sector.

If the data transfer of the disk is serial and the interface of the processor parallel, as is often the case, then an obvious necessity is to perform parallel to serial conversions during output from the processor and serial to parallel conversions during input to the processor. This general process is often accomplished by a two-level register; one level is a serializer, and the second level, a buffer. This allows the data stream to be nearly continuous to and from the disk. If a 24-bit word is transferred between the processor and the buffer (and this is to be accomplished as a parallel transfer), the words in and out of the serializer should be 24 bit times plus an extra 1 or 2 bit times allotted for the processing transfer between serializer and buffers. The parallel transfer occurs in one of the extra bit times just mentioned in the last sentence. Therefore a 24-bit word on the disk is 24 bits plus 2 bit positions in which data are not recorded. The transfer between the buffer and the processer occurs at the processor's convenience (as long as the convenience period is no longer than the time required to serialize the second word). In other words, during the serialization of a word, the previous word serialized waits in the buffer for transfer to the processor if the data flow is to the processor. If the data flow is from the processor, the word transferred from the processor memory waits in the buffer until the previous word clears from the serializer onto the disk.

The logic for the PCU shown in Fig. 13-15 includes a decoder section which starts, stops, and tests the disk's operating condition. The decoder also transfers the instruction address word into the disk address register where it is held. The buffer and serializer, as just described, are of course a major part of the logic. The control logic for the PCU involves those elements that time and control the process. Since the disk file normally

operates asynchronously with the processor, the control timing will normally come from the disk file itself. As a result, the timing pulses to serialize (P_1-P_{24}) and the buffer transfer pulse P_{25} are all derived by counting
down bit internal-clock pulses from a track in the disk. This counter, the

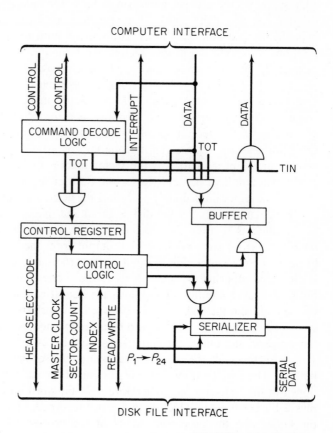

FIG. 13-15   Disk file PCU.

logic for recognizing a sector match, and the logic to allow the data transfer
to start and end at the proper points all are included in the control block.
Matching circuits at the interface as required will also be a part of the PCU.
They are also indicated in Fig. 13-15.

Table 13-6 includes an estimate of the parts complexity of the disk-file
PCU. This list allows the reader to compare the relative complexities of
the two PCU's described in this chapter.

Although nothing has been proposed so far for adding or checking
parity, this check could easily be incorporated into the system. In a *serial*

TABLE 13-6

Disk-file PCU, approximate parts count

Function	Quad 2-input NAND	Dual 4-input NAND	8-input NAND	Flip- flop	One- shot	Dual power NAND	Dual EX-OR	Misc.	Total function
Command decode	5	5	2	4	2	2			20
Control logic	14	29	8	17	4	2		3	77
Buffer- serializer	8	1		48			48		105
Interface						52			52
TOTAL	27	35	10	69	6	56	48	3	254

process (which is what data transfer on and off a disk usually is), the parity bit can be added as in any serial transfer (reading the setting on a flip-flop) and can be checked just as readily, if desired, by counting the "1's" or "0's" and the parity flip-flop setting. The parity bit could be stored in the P_{26} position in the word cell.

SUMMARY

This chapter has outlined some of the normal peripheral equipment used with modern processors. The early sections of the chapter discussed mechanical devices which operate on holes punched in paper tape or Hollerith cards. Also mentioned briefly were mechanical printers, primarily those using a rapidly rotating drum and individual print hammers for each column.

A section followed on bulk storage devices with emphasis on incremental tape readers, continuous-run tape readers, and disk files. These devices were briefly described and their characteristics compared. Then, the general PCU device is described. The PCUs are employed to connect the computer input–output with the actual peripheral device. The use of a matching device between the input–output and peripheral interfaces permits the processor a wide latitude in the selection of potential peripherals.

The chapter concluded with two PCU examples: (1) a continuous-run magnetic tape; and (2) a disk file.

REVIEW QUESTIONS AND PROBLEMS

13-1. What are some of the advantages in using photoelectric sensing of holes in mechanical reading equipment?

13-2. Describe how an incremental tape read-recorder differs from a continuous-run magnetic-tape machine.

13-3. Compare an incremental tape read-recorder with a paper-tape punch and reader. What advantages does the incremental tape machine have? What advantage does the paper-tape machine have?

13-4. Describe how a CRT display is used. List a number of uses and examples of each use.

13.5. Define a bulk-storage memory. How does it differ from an internal memory?

13-6. What are some reasons for using a disk file rather than a magnetic-tape transport?

13-7. What is a PCU? Describe its major component parts.

13.8. The PCU described for the continuous-run magnetic tapes could be simplified to the extent that the word buffer can be left out. What effect does this have on the programming for loading and unloading data from the continuous-run magnetic-tape unit?

13-9. Design a simple PCU for a CRT display. Assume the display interface is 29 bits. Use the data in Fig. 13-8 and Table 13-2. Make whatever other assumptions are necessary. List the assumptions.

13-10. What size single disk is needed to hold 1×10^6 24-bit words if 100 tracks are allowed and the bit packing density is no more than 1000 bits per inch along the track and the heads can be spaced 20 to the inch? (Assume that the inner and outer tracks each have the same number of sectors, that recording is serial, and that each word occupies a sector by itself.)

COMPUTER
HARDWARE DESIGN   **14**

This chapter concludes the discussion of the basic digital computer. However, there remain many topics relating to the design of a digital computer, including those factors that must be considered when matching it to the requirements of the problems it will be expected to solve. In addition, the economic factors must be studied. It makes little sense to design a computer that costs more to purchase, more to operate, and more to maintain than another design that will accomplish the same results—unless there is some technical reason why the competitive design is unusable.

The processor type must be established along with the necessary instruction repertory. This requires further study of the operational requirements. Now, when all the factors that affect the design have been considered, insofar as possible using the assumptions made, it is time to start the detailed design. This involves establishing the instruction format, or structure, flow-charting in detail all instructions, defining the processor organization, detailing both the logic and circuit designs, detailing the designs of the interface, plotting the operation timing charts, detailing the mechanical design of the packaging, and establishing the internal cooling method for the device.

This chapter concludes with a brief discussion of a specimen special-purpose computer. This is done to demonstrate how the components of a computer mesh together in a final configuration. In a sense, it summarizes Chapters 9 through 12. The assumption is made here that the design is required for a special-purpose machine. A study of the requirements of the problem should lead to an optimum design of a computer to solve the class of problems considered. Yet because a computer must concern itself with a spectrum of applications, another approach might be to consider the best similar design now on the market and provide a new design that is faster in performance, less expensive to buy, easier to use, better equipped with available software, and uses the latest technology. Whatever the criteria defining the new design, there must be reasons for the investment of the money, time, and effort. It is important that these reasons for the venture are well known to the designers, the management of the company, and to the potential customers. And finally, some parting thoughts: Make sure that all concerned know the product's components, its purposes, its approximate price, its market targets, that all the technology required to design the machine is truly available within the design time span, and also that some thought has been given to how the design fits into operational systems. Consideration of these factors may save a company much grief at a later time and avoid the potential development of a beautiful white elephant that no one needs or will buy.

SYSTEMS DESIGN

The design of a new data processor depends to a large extent on defining (as accurately as possible) the spectrum of uses and computer organization requirements to satisfy this spectrum. This definition process is often termed *systems analysis*. Essentially it involves a systematic listing and evaluation of many factors.

First, a definition could be prepared of what the central processor does for the system. If the various equations which must be solved in the course of a computation, are known, a study should be initiated to determine the *optimum* methods of solution. This study should lead to a tentative list of types of instruction, an estimate as to the total number of stored instructions required, and the time to perform the solutions. Secondly, the *accuracy* of the data and the required number of solution iterations should be considered. From these two considerations, a reasonable estimate of the total number of instructions to be stored and the accuracy of the numerical data required for the mathematical functions under consideration can be obtained.

This general process must be repeated for all possible expected operational function groups and a reasonable safety factor allowed. From this analysis, then, evolves a tentative estimate of the memory size, a tentative listing of instruction repertory, the general speeds required for the calculations, data transfer, etc., and a tentative word length. The word length is usually a compromise. A shorter word length means that the planes in the memory will be reduced to a minimum, but the word may not be of sufficient bit length to represent numerical quantities to the required accuracies. Also, the instructions must have sufficient bits to provide the necessary address codes, the necessary address modification bits (variant code) and the necessary bits for a suitable operation code. Because of the need to conserve hardware and at the same time not limit the processor capability unduly, it is normal to perform compromise, or "trade off," studies of one approach versus another. On the basis of the relative expected performances, a selection of the most promising approach is made. For instance, the subject of word length is a common subject of compromise studies. Supposing a word length is chosen to satisfy the length necessary for *all* instructions. However, the word length is not long enough to represent all data to sufficient accuracy. The trade-off study would consider the possibility of using double-length word arithmetic processes for those process steps where high accuracy is necessary. It may turn out that the number of calculations required are few, but they may occur at a point in the problem solution when the extra time cannot be allowed. In this case, then, a longer word length than the minimum necessary to handle the instructions alone must be used. The designer can then consider possibly packing two instructions to a word or other possible approaches to efficient use of the allotted word length.

The above discussion was just a sample of the reasoning involved in design decisions, factors which cannot be ignored. Some of these include, the peripheral equipment to be employed, whether buffering is necessary, whether standard word length must be adhered to for standardization reasons, etc.

Under any circumstance, the designer *must* allow for *growth* in his design. It is most unlikely that he can predict the exact repertory of instructions required, the data storage exact requirements, or the peripherals and interfaces with other equipment that the system may have to use in the future. For some reason, it rarely happens that a computer will always be restricted to the actual application for which it was originally designed. Someone is bound to propose its use for other purposes.

Depending on the class of applications, the system design process also involves both the consideration of human factors, and style requirements.

Human factor considerations are especially important in military applications where each control and display must be where the operator expects to find it and in a manner that will indicate to him instinctively the proper action to take. Styling is important for attractiveness and from the competitive standpoint. All other things being equal, the model with the most pleasing appearance and styling has the best chance in the competitive market.

In addition, early in the design, the hardware and software designers must jointly decide on maintenance and trouble-shooting procedures. How much trouble shooting and fault isolation and location can the computer do by itself? What sort of displays are required to show if a fault exists? What is the easiest way to locate a fault in a specific replaceable module? All these questions are important to any user, and he wants a design that is not only trouble free but easy to maintain. In addition, once a failure is pin-pointed, is the defective component easily and quickly replaced? Although high reliability is desired, a reasonable maintenance and easy location and repair of failures is even more inviting in many situations.

THE PROCESSOR TYPE

Once the system requirements have been established, a system specification should be written and distributed to all concerned with the computer design. This specification should outline the memory size, the basic word lengths, the instruction repertory, the computation and data-transfer speeds, the input–output interface approaches, and any bulk storage requirements. If there are physical restrictions because of the expected application, these should also be detailed in the system specification as well as reliability and maintenance goals.

In general, however, there is a second step to the definition of the processor type. Within the guide lines set by the initial specification, a great deal more detail must be worked into the revisions of these specifications. For instance, a preliminary block diagram must be prepared outlining the proposed organization of the processor components. For the data processor, this should clearly show whether the data transfers are serial or parallel, what provisions are to be included for modifying instructions, what control registers, transfer registers, index registers, and counters will be necessary, etc. More detail should be proposed for the input–output interface. For instance, what control and clock-pulse system will be used? Between what registers and the input–output bus is the data transfer to occur? How are the buffer transfers to be handled? All of these are important questions in defining a system.

In the same manner, the details of data transfers between memory and processor and between memory and input–output should be considered, as should the technique of incremental additions of memory to be added to the system and how it will be controlled from the present instruction repertory. In addition, a basic decision must be made as to the memory organization. This decision will as much determine the overall processor speed in modern computers as will the organization of the processor logic. Generally, in modern machines, the word transfer times (to and from the memory) is the limiting factor in increasing the computational speeds.

It is at this approximate point in the design process that the logic circuit types are chosen, that a basic mechanical configuration is decided, and preliminary estimates made of the total volume, total weight, and total power requirements of the finished data processor.

Any compatibility standards with other computers of the product line in terms of interface specifications and software that will work in common with computers of the product line should also be included in the specification for everyone's information.

DETAILED DESIGN

The detailed design of the hardware, and the software, too, can begin when the final system specifications are established. The detailed design includes many steps. Only those steps pertaining to the hardware design will be mentioned here.

1. *Detailed system design.* This includes establishment of the final instruction format. Work out the detailed algorithms for each of the arithmetic processes. Establish the approximate timing. Work out the detailed timing charts and flow charts for each instruction operation. Decide whether to use a microprogramming approach (see Chapter 11).
2. *Detailed logic design.* Establish the logic organizations, both on the combinational level, and at the individual gate level. Write the logic equations, or prepare the logic diagrams of all component sections.
3. *Detailed circuit design.* Establish the circuit type and its operation levels for reliable operation, susceptibility to noise, power dissipation, noise radiation characteristics, power supply levels, total power required, and detailed component positioning. In addition the *clock* system must be designed so that its timing is within proper limits at every point in the system.
4. *Detailed packaging design.* This task involves the general problem of mechanically mounting circuit boards, chassis, and cables. It involves studies of heat transfer and removal and also any special design features that must be included to permit the design to function in the expected environment or to specific environmental specifications.

5. *Reliability analysis.* For military applications, a detailed reliability analysis and calculations of expected failure times is normally required.

The above breakdown of tasks are tentative and included to show only a general range of design responsibilities. There are many more details that the designers must face, but these are solved as they arise. The above mentioned factors are typical and sufficient to acquaint the reader with the scope of computer design.

A SPECIMEN COMPUTER

For the sake of completing the tasks begun in Chapter 9 and continuing through Chapter 12, this section introduces a sample computer. This sample is a hypothetical computer in every respect, having no relationship to any practical design known to the author. The organization described, however, is intended to illustrate the relationships between the previously introduced computer sections, and should serve to tie the previously expressed ideas into a final package.

A number of assumptions are required at the outset. First, assume a 12-bit word for both instruction and data. For most applications this word length is too short, but for purposes of illustration and simplicity, it is sufficient. If 6 bits are allowed for addressing, then the memory would be limited to 64 words, obviously an unreal assumption, but still sufficient for our illustration. The other 6 bits in the instruction can be used as follows: 4 for operator code (permitting 16 instruction types) and 2 for a *variant* indication. These last two bits indicate whether or not the index registers are to be used to modify the program sequence.

The transfer of data and instructions generally will be serial, except in a few special instances.

This latter assumption might also be considered too restrictive and time consuming since it is usually preferred to transfer and decode instructions in parallel lest the computer speed suffer unduly. Nevertheless, the assumptions made in the illustrative or specimen computer could be real assumptions with some basis in fact, particularly where speed is not a major requirement.

The organization of the hypothetical serial processor is presented in Fig. 14-1.† The ordinary division into sections is along traditional lines of memory, input–output, arithmetic section, and control. Also, in the traditional fashion, all control signals (pulses, levels, etc.) emanate from the control section and are derived from a basic 2 MHz oscillator source. It is the design of this control section that becomes the most challenging task

† See attached foldout page (facing page 338).

associated with the development of the computer. This chapter will not become involved in the detail of this design, as it follows the principles outlined in Chapter 11 and elsewhere in this text.

The Memory Section

The memory section is organized along the principles discussed in Chapter 10. There is, of course, a memory-core stack. For the purposes of illustration, the memory has been assumed to contain only 64 words of 12 bits each. This, of course, is not a sufficient storage for any practical computer. The four sets of decoders and $X-Y$ drivers are shown in block form. Also, the inhibit drivers and the 12 sense amplifiers are obviously present. What do these latter components indicate about the organization of the core stack system? The MAR and the MBR are also clearly indicated. The other gates, clock pulses, and control signals that appear on them are for timing their operation. The student is referred to the glossary (Table 14-1) for an explanation of the symbols. Note that, to simplify the explanation, only AND, OR, and INHIBIT gates are employed in the figure. In any practical system, NAND or NOR logic would be more likely. The last point to mention regarding the memory is that the data transfer from the cores to the MBR is a parallel transfer, whereas data flow to and from the MBR and other points in the processor is serial. The operand address transferred to the MAR is also serial, but its effect is parallel on the decoders.

The Input–Output Section

The input–output section represented in Fig. 14-1 is elementary in its simplicity. It consists of a transfer register that both accepts and transfers data to or from the peripheral devices in parallel form. Also associated with the data transfer is a group of strobes, as described in Chapter 12, which indicates whether the data is an instruction, a number, or a discrete. The transfers (internal to the computer *input* and *output* bus) are serial. Would this input–output system be described as a direct or a buffered input–output system?

The Arithmetic Section

This section closely follows the serial arithmetic section discussed in Chapter 9. For simplicity, however, only the hardware operations of addition and multiplication are emphasized, although the necessary hardware is included for division also. The strobes and control levels originate generally within the control section, with the exception of the arithmetic unit

TABLE 14-1

Glossary of control signals and terms, applied to Fig. 14-1

C	Clock pulse
t_n	Timing pulse n. There are 14 timing pulses t_0 to t_{13}.
ϕ_n	There are two phase intervals each of 14 timing pulse duration:

ϕ_1: The interval during which the instruction is clocked to MAR and the operation code is sent to the operation code register. It is during this interval that command alterations take place, such as replacing the instruction counter contents. The instruction counter transfer to the MAR occurs at the beginning of this period. This has been termed the *program* interval.

ϕ_2: This is the interval during which program execution occurs. It is the *operation* interval and supports such activities as transfer operations, arithmetic operations, and input–output operations. It is frequently one 14-clock-pulse interval in length but may be extended for such operations as multiply and divide.

W	The control strobe that times the memory write operation.
R	The control strobe that times the memory reading operation
C^*	Symbol used here for complementing circuit logic
I	This is the inhibit-memory-bit strobe used during the memory write operation when the present memory contents are to be maintained. It is clocked into those bit positions where a "0" is to be recorded. The MBR contents determines.
S_1–S_{10}	The timing interval for the multiply process. This may amount to 10, or less, ϕ intervals. With "0's" in the multiplier and a fast shift it can reduce multiply time.
Decoder outputs	These levels are obtained by decoding instructions. They are employed for opening gates which assist in executing the instructions specified. The ones shown in the figure are just a few of the required levels. Those listed include:

Decode level	Function
Trans in	Transfer data in
Trans out	Transfer data out
Add	Addition process
Mult	Multiply process
Div	Divide process
M Trans	Transfer to memory
W-B load	Word-buffer load
Int Res	Reset interrupt flip-flop
Load A (M, Q, etc.)	Load the buffer or register identified

Other strobes	These are narrow-pulse strobes that are employed generally in the output or input transfers. They include:

Strobes	Function
TIN	Strobe data in to I/O buffer
TOT	Output strobe to peripheral devices
CON	External command transfer strobe
Acknow'ge	Acknowledge that TOT, TIN, CON, etc., has been completed successfully by processor
Resp	Response from peripheral that it accepts CON, TIN, TOT command

timing. The approach suggested here for arithmetic unit control is the one proposed by Fig. 9-16. In this figure the arithmetic cycle, depending on the process in operation, is controlled by a counter and other elements in the arithmetic control logic subsection. As previously stated in the memory paragraph of this chapter, the timing and control signals are intended to be identical with those used in earlier chapters; however, there may be minor differences in control level symbols. As for the original discussion, during an add command the contents of A is added with the contents of the MBR. For multiply, the multiplicand is transferred to M and the multiplier to Q. The Q register may be used to absorb the overflow product of the multiply operation, if it is to be retained. The sign control logic operates identically with that proposed in Chapter 9.

The Control Section

This general section has the obvious assignment of providing the control levels and timing pulses to all other sections. It also serves to decode instructions which in turn sees that the proper strobes and levels are formed and distributed on schedule. The system of control is the type associated with one-address instructions. The output of the instruction counter provides successive memory addresses for instructions to be employed.

For normal sequencing of instructions, the instruction counter is gated to the MAR, where the actual working instruction is retrieved from the memory address specified by the instruction counter's contents. This instruction is then executed, and a "1" added to the instruction counter's contents. Thus the incremented instruction counter now calls for the next instruction from the next higher memory address. For normal instruction sequencing this is the procedure of control shown in Fig. 14-1. The gating to the MAR is parallel to reduce the fetch-instruction operation time.

Although there are many ways to modify instructions, the index register approach is one of the better known. The method chosen to illustrate the general process is to incorporate two address modification registers. A jump requirement is indicated by the generation of a two-bit variant code. This code identifies whether the instruction counter proceeds in its normal mode or not. The generation of the proper code stops the instruction counter's *normal* transfer and instead transfers its contents to the instruction counter storage. Immediately thereafter, depending on the variant code, one of the address modification registers is transferred to the instruction counter and replaces the former contents. The instruction counter operation now proceeds with its normal sequence, and the new contents govern operations. Upon completion of the jump routine, the former instruction counter contents can be retrieved from its temporary storage and restored to the instruction counter where it continues the original program, as if never interrupted.

The original loading of the instruction counter and address modification registers is by program. For illustration, these registers were represented as logic hardware (flip-flops, gates, etc.). In a practical computer, they might be storage locations in the main memory or, more likely, storage locations of a special high-speed memory often designated a *control memory*. If no number was loaded into the instruction counter originally, the processing of memory addresses would start at position 000...

In the particular organization of modification registers chosen, the entire contents of the register replaced the contents of the instruction counter. In the index register method, the contents of these modification registers (now called index registers) are often logically combined or simply added to the instruction counter contents and thereby modify the instruction address. Also, an index register can often be loaded with a number that is decremented at every program step, or in some other manner. In this way, the number of program steps in a subroutine can be tallied. This general operation could have been specified in this example with only a moderate redesign. It is a point a designer should consider.

As suggested by the block diagram, a *jump* instruction could be originated by an input–output device (peripheral) generating an *interrupt*. In this case, the computer's present operation would be frozen until the *index register* instruction called for by the *jump* was executed. If the *jump* called for reloading the instruction counter, an entire subroutine could be initiated and completed before the processor returned to the original instruction counter setting and routine.

The index register technique is an illustration of merely one of several ways to modify a program routine according to events occurring during the computation process. It is an example of just one of the simple tools that lend so much power to data processing machinery.

One other point should be mentioned, i.e., the employment of *variant* bits in instruction formats. In some instruction organizations, two or more bit positions will normally contain "0's." This means that the instruction should be executed in the normal manner. Should an operation occur that requires an index register operation, a coding of "1's" and "0's" appears in the *variant* position. This involves employment of the index register to modify the instruction (as it is designed to do in this particular machine). The code often identifies which index register is to operate. The bit codes appearing in the variant position are placed there by the *jump* criteria encountered during a process. (The variant bit approach for instruction formats was not discussed. This process is mentioned here, however, because it is a popular technique in many systems.)

SUMMARY

This chapter has summarized many of the considerations that form a part of the systems analysis process leading to the definition and detailed design of a data processor. A short discussion was included of the design phase that defines the characteristics of the designated processor. The chapter concluded with an example of a computer and a description of its general details.

REVIEW QUESTIONS AND PROBLEMS

14-1. Prepare a list of those factors a systems designer must concern himself with when defining a system.

14-2. Prepare a tabulation of those tasks to be accomplished in order to write a final specification for a new processor.

14-3. Draw a block diagram of a PCU for a simple printer to be attached to the input–output bus of the sample processor described in this chapter. Assume the necessary control lines and that the word buffer, if one is needed, is in the printer.

14-4. Suppose an 18-bit word is allowed for the sample computer. Assume also that 32 commands are required. How many words of memory are now permitted? Assume each memory word is to be directly addressable.

14-5. Assume the computer is to require add time cycles of the order of 10 μsec. This cycle requires fetching, decoding, and executing the instruction. What basic changes would you recommend in the design of the sample computer to acomplish this?

ANALOG AND HYBRID METHODS 15

This chapter covers much supplementary material not specifically germane to other chapters. Because of the wide use of analog techniques and their relationship to hybrid systems, a considerable portion of this chapter is devoted to *operational amplifiers* and analog computing methods. This is followed by the digital equivalent of analog integrators, i.e., the *digital integrator*. The digital integrator is sometimes referred to as a *hybrid* device because it performs a function similar to the analog integrator. Computing devices employing digital integrators are similar in organization to analog differential analyzers. In the final sections of the chapter, computing methods employing *counters* are covered briefly. The techniques covered in this chapter have been used in the design of specialized test devices where high computational rates are not required, and the design concepts may be of interest to those interested in unusual approaches. In the past, such inexpensive counter devices as the *Deketron* tube have proved useful for this kind of operation. With low-cost I-Cs now available perhaps more extensive uses of counter techniques will become popular.

The digital processors discussed in Chapters 1 through 14 were of the general-purpose whole-number (integral) type. Most digital computers employed today are of this general classification. A second type, that has special interest in areas where its characteristics can be used to advantage is the *incremental computer*. This computer operates with numbers that are updated from a previous number. This updating continues during the course of the solution. For some processes it is much faster than whole number processing, but errors will be propagated along as the solution continues. For instance, by using an incremental computer, a complete multiplication can be accomplished in two word times. This same operation in a whole-number serial computer can take as many word times as there are bits in the multiplier.

The *digital differential analyzer* is an example of an incremental computer. There are many other examples some of which are probably nearer the basic definition. In special applications such as navigation, guidance, or vehicular control, the actual integration of accelerometer data can be accomplished in a separate *incremental section*. The output of this section may then serve as an input to the conventional whole-number (integral) computer. The reason for such organization is that accelerometer data require high processing rates, and this can be accomplished more economically in specialized incremental processors.

In Chapter 12, A/D and D/A conversions were discussed. These topics could have been covered in this chapter under the heading of hybrid techniques since they embrace both the analog and digital categories.

Hybrid processors are devices which are analog for some portion of their organization and digital for other portions. A typical hybrid processor might have analog inputs and outputs, but the internal processing would be digital. Such an example is a computer whose inputs are from A/D converters, multiplexed or otherwise, and whose outputs are D/A converters. Processors employed in control applications and in many types of data processing, such as the processing of test data from analog sensors, are in reality hybrid systems. Another type of application of a hybrid system could be the actual programming of interconnections of an analog machine by a digital processor. The analog connections required would be stored in the memory of the digital processor, and the execution of the program would complete the analog interconnections. This particular example is roughly the reverse of the first one described.

The advantage of hybrid systems lies, of course, in using either analog or digital technology where each has the most advantage. In digital systems, to store commands and data words indefinitely and to manipulate these by programs are techniques not easily accomplished by analog methods. The inherent high accuracy of digital calculation and the number of significant figures also favors this type of computation where required. On the other hand, analog systems operate continuously and many sensing devices are best designed as analog devices. The following sections of this chapter explore some of the devices and approaches of analog-digital hybrid technologies.

OPERATIONAL AMPLIFIERS

Operational amplifiers perform numerous valuable functions in analog systems. These circuits are characterized by extremely high input impedances (as near infinity as is practical) and high voltage gains. The dynamic range of the output and the output power capabilities may vary with the application. The frequency and bandwidth again vary with the application.

The amplifier is usually employed as part of a network. The network itself is a *feedback* network and may consist of resistors, inductors, capacitors, and nonlinear elements such as diodes. The feedback network may be fairly complex, which in turn gives rather complex frequency gain characteristics to the complete operational circuit.

In most applications it is necessary to limit amplifier *drift* to extremely low-values over the range of interest. Any drift components appearing in early stages or at the amplifier input are amplified by the amplifier and this will appear as an error in the system. In the case of d-c amplifiers, the drift component at the input cannot be identified from the low-level d-c signals. If this error component is constant, however, it is termed *a bias,* and this bias may be compensated by an adjustment. The "error" drifts that are difficult to compensate for may be those caused by temperature changes of components, current leakage, noise in low-level amplifier stages, etc.

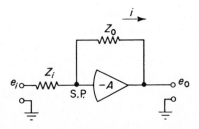

In an operational amplifier S.P. is at virtual ground. If the input impedance of the amplifier is very high

$$i Z_i = i Z_0$$

$$i = \frac{e_i}{Z_i} = -\frac{e_0}{Z_0}$$

Therefore $e_0 = -\frac{Z_0}{Z_i} e_i$ (if $A \gg 1$)

FIG. 15-1 Operational amplifier.

A typical operational amplifier is shown in Fig. 15-1. The gain characteristics of the overall circuit are a function of the external impedance
networks only in the ideal case. The high gain of the amplifier keeps the
error from this assumption negligible.

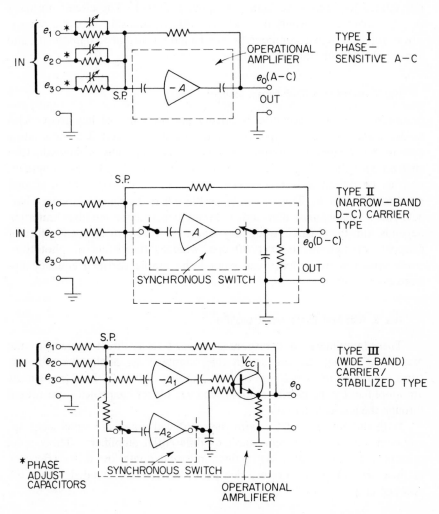

FIG. 15-2   Operational amplifier organization.

In practice, operational amplifiers occur in three types. Figure 15-2
illustrates by block diagram the differences in the organization of the three
types.

Type 1. Alternating-Current Operational Amplifier

This circuit is a high-gain amplifier adjusted to have a bandpass about the frequency of interest. Ideally it accepts modulated signals (of which the modulation component carries the intelligence, and the phase of the carrier related to a reference indicates signal polarity). The circuit normally rejects carrier components not in 0 or 180° relationship with the carrier. These rejected signal components are called *quadrature components* and serve only to saturate the amplifier prematurely.

Type 2. Narrow-Band Direct-Current Amplifier

These amplifiers accept a relatively narrow band of low frequencies to d-c voltages. In this type, the input signal is converted to alternating current by a vibrator-chopper or synchronous (usually semiconductor) switch. The alternating current is internally amplified in the a-c amplifier, and at the output it is reconverted back to direct current by a second synchronous switch. This circuit is usable when the signal response characteristics can be limited to a few cycles per second, but this limitation depends on the carrier frequency chosen. Electromechanical vibrator choppers operate to about 1200 cps, whereas transistors or phototransistor synchronous switches can extend the usable carrier frequency upward considerably.

Type 3. Wide-Band Direct-Current Amplifier

These amplifiers have responses upward from direct current to the megahertz range. In one design they combine essentially the vibrator-carrier amplifier of type 2 with the a-c amplifier of type 1. Low frequencies are amplified by the carrier section, whereas higher frequencies are routed through the a-c section only.

With the advent of I-Cs, with their reduced noise and small size, operational amplifiers are being built as differential amplifiers. These units possess wide bandwidths, high gains, and moderately low drifts. Because of their size, even temperature compensation can be included within the package (Fig. 15-2).

ANALOG MATHEMATICAL OPERATIONS

The following paragraphs describe some of the more elementary operations performed by analog elements. To understand the complete operation of an analog computer, it is necessary to study how the mathematical processes are accomplished. The techniques are not at all similar to the digital processes discussed previously. Further, analog computers are organized by interconnecting the elements in a configuration that represents an *analog* (hence the name *analog* computer) of the actual system to be simulated. The description of analog computation processes begins directly with a brief outline of analog adders.

Summation

The sum of analog quantities is determined basically by allowing weighted currents, each representing an individual quantity, to add together in a common resistance. The basic network is represented by Fig.

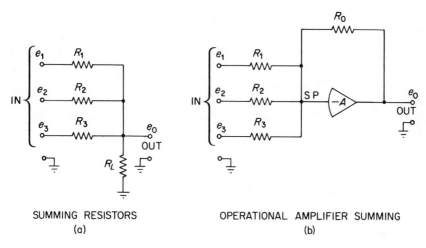

SUMMING RESISTORS
(a)

OPERATIONAL AMPLIFIER SUMMING
(b)

FIG. 15-3   Analog summation with resistors.

15-3. When the resistor value $R_1, R_2, \ldots, R_n$ are equal, the output voltage will be ideally

$$e_o = \left(\frac{R_L}{R_1 + R_L} \right)(e_1 + e_2 + e_3, \ldots, e_n)$$

In most analog computers the summation network is combined with an operational amplifier. This technique has the advantage of a more accurate solution with greater isolation of the sources and loads. Such an example is given by Fig. 15-3*b*. Here the output is proportional to

$$e_o = \left(\frac{R_o}{R_1} e_1 + \frac{R_o}{R_2} e_2 + \cdots + \frac{R_o}{R_n} e_n \right)$$

Note that the ratio of R_o to the input resistors $R_1, R_2, \ldots, R_n$ determines the *scaling* of the input signals. Here scaling means multiplying the input signals by a ratio—in this case, the ratios: R_o/R_1, R_o/R_2, ..., R_o/R_n. For the operational amplifier to perform its function accurately, the voltage gain must be extremely high and the input impedance to the amplifier itself must load point S (the summing point) a negligible amount. Note, also the output is inverted from the input as identified by the negative sign attached to the results.

Multiplication by a Variable

Although scaling the input resistors of Fig. 15-3 permits a fixed multiplication of the individual input analog quantities, an adjustable multiplication may be obtained by use of a potentiometer (usually called simply a *pot*). Pots can be wound to high precision and with little error from the ideal linear value. The output of the pot is proportional to the voltage across the pot multiplied by the position of the arm where the position is represented as a ratio. At the lower end extremity, the ratio is 0 and at the higher end, it is 1.0. In between, the ratio assumes any value depending on the ratio of the distance from the starting point (low end). Examples of the output to be expected from a pot are given in Fig. 15-4.

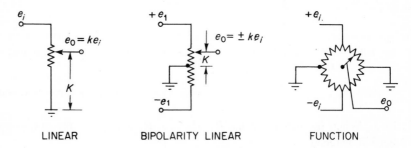

LINEAR   BIPOLARITY LINEAR   FUNCTION

FIG. 15-4   Potentiometers as computing elements.

Pots are often wound to have other than linear tapers. These pots can be designed to give special functions over limited and, in many cases, extended ranges. In either case, the pot is wound with a nonlinear taper to compensate for known loading of output circuits attached to the pot.

A full-fledged analog multiplier (Fig. 15-5) can be constructed if we take the pot just described and drive the wiper arm with a servomotor. If the voltage to the pot is x and the voltage that positions the servo is y, the output from arm z of pot 2 will be $z = xy$ for a linear pot. Should pot 2 have a taper representing some function $f(y)$, then the output would be $z = x f(y)$.

Although the design illustrated by Fig. 15-5 is a time-honored one, it suffers from relatively low speeds as a function of the maximum dynamic

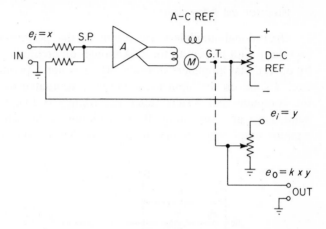

FIG. 15-5   A servo analog multiplier.

response time of the electromechanical servos. Modern devices, such as Hall multipliers, are now commercially available, and these devices will perform analog multiplication at electronic speeds, perhaps at reduced accuracy at times, but at substantially less cost. Other all-electronic methods are available, but these methods are left to reference books on the subject.

Division

A direct way of performing division is by the servo technique introduced in the past section. The organization of an analog divider is illustrated by Fig. 15-6. The reader will note, of course, that the pot is now

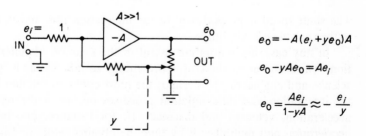

$$e_0 = -A(e_i + y e_0)A$$

$$e_0 - y A e_0 = A e_i$$

$$e_0 = \frac{A e_i}{1 - yA} \approx -\frac{e_i}{y}$$

FIG. 15-6   Analog divider.

in the feedback path of the amplifier. Again, as for the multiplier, the arm y can be positioned with a servo in order that y will be represented by a voltage.

Integration and Differentiation

Operational amplifiers are useful in the performance of integration, especially with respect to time. Although differentiation may be performed by operational amplifiers theoretically, it is not a popular method in practice. (Noise on the input leads will be accentuated by differentiation, and the computational results suffer accordingly.) Integrators, on the other hand, have an attenuating effect on circuit noise. The typical analog integrator employing an operational amplifier is shown in Fig. 15-7. By

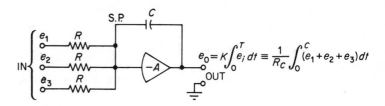

FIG. 15-7 Analog electronic integrator using an operational amplifier.

rearranging the organization of the problem to be solved, analog integrators can usually be substituted for analog differentiators.

An electromechanical integrator is sometimes used in analog systems. In this design a servo is constructed where the feedback is taken from a rate generator or tachometer. Here a velocity signal (rate-generator output) is summed with an input voltage e_i'. The servo shaft's total turns will be proportional to the integral of e_i; or,

$$\theta_t = k \int_0^t e_i \, dt$$

The shaft speed is proportional to the integration rate and is proportional to the variable e_i's amplitude.

In any case integrators are useful in the solution of differential equations (a common method of representing certain dynamic processes of science and engineering). Perhaps the most common relationship between the integration and differentiation processes occurs in the relationship of acceleration, velocity, and distance. If, for instance, one takes average *acceleration* and multiplies it by *time,* he obtains *velocity*. Likewise, if he takes average *velocity* and multiplies it by *time,* he computes *distance*. In the reverse direction, *distance* divided by *time* is *velocity,* and *velocity* divided by *time* is acceleration.

In mathematics or physics, this relationship is represented by *differentials* or *integrals.* The following relationships are defined:

$$\text{velocity} = \frac{\Delta \text{ change in distance}}{\Delta \text{ change in time}} = \frac{\Delta s}{\Delta t} = \frac{ds}{dt}$$

in the limiting case of Δs going to zero and Δt going to zero.

$$V = \frac{ds}{dt}$$

where V is the differential of s with respect to t. This is an example of the differentiation process where s is differentiated. Also,

$$a = \frac{dv}{dt}$$

where a is the differential of v with respect to t. This is a second example of a derivative process.

Also we could write the second differential of s, which turns out to be acceleration, as follows:

$$\frac{d}{dt}\left(\frac{ds}{dt}\right) = \frac{dv}{dt} = a$$

$d^2s/dt^2 = a$ is a second notation used extensively. In this case a is said to be the second differential of s with respect to time t.

The inverse process of differentiation is integration. For example, if

$$\frac{dv}{dt} = a$$

we can write $dv = a\ dt$. We can integrate both sides and we then have

$$v = \int a\ dt$$

where

$$\int_a^b (\ldots)\ dt$$

indicates the limits of integration are over the time interval of a to b.

Here velocity is the integral of a over the interval of time t. The value of v can also be integrated over a time t to obtain s, e.g.,

$$s = \int_0^t v\ dt = \int_0^t \left(\int_0^t a\ dt\right) dt$$

In other words s may be obtained by performing a double integration on acceleration, *a*. This process, e.g., is the way inertial navigation systems operate. Accelerometers sense the acceleration of the craft in a given direction and electronic integrators perform a double integration, which gives the distance *s* the craft travels in that direction.

Therefore, the integrator described previously is a device which performs the process of integration, or it performs

$$E_o = k \int_0^t e_i \, dt$$

where *k* is a scale factor normally equal to $1/RC$ and the integration is performed from time equals zero to time equals *t*. If there are several inputs, the outputs will be

$$E_o = k_1 \int_0^t e_1 \, dt + k_2 \int_0^t e_2 \, dt + k_3 \int_0^t e_3 \, dt + \cdots$$

Or, if $k_1 = k_2 = k_3 \ldots = k_n$,

$$E_o = k_1 \int_0^t (e_1 + e_2 + e_3 + \cdots) \, dt$$

Other Analog Techniques

The analog techniques described up to this point have assumed the variables were d-c functions. Operational amplifiers can be designed to operate with a-c variables, but, because of phase shifts between the a-c carriers, it is more difficult to perform summations. For integration, it is necessary to go to more elaborate electromechanical servointegrators. However, some analog processes are more conveniently handled with a-c variables, and these often involve trigonometric quantities such as sine, cosine, etc. A device, called a *resolver,* converts shaft angles to voltages which represent the sine or cosine function of the shaft angle. In conjunction with a servo, an a-c resolver is a convenient way to obtain such quantities, or $y = x \sin \theta + x \cos \theta$. Although d-c resolvers in the form of specially wound pots do exist, they are often quite expensive compared with their a-c counterparts of equal accuracy.

Special functions whether trigonometric, logarithmic, or, for that matter, even described by a mathematical equation can be provided by devices defined as *function generators.* Function generators often consist of pots wound to represent the function required. Another widely used method is to use nonlinear elements whose voltage or current characteristic approach the desired function. General-purpose function generators are available in which the nonlinear characteristic is adjustable. The particular designs of these employ diodes whose cathode (or anode) is brought to a reference voltage adjustable by the operator. The desired nonlinear curve is approximated by adjusting the reference voltage to the individual diodes of the network. Figure 15-8 presents an example of this technique.

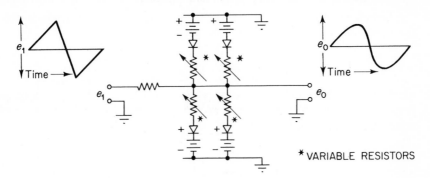

FIG. 15-8   Diode function generator.

Again operational amplifiers can employ diode networks in the feed-back path to obtain special nonlinear, or shaping, effects. One of the powerful advantages of the analog computer method is the fact that non-linear effects (saturation, hysteresis, limiting, etc.) are easily simulated in problem solutions by employing diodes as clamps. The clamping effect is obtained by connecting the diode terminals to the desired reference voltage. The reference voltage, being adjustable, allows a tailoring of the function curve.

Solving Equations with Analog Elements

In the usual analog computer, the elements described in the last section are patched together in such a way that the configuration will *simulate* the problem and its solution. A simple example would be the solution of two simultaneous algebraic equations. For example, solve

$$ax + by = k_1 \qquad (1)$$
$$cx + dy = k_2 \qquad (2)$$

Solve for x and y:

$$x = \frac{k_1}{a} - \frac{b}{a}y \qquad y = \frac{k_2}{d} - \frac{cx}{d}$$

The solution for these equations can be obtained by interconnecting operational summing amplifiers in the configuration shown in Fig. 15-9. The value of resistors chosen at the summing inputs will *scale* the variable of the problem. Note that a/b of the summing resistor give $(b/a)x$, where x is the variable. For simple inversion of the variable, the ratio of R_o to R is $1:1$.

Integrators and summing amplifiers together will readily solve differ-

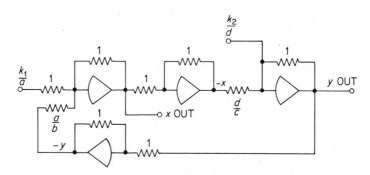

FIG. 15-9   Mechanization of simultaneous equations.

ential–integral equations of many types. To illustrate the process, assume the solution of the following equation is desired:

$$a \frac{d^2y}{dt^2} + b \frac{dy}{dt} + ay = f(t)$$

The solution of this differential equation is obtained by solving the equation for the highest order derivative (the $a(d^2y/dt^2)$ term). The $f(t)$ is some arbitrary forcing function and is often a step of voltage, a sine wave, or other signal for which the solution is desired. The normal way to solve this problem is to interconnect the necessary elements in the proper configuration. The forcing function is injected at the proper point. The solution is obtained on a chart, x–y plotter, or oscilloscope in a plotted curve form. The operator applies the forcing function, and the plotter will plot a curve of y or dy/dt or dy^2/dt^2 depending on where it is connected in the system. To organize the elements most readily, the equation is solved for d^2y/dt^2. To obtain dy/dt, the original d^2y/dt^2 term is integrated and inverted. To solve for y, the dy/dt term is integrated and inverted. To solve for d^2y/dt, we have

$$a \frac{d^2y}{dt^2} = f(t) - \frac{b \, dy}{dt} - ay$$

or

$$\frac{dy^2}{dt^2} = \frac{f(t)}{a} - \frac{b \, dy}{a \, dt} - y$$

This last equation, then, is the one that is interconnected by the analog elements. Figure 15-10 is an example of how this is accomplished. The student should trace the connections through to ensure his understanding of the general process.

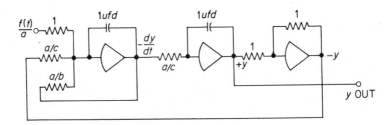

FIG. 15-10   Differential equation solution connections.

The above description of analog computation was on a very elementary plane. In actual practice, there are several other factors that must be considered. Some of these factors include:

Scaling. The values of resistors at the summing inputs must be chosen carefully so that the range of variables, when scaled, is within the range that can be handled by the summing amplifiers and integrators.

Initial conditions. For many problems the integrating capacitors must be charged to some initial value or must be discharged from a previous run.

Saturation limits. An operational amplifier within the system cannot saturate (become nonlinear) during the solution time interval. Intentional saturation devices are often used purposely to simulate a desired non-linearity, when a study of the nonlinearity is intended. Amplifiers that saturate unintentionally destroy the solution, and the operator must rescale the problem or look for errors in his interconnections.

This section very briefly described two possible ways that operational amplifiers can be connected to solve problems. There are a multitude of other problems that have been put to analog computers (in this case, analog differential analysis). However, now that the digital computer has become so common, most solutions for this type of problem can be accomplished on digital computers with appropriate numerical analysis techniques to prepare suitable programs. Nevertheless, there has been a sort of marriage of the analog techniques with digital techniques in the development of DDAs (digital differential analyzers). In a sense, the DDA is a digital EDA (electronic differential analyzer). In its implementation, digital integrators are used instead of analog integrators. A following section describes the elements and the organization of a DDA.

COUNTER COMPUTING TECHNIQUES

If time allows for the slower speeds, counters themselves will compute. For this method, the number of pulses in a pulse train represents the number to be processed. For instance, 7 would be indicated by seven pulses, 3 by three pulses, etc. To add two numbers in this form, it is merely necessary to sum the total pulses from both numbers in a binary counter. Of course, the counts from the two number words to be summed must not coincide or overlap. Figure 15-11 outlines the process of addition and subtraction by counters.

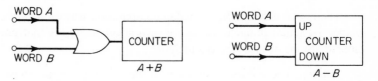

FIG. 15-11 Counter methods of addition.

If an up-down counter is used, the process of subtraction results. Again the restriction that the two pulse trains cannot overlap must be respected.

During the processing of numbers in this form, the result and sum will appear in the binary counter as *a binary number*. If this number is to be processed further, it must be reconverted to a pulse train. Actually, to reconvert is not difficult. All that is done is to subtract (count down) until the counter is empty (reads 000...). Logic associated with the counter detects the 000... condition and closes a gate, which cuts off the count-down clock. The total count of count-down clocks employed is the original contents of the counter.

Multiplication of two numbers is relatively easy if one number is in binary form and the other number in pulse-train form. The number in pulse-train form is the input to a binary counter. Each stage of the binary counter serves as an input to one side of a separate AND gate. The other input to the AND gate is the second number in binary form. All AND gates are combined in an OR gate which is the output. The output of each stage of the counter is converted to a pulse. This pulse is emitted through the AND gate if the binary digit is a "1." The total count through the OR gate will be the product of x and y. Again, the timing must be controlled so that the outputs of the AND gates are staggered with each other. The counter on the output must be fast enough to read *all* pulses generated and gated through the individual AND gates. The process just described is illustrated in Fig. 15-12.

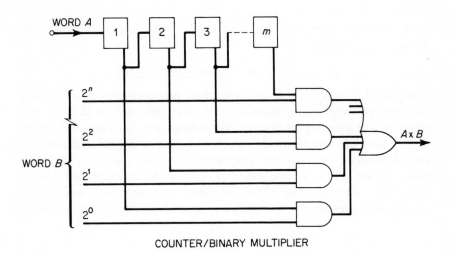

COUNTER/BINARY MULTIPLIER

FIG. 15-12   Counter multiplication.

Division can also be performed by combining the multiplier just described with an up-down counter. The binary multiplier is employed here in a feedback mode in much the way the pot was in the analog divider illustrated in Fig. 15-6. Likewise, integration and differentiation are possible. Integration is the total sum of inclusive pulses that occur up to a reference time. Differentiation is the rate of change of count that occurs in a small measured interval of time.

Although these methods are interesting, their application has been limited to special systems, generally where the computational speeds are relatively low such as a few operations per second, perhaps. The notable exception to this last statement is the digital differential analyzer next described.

THE DIGITAL DIFFERENTIAL ANALYZER

The basic element of the DDA is the *digital integrator*. Individual digital integrators can be interconnected in much the same way as analog integrators; hence, the technique of interconnecting blocks to simulate the characteristic equation is also employed here.

There are some differences between the electronic analog integrators and the digital integrators that should be noted, however. The analog integrator solution is

$$E_o = \int_0^t e_i \, dt$$

(Note that the output E is the integral of e_i with respect to time.) The digital integrator solution is

$$\Delta z = y \, \Delta x \qquad \text{or} \qquad z = \sum \Delta z = \sum y \, \Delta x$$

The symbol $\sum$ stands for summation. This processing differs in two ways from the previous analog solution. The first difference is that the integration is *not* with respect to time. The output of a signal digital integrator is Δz, where the variable of the solutions are y and Δx, none of which are time dependent. The second difference is that the output is Δz rather than z, which means an integration of Δz must be accomplished before z is available directly. The EDA integrator, of course, will compute the corresponding results if $y = e_i$ and $dt = \Delta x$ and the integration of resulting

$$\int_0^t e_i \, dt$$

will be accomplished.

The implementation of a digital integrator is illustrated by Fig. 15-13.

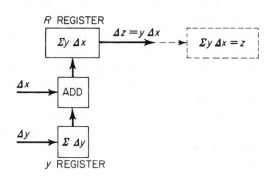

FIG. 15-13   Digital integrator mechanization.

The Y register contains the current value of y. It is updated periodically by a change in y (or Δy). This change is normally a $+$ pulse for a $+1$ increment (or a $-$ pulse for a -1 increment.) Periodically, the y register, which contains $\sum \Delta y$ is gated to the R register at Δx intervals; therefore, the R register contains $\sum y \, \Delta x$.

At every Δx interval, the contents of the R register is updated by a new addition of the contents of the y register; hence, this register fills up rapidly. Once the R register is full, additional summations of y cause overflow of the R register. The overflow is equal to $\Delta z = y\,\Delta x$. Although this overflow is Δz and not z, an integration of Δz in a second integrator develops z, or performs the complete integration process $z = \int y\,dx$.

The comparison was made earlier with the analog integrator. Although, there is correspondence, the similarity of the digital integrator to Lord Kelvin's original mechanical integrator is more exact. In this design, the x was represented by a flat disk that contacts (at right angles to the radius) and rotates a small wheel. The radial distance of the small wheel from the center of the disk is variable and represents y. The rotation of the small wheel represents $y\,\Delta x = \Delta z$; consequently, comparison of the Kelvin integrator and the digital integrator is amazingly close.

The digital integrator, in addition to performing integration, can be used to perform multiplication. In this application, three integrators are required. The multiplication occurs because of a theorem of differential calculus which states that

$$d(xy) = x\,dy + y\,dx$$

The quantities $x\,dy$ and $y\,dx$ are obtained by two separate integrators of the type discussed. They are both summed together to give $d(xy)$. Upon a second integration $d(xy)$ yields xy.

SUMMARY

This chapter has introduced the student to analog and hybrid methods of calculation. It was included at the end of the text because of the increasing interest in combined analog/digital, or hybrid, techniques.

The introductory paragraphs discussed the advantages and disadvantages of analog, digital, and hybrid systems. The incremental computer organization was mentioned. Then a section described operational amplifiers, a major tool in the analog arsenal. The various analog arithmetic processes—analog summation, multiplication, division, integration, and general function generation—were explained. Two examples were given of analog equation solving. These include simultaneous algebraic equations and a second-order differential equation. Counter-computing techniques were described briefly. These methods can be interesting when the time of solution is relatively slow. The chapter concluded with a short description of a digital integrator. Digital integrators and adders may be used to construct DDAs; but the student is referred to specialized texts for a description of their operation in detail.

REVIEW QUESTIONS AND PROBLEMS

15-1. What is the basic difference between an incremental and whole-number computer?

15-2. What is a hybrid computer?

15-3. What is an operational amplifier? What are its characteristics? Where is it used in analog computation?

15-4. Design an analog amplifier that will sum. The variable output polarity will be the inverse of the input polarity. Assume unity gain. Given:

e_1 multiplied by the ratio $\frac{3}{4}$
e_2 multiplied by the ratio $\frac{1}{5}$
e_3 multiplied by the ratio 1

Find the summation equation.

15.5. What is the output of the amplifier in Problem 15-4 if

$l_1 = -1$ volt
$l_2 = +2.5$ volts
$l_3 = +0.5$ volts

What would be the effect of doubling the value of R_o?

15-6. Explain in your own words the operation of an analog divider.

15-7. What is the application of analog electronic integrators? What is a limitation to the integrator process by the analog integrator described in this chapter?

15-8. Describe an analog system that will solve the algebraic equation

$$3x + 5y = 3$$
$$2x - y = 7$$

15-9. Show the organization of an analog system that will solve the differential equation:

$$4\frac{d^3y}{dt^3} + \frac{2d^2y}{dx^2} = 3y = f(t)$$

15-10. What are counter-computing techniques? What is the restriction in this method? What are its potential advantages?

15-11. What is the functional difference between a digital integrator and an analog integrator?

15-12. The digital integrator is more closely comparable to the Kelvin integrator than the analog integrator. Explain.

LOGIC
SYMBOLS†

A

1. "AND" GATES

2. "OR" GATES

(Cont. next page)

† From MIL-STD-806B (U.S. Department of Defense, Washington, D.C.).

361

3. EXCLUSIVE "OR"

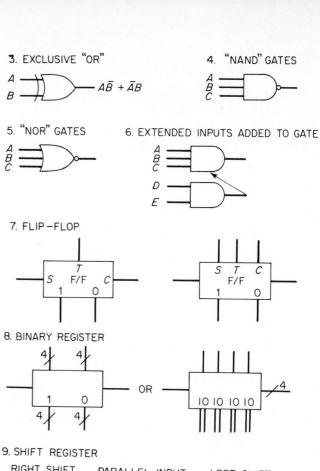

$A\bar{B} + \bar{A}B$

4. "NAND" GATES

5. "NOR" GATES

6. EXTENDED INPUTS ADDED TO GATE

7. FLIP–FLOP

8. BINARY REGISTER

OR

9. SHIFT REGISTER

RIGHT SHIFT INPUT   PARALLEL INPUT   LEFT SHIFT INPUT

SERIAL INPUT

$S R S R S R$
SR (G)
$1 0 1 0 1 0$

SERIAL OUTPUT

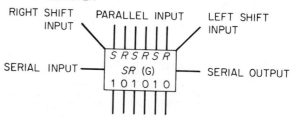

10. SINGLE SHOT FUNCTION

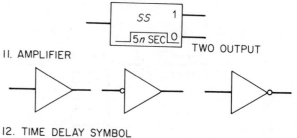

SS   1

$5n$ SEC   0   TWO OUTPUT

11. AMPLIFIER

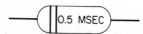

12. TIME DELAY SYMBOL

0.5 MSEC

SELECTED
BIBLIOGRAPHY **B**

General

Thomas C. Bartee, *Digital Computer Fundamentals*. New York: McGraw-Hill Book Company, 1960.

Burrough's Corporation, *Digital Computer Principles*. New York: McGraw-Hill Book Company, 1961.

Ivan Flores, *Computer Logic*. Englewood Cliffs, N.J.: Prentice-Hall, Inc., 1960.

Engineering Research Associates, *High-Speed Computing Devices*. New York: McGraw-Hill Book Company, 1950.

R. K. Richards, *Arithmetic Operations*. Princeton, N.J.: D. Van Nostrand Co., Inc., 1955.

R. K. Richards, *Digital Computer Components and Circuits*. Princeton, N.J.: D. Van Nostrand Co., Inc., 1957.

Paul Siegel, *Understanding Digital Computers.* New York: John Wiley and Sons, Inc., 1961.

Calculating Machines, Encyclopedia Britannica, 1958 ed.

Y. Chu, *Digital Computer Design Fundamentals.* New York: McGraw-Hill Book Company, 1962.

R. S. Ledley, *Digital Computer and Control Engineering.* New York: McGraw-Hill Book Company, 1965.

Litton Systems Division, *Digital Computer Fundamentals.* Englewood Cliffs, N.J.: Prentice-Hall, Inc., 1965.

A. Booth and K. H. V. Booth, *Automatic Digital Calculations.* London and Washington: Butterworth Scientific Publications, 1953.

Ivan Flores, *Computer Design.* Englewood Cliffs, N.J.: Prentice-Hall, Inc., 1967.

Switching circuit theory

Montgomery Phister, Jr., *Logical Design of Digital Computers.* New York: John Wiley and Sons, Inc., 1958.

W. Keister, A. E. Ritchie, and S. H. Washburn, *The Design of Switching Circuits.* Princeton, N.J.: D. Van Nostrand Co., Inc., 1951.

N. E. Staehler, An application of boolean algebra to switching circuit design. *Bell System Tech. J.,* Mar., 1952.

C. E. Shannon, Symbolic analysis of relay and switching circuits. *AIEE Trans.* **57,** 1938.

E. W. Veitch, A chart method for simplifying truth functions. *Computing Machinery,* May, 1952.

G. Karnaugh, The map method for synthesis of combinational logic circuits. *AIEE Trans.* Pt. 1, Nov., 1953.

Boolean algebra

George Boole, *An Investigation of the Laws of Thought.* New York: Dover Publications, Inc., 1954.

E. V. Huntington, *The Algebra of Logic.* Providence, R.I.: American Mathematical Society, 1904.

Programming

D. D. McCracken, *Digital Computer Programming.* New York: John Wiley and Sons, Inc., 1957.

Circuits

R. F. Lee and E. L. Daniel, Investigation of integrated logic circuits for application in systems operating above 1.0 mc. St. Petersburg, Fla.: Honeywell memorandum (unpublished).

A. Pressman, *Design of Transistorized Circuits for Digital Computers*. New York: John F. Rider, Inc., 1959.

GLOSSARY
OF TERMS

This glossary was adapted from that appearing in the text, *Computer Logic* by Ivan Flores, first published by Prentice-Hall in 1960. It has been updated here by the addition of over 100 terms to make it suitable to the task at hand—namely, definition of the terms employed in the present book in the way that the author intends them to be interpreted. [These newly added terms are identified by a symbol (A).] Where they were not relevant to this text, a few terms were dropped from Dr. Flores' listing. The reader is directed to the reference for source designations of the terms used.

A

-ac. A suffix meaning "automatic computer," as in ENIAC, SEAC.

access, arbitrary. Access to storage under conditions in which the next position from which information is to be obtained is in no way dependent on the previous one.

access, random. See *access, arbitrary.*

access time. The time interval between the instant at which the arithmetic unit calls for information from the memory unit and the instant at which the information is delivered from storage to the arithmetic unit. The time interval between the instant at which the arithmetic unit starts to send information to the memory unit and the instant at which the storage of the information in the memory unit is completed. In analog computers, the value at time *t* of each dependent variable represented in the problem is usually immediately accessible when the value of the independent variable is at time *t,* and otherwise not accessible.

accumulator. The register and associated equipment in the arithmetic unit in which are formed sums and other arithmetical and logical results; a unit in a digital computer where numbers are totaled, i.e., accumulated. Often the accumulator stores one quantity and upon receipt of any second quantity, it forms and stores the sum of the first and second quantities.

accuracy. Freedom from error. Accuracy contrasts with precision; e.g., a four-place table, correctly computed, is accurate; a six-place table containing an error is more precise, but not accurate.

acknowledge. A reply strobe to the "response" strobe, generally in the direction of the computer. (*A*)

adder. A device capable of forming the sum of two or more quantities.

adder, full. A functional unit which produces outputs corresponding to the sum and carry of binary addition for inputs corresponding to the addend, augend carry-in bits.

addition, signed. Addition of two numbers whose signs may be either plus or minus. The results of the addition will have the sign of the largest of the two numbers, and if the numbers have unlike signs, a numerical subtraction results. (*A*)

address. A set of characters which identifies either a register, a location in storage, or a device in which information is stored; a label, usually in the form of numerical coordinates.

address, absolute. The label(s) assigned by the machine designer to a particular storage location; specific address.

address part. In an instruction code the part that specifies an address. See *code, instruction.*

address, relative. A label used to identify a word in a routine or subroutine with respect to its position in that routine or subroutine. Relative addresses are translated into absolute addresses by the addition of some specific "reference" address, usually that at which the first word of the routine is stored;

e.g., if a relative address instruction specifies an address and the address of the first word of the routine is k, then the absolute address is $n + k$.

address, symbolic. A label chosen to identify a particular word, function, or other information in a routine, independent of the location of the information within the routine; floating address.

allocate. To assign storage locations to the main routines and subroutines, thereby fixing the absolute values of any symbolic addresses. In some cases allocation may require segmentation.

amplifier. A device for increasing the amplitude of electric waves by the control exercised by the input over the power supplied to the output of the amplifier. See also *amplifier, buffer* and *amplifier, torque.*

amplifier, buffer. An amplifier used to isolate the output of any device, e.g., oscillator, from the effects produced by changes in voltage or loading in subsequent circuits.

amplifier, differential. An amplifier with dual inputs such that input signals which are equal and opposite (180° phase) both drive the output in the same phase. Two signals of equal phase and amplitude on the dual inputs will tend to cancel each other. (*A*)

amplifier, operational. A high gain amplifier of high input impedance, about which a feedback loop is connected from output to summing point. The characteristics of the complete circuits (amplifier and feedback) are determined primarily by the feedback loop characteristics. (*A*)

amplifier, torque. A device which produces an output turning moment in proportion to the input moment, wherein the output moment and associated power is supplied by the device, and the device requires an input moment and power smaller than the output moment and power.

analog. The representation of numerical quantities by means of physical variables, e.g., translation, rotation, voltage, resistance; contrasted with "digital."

analyzer, differential. An analog computer designed and used primarily for solving differential equations.

AND. A logical operator which has the property that for two statements P and Q, the statement "P and Q" is true or false according to the following table:

P	Q	P *and* Q
false	false	false
false	true	false
true	false	false
true	true	true

The AND operator is represented by a centered dot ($\cdot$), or by no sign as in $P \cdot Q$ or PQ.

AND-**gate.** See *gate.*

arithmetic unit. That portion of the hardware of an automatic computer in which arithmetical and editing operations are performed.

assemble. To integrate subroutines (supplied, selected, or generated) into the main routine, by adapting, or specializing to the task at hand by means of preset parameters, by adapting, or changing relative and symbolic addresses to absolute form, or incorporating, or placing in storage.

asynchronous. See *computer, asynchronous.*

attenuate. To obtain a fractional part or reduce in amplitude an action or signal.

automatic controller. A device which controls a process by (1) automatically receiving measurements of one or more physical variables of the process, (2) automatically performing a calculation, and (3) automatically issuing suitably varied actions, such as the relative movement of a valve, so that the process is controlled as desired; for example, a flyball governor on a steam engine; an automatic pilot.

automation. Process or result of rendering machines self-acting or self-moving; rendering automatic. Theory, art, or technique of making a device, machine, or an industrial process more automatic. Making automatic the process of moving pieces of work from one machine tool to the next.

B

base. A number base; a quantity used implicitly to define some system of representing numbers by positional notation; radix.

beam, holding. A diffused beam of electrons used for regenerating the charges stored on the screen of a cathode ray storage tube.

beta (β). The conversion gain factor for a transistor. It is generally defined as change in collector current caused by a change in base signal current expressed as a ratio: $\beta = \Delta_{ic}/\Delta_{ib}$. (*A*)

bias. The average d-c voltage maintained between the cathode and control grid of a vacuum tube.

bias, forward. The circuit, transistor, tube, diode involved has applied to it a voltage which causes it to conduct (*turned-on*). (*A*)

bias, reversed. The circuit, transistor, tube, or diode involved has applied to it a voltage which causes it to cease conduction (*turned-off*). (*A*)

binary. A characteristic or property involving a selection, choice, or condition in which there are but two alternatives.

binary-coded decimal notation. One of many systems of writing numbers in which each decimal digit of the number is expressed by a different code written in binary digits. For example, the decimal digit 0 may be represented by the code 0011, the decimal digit 1 may be represented by the code 0100, etc.

binary digit. A digit in the binary scale of notation. This digit may be only 0 (zero) or 1 (one). It is equivalent to an "on" condition or an "off" condition, a "yes" or a "no," etc.

binary notation. The writing of numbers in the scale of two. The first dozen numbers zero to eleven are written 0, 1, 10, 11, 100, 101, 110, 111, 1000, 1001, 1010, 1011. The positions of the digits designate powers of two; thus 1010 means 1 times two cubed or eight, 0 times two squared or four, 1 times two to the first power or two, and 0 times two to the zero power or one; this is equal to one eight plus no fours plus one two plus no ones, which is ten. Also called natural binary.

binary number. A number written in binary notation.

binary point. In a binary number, the point which marks the place between integral powers of two and fractional powers of two, analogous to the decimal point in a decimal number. Thus, 10.101 means four, one half, and one eighth.

binary-to-decimal conversion. Converting a number written in binary notation to one written in decimal notation.

biquinary notation. A scale of notation in which the base is alternately 2 and 5. For example, the number 3671 in decimal notation is 03 11 12 01 in biquinary notation; the first of each pair of digits counts 0 or 1 units of five, and the second counts 0, 1, 2, 3, or 4 units. For comparison, the same number in Roman numerals is MMMDCLXXI. Biquinary notation expresses the representation of numbers by the abacus, and by the two hands and five fingers of man; and has been used in some automatic computers.

bit. A binary digit; a smallest unit of information; a "yes" or a "no"; a single pulse position in a group of possible pulse positions.

block. A group of consecutive machine words considered or transferred as a unit, particularly with reference to input and output. In a programming flow chart, an assembly of boxes, each box representing a logical unit of computer programming.

bobbin core. See *tape-wound core.*

Boolean algebra. An algebra dealing with classes, propositions, on-off circuit elements, etc., associated by operators AND, OR, NOT, EXCEPT, IF . . . THEN, etc.

Boolean calculus. Boolean algebra modified to include time, thereby providing an algebra or calculus for: states and events; additional operators such as AFTER, WHILE, HAPPEN, DELAY, BEFORE; classes whose members change over time; circuit elements whose on-off state changes from time to time such as delay lines, flip-flops, and sequential circuits; so-called step-functions, and their combinations, etc.

Boolean function. A mathematical function in Boolean algebra; examples of common functions are $c = a$ OR $b = a + b$, $c = a$ AND $b = a \cdot b$, $c =$ NOT-$a = \overline{a}$, $c = a$ EXCEPT $b = a \cdot \overline{b}$, $c =$ NEITHER a NOR $b = \overline{a} \cdot \overline{b}$.

bootstrap. In a programming flow chart, a logical unit of computer programming surrounded by a rectangle and treated as a unit. Often identified by requiring transfer of the instructions referred to therein into and out of the rapid memory of the computer.

breakpoint. A point in a routine at which the computer, under the control of a manually set switch, will stop for an operator's check of the progress of the routine.

branch. See *conditional jump*.

buffer. Storage between the input–output equipment and the computer where information is assembled in easily absorbed units: storage between the main memory and the computer where information is rapidly accessible.

buffered channel. A method of interfacing devices with a computer. The buffer channel contains memory addressing capability and the ability to count transferred words. Word transfers occur under device control and without individual word-transfer instructions from the computer. (*A*)

bus. A path over which information is transferred, from any of several sources to any of several destinations. An electrical conductor capable of carrying a large current; a trunk; a heavy wire, line, or lead.

business processing. Operation that features the computer's ability to process large quantities of data. The input–output transfers are usually numerous, whereas the calculations are less numerous than for scientific processing. (*A*)

C

call in. To transfer control of a digital computer temporarily from a main routine to a subroutine, which is inserted in the sequence of calculating operations temporarily to fulfill a subsidiary purpose.

call number. A set of characters identifying a subroutine, and containing information concerning parameters to be inserted in the subroutine, or information to be used in generating the subroutine, or information related to the operands.

call word. A call-number which fills exactly one machine word.

canonical. A Boolean function whose terms contain all variables (or their compliments). This is the unreduced form of the Boolean function in minterm or maxterm form. (*A*)

capacity. The number of digits or characters which may regularly be processed in a computer, as in "the capacity is ten decimal digit numbers." The upper and lower limits of the numbers which may regularly be handled in a computer, as "the capacity of the computer is $+.00000\ 00001$ to $.99999\ 99999$." Quantities which are beyond the capacity of the computer usually interrupt its operation in some way.

capstan. The rotating shaft on a magnetic tape recording and/or reading device which is used to impart uniform motion to the magnetic tape on command.

card. A document of constant size, thickness, and shape adapted for punching in a pattern which has meaning. The punched holes are sensed electrically by wire brushes, mechanically by metal fingers, or photoelectrically. Also called "punch card." Punch cards are $7\frac{3}{8}$ inches long and $3\frac{1}{4}$ inches wide and contain 80 or 90 columns in each of which any one or more of several hole sites may be punched.

card column. One of a number of columns (45, 80, or 90) in a punch card into which information is entered by punches.

card feed. A mechanism which moves cards one by one into a machine.

card field. A set of card columns fixed as to number and position, into which the same item of information is regularly entered; for example, purchase order numbers of five decimal digits might be punched regularly into the card field consisting of card columns 11 to 15.

card punch. A mechanism which punches cards, or a machine which punches cards according to a program.

card reader. A mechanism that causes the information in punch cards to be read, usually by passing them under copper wire brushes or across metal fingers.

card stacker. A mechanism that stacks cards in a pocket or bin after they have passed through a machine. Sometimes called *card hopper*.

carriage, automatic. A typewriting paper guiding or holding device which is automatically controlled by a program so as to feed forms or continuous paper to a set of impression keys and to provide the necessary space, skip, eject, tabulate, and other operations.

carry. A signal or expression, produced as a result of an arithmetic operation on one digit place of two or more numbers expressed in Positional Notation and transferred to the next higher place for processing there. A signal or expression as defined in (1) above which arises in adding, when the sum of two digits in the same digit place equals or exceeds the base of the number system in use. If a carry into a digit place will result in a carry-out of the same digit place, and if the normal adding circuit is bypassed when generating this new carry, it is called a High-Speed Carry, or *Standing-on-*

Nines Carry. If the normal adding circuit is used in such a case, the carry is called a *Cascaded Carry.* If a carry resulting from the addition of carries *is not* allowed to propagate (e.g., when forming the partial product in one step of a multiplication process) the process is called a *Partial Carry.* If it *is* allowed to propagate the process is called a *Complete Carry.* If a carry generated in the most significant digit place is sent directly to the least significant place (e.g., when subtracting numbers using 9's complements addition), that carry is called *End-Around Carry.* In direct subtraction, a signal or expression as defined in (1) above which arises when the difference between the digits is less than zero. Such a carry is frequently called a *Borrow.* The action of forwarding a carry. The command directing a carry to be forwarded.

cascade control. An automatic control system in which control units are associated in a sequence, where each control unit regulates the operation of the next control unit in the sequence.

cathode ray tube. A large electronic vacuum tube with a screen for visual plot or display of output in graphic form by means of a proportionally deflected beam of electrons. A large electronic vacuum tube containing a screen on which information, expressed in pulses in a beam of electrons from the cathode, is stored by means of the presence or absence of spots bearing electrostatic charges. This capacity usually is from 256 to 1024 spots.

cell. Storage for one unit of information, as one bit, one character, or one machine word. More specific terms (*column, location, block*) are preferable since there is little uniformity in the use of the term *cell.*

centralized control. A computer for which all processing is controlled by a single operational unit is said to have *centralized control.* Otherwise, the computer has *decentralized control,* in which case requests for processing are issued by the *main control unit* to *auxiliary control units,* each of which assumes control of a portion of the processing and surrenders control to the main unit on completion of the auxiliary task.

channel. See *drum, magnetic storage.*

character. A decimal digit 0 to 9, or a letter A to Z, either capital or lower case, or a punctuation symbol, or any other single symbol (such as appear on the keys of a typewriter) which a machine may take in, store, or put out. Representation of such a symbol in a pattern of ones and zeros representing a pattern of positive and negative pulses or states is called a *character code.*

check. A means of verification of information.

check, built-in or automatic. Any provision constructed in hardware for verifying the accuracy of information transmitted, manipulated, or stored by any unit or device in a computer. Extent of automatic checking is the relative proportion of machine processes which are checked or the relative proportion of machine hardware devoted to checking.

check, duplication. A check which requires that the results of two independent performances (either concurrently on duplicate equipment or at a later time on the same equipment) of the same operation be identical.

check, forbidden combination. A check (usually an automatic check) which tests for the occurrence of a non-permissible code expression. A *self-checking code* (or error-detecting code) uses code expressions such that one (or more) error(s) in a code expression produces a forbidden combination. A *parity check* makes use of a self-checking code employing binary digits in which the total number of ones (or zeros) in each permissible code expression is always even or always odd. A check may be made for either even parity or odd parity. A *redundant check* employs a self-checking code which makes use of redundant digits called check digits.

check, mathematical or arithmetical. A check making use of mathematical identities or other properties, frequently with some degree of discrepancy being acceptable; e.g., checking multiplication by verifying that $A \cdot B = B \cdot A$, checking a tabulated function by differencing, etc.

check, modulo *N*. A form of check digit, such that the sum of the digits in each number A operated upon is compared with a check digit B, carried along with A and equal to the remainder of A when divided by N, e.g., in a "modulo 4 check," the check number will be 0, 1, 2, or 3 and the remainder of A when divided by 4 must equal the reported check number B, or else an error or malfunction has occurred; a method of verification by congruences, e.g., casting out nines.

check, odd-even. See *check, parity*.

check, parity. A summation check in which the binary digits, in a character or word, are added (modulo 2) and the sum checked against a single, previously computed parity digit; i.e., a check which tests whether the number of ones is odd or even.

check, programmed. A system of determining the correct program and machine functioning either by running a sample problem with similar programming and known answer, including mathematical or logical checks such as comparing A times B with B times A and usually where reliance is placed on a high probability of correctness rather than built-in error-detection circuits or by building a checking system into the actual program being run and utilized for checking during the actual running of the problem.

check, redundant. A check which uses extra digits, short of complete duplication, to help detect malfunctions and mistakes.

check, summation. A redundant check in which groups of digits are summed, usually without regard for overflow, and that sum checked against a previously computed sum to verify accuracy.

check, transfer. Verification of transmitted information by temporary storing, re-transmitting and comparing.

check, twin. A continuous duplication check achieved by duplication of hardware and automatic comparison.

checking, marginal. To determine computer circuit weaknesses and incipient malfunctions by varying the power applied to various circuits, usually by a lowering of the d-c supply or filament voltages.

chip. The body portion of a transistor, diode FET-MOS, or integrated circuit device. It is the finished segment of the device taken from the wafer after the planar process, etc. is complete. (*A*)

clear. To make all bits zero (or sometimes one) in a storage device.

clock, master. The source of standard timing signals required for sequencing computer operation, usually consisting of a timing pulse generator, a cycling unit, and sets of special pulses that occur at given intervals of time. Usually in synchronous machines the basic frequency utilized is the clocking pulse.

closed shop. A computing installation in which programs and routines are written only by the professional staff of programmers.

code. The machine-language representation of a character. The *instruction code* is the set of symbols which conveys to the computer the operation which it is to perform. The instruction code always specifies a process; it usually specifies one or more operand addresses; it may specify the address of the next order; it may specify additional information such as a cycle index or breakpoint. The *coded instruction code* or machine-language operation code may sometimes be referred to as a code.

code, Baudot. A teletype code usually, but not necessarily, restricted to five bit levels. It has a distinctive start and stop indication permitting characters to be asynchronous, one from another. (*A*)

code, error correcting. Binary bits are added to the binary word which make it possible to correct errors on the basis of these added bits. From the arrangement of bits and parity-type checks, a particular bit error can be detected in the word and, therefore, the error can be corrected. (*A*)

code, excess-three. A binary-coded notation for decimal digits which represents each decimal digit as the corresponding binary number plus three; e.g., the decimal digits 0, 1, 7, 9 are represented as 0011, 0100, 1010, 1100, respectively. In this notation, the 9's complement of the decimal digit is equal to the 1's complement of the corresponding four binary digits.

code, instruction. The set of symbols which conveys to the computer the operation which the programmer desires it to perform. The instruction code always specifies a process; it may specify operand addresses; it may specify the address of the next order; it may specify auxiliary information, such as a cycle index register or a breakpoint; see *code, multiple-address.*

code, interpreter. A code which is acceptable to an interpretive routine.

code, multiple-address. When the instruction code specifies no operands nor the next instruction address, since these are implicit in the order structure, the code is called a *zero address code*. The number of operand or result addresses specified in the code may be used to describe it; thus, a *two address code* is one where two operand addresses are specified. If the address of the next instruction is part of the code, the phrase "plus one" is added to the description. Thus, a *one-plus-one address code* specifies one operand address and the address of the next instruction.

code, natural binary. A machine language wherein the code corresponds exactly to the binary numbers used in counting.

code, natural-binary coded decimal. Sometimes *NBCD* or *8421*. A code which uses the four-bit binary number to represent each decimal digit, thus:

0—0000	1—0100	8—1000	F—1100
1—0001	5—0101	9—1001	F—1101
2—0010	6—0110	F—1010	F—1110
3—0011	7—0111	F—1011	F—1111

where F is a forbidden combination.

code, operational. That part of an instruction which designates the operation to be performed.

code, self-complementing. A machine language for which the code of the complement of a digit is the complement of the code of the digit.

coder. A person who translates a sequence of instructions for an automatic computer to solve a problem into the code acceptable to that machine.

coding. The list, in computer code or in pseudo-code, of the successive computer operations required to solve a given problem.

coding, absolute, relative, or symbolic. Coding in which one uses absolute, relative, or symbolic addresses, respectively; coding in which all addresses refer to an arbitrarily selected position, or in which all addresses are represented symbolically.

coding, alphabetic. A system of abbreviation used in preparing information for input into a computer such that information is reported in the form of letters, e.g., New York as NY, carriage return as CN, etc.

coding, automatic. Any technique in which a computer is used to help bridge the gap between some "easiest" form, intellectually and manually, of describing the steps to be followed in solving a given problem and some "most efficient" final coding of the same problem for a given computer; two basic forms are defined under *routine, compiler* and *routine, interpretive*.

coding, minimum latency. See *minimum-access programming*.

coding, numeric. A system of abbreviation used in the preparation of information for machine acceptance by reducing all information to numerical quantities; in contrast to alphabetic coding.

coercive force, II_c. The magnetizing force at which the magnetic flux density is zero when the material is in a *symmetrically cyclically magnetized condition*. [*Note*: Coercive force is not a unique property of a magnetic material, but is dependent upon the conditions of measurement.]

coercivity. The property of a magnetic material measured by the *coercive force* corresponding to the *saturation induction* for the material. [*Note:* This is a quasi-static property only.]

coincident-current selection. The selection of a magnetic cell for reading or writing, by the simultaneous application of two or more currents.

collate. To combine two sequences of items of information in any way such that the same sequence is observed in the combined sequence. For example, sequence 12, 29, 42 and sequence 23, 24, 48 may be collated into 12, 23, 24, 29, 42, 48. More generally, to combine two or more similarly ordered sets of items to produce another ordered set composed of information from the original sets. Both the number of items and the size of the individual items in the resulting set may differ from those of either of the original sets and of their sum.

collator. A machine which has input card feeds, output card pockets, and stations at which a card may be compared or sequenced with regard to other cards, so as to determine the pocket into which it is to be placed. The machine is particularly useful for matching detail cards with master cards, for merging cards in proper sequence into a file of cards, etc.

column. The place or position of a character or a digit in a word or other unit of information. One of the characters or digit positions in a positional-notation representation of a unit of information. Columns are usually numbered from right to left, zero being the rightmost column if there is no decimal (or binary, or other) point, or the column immediately to the left of the point if there is one. A position or place in a number, such as 3876, written in a scale of notation, corresponding to a given power of the radix. The digit located in any particular column is the coefficient of the corresponding power of the radix; thus, 8 in the foregoing example is the coefficient of 10^2.

combinational. In computer logic, this term refers to a group of logic elements connected together to form a higher-level logic subgroup. (*A*)

command. See *instruction*.

comparand. One of the words which the computer compares when executing a given comparison order.

comparator. (1) A circuit which compares two stored codes and supplies an indication of agreement or disagreement; or a mechanism by means of which two items of information may be compared in certain respects, and a signal given depending on whether they are equal or unequal. (2) A device for comparing two different transcriptions of the same information to verify agreement or determine disagreement.

compare. To determine the relative order of two computer words or sets of symbols by some predetermined criteria. The result of such a comparison is equality if the comparands are identical or greater than or less than according to whether the first comparand precedes or follows the second comparand in the predetermined ordering.

compiler. A program-making routine, which produces a specific program for a particular problem by the following process: (1) determining the intended meaning of an element of information expressed in pseudo-code; (2) selecting or generating (i.e., calculating from parameters and skeleton instructions) the required subroutine; (3) transforming the subroutine into specific coding for the specific problem, assigning specific memory registers, etc., and entering it as an element of the problem program; (4) maintaining a record of the subroutines used and their position in the problem program; and (5) continuing to the next element of information in pseudo-code.

complement. A quantity which is derived from a given quantity, expressed in notation to the base n, by one of the following rules. (a) Complement on n: subtract each digit of the given quantity from $n - 1$, add unity to the rightmost digit, and perform all resultant carries. For example, the 2's complement of binary 11010 is 00110; the 10's complement of decimal 679 is 321. (b) Complement on $n - 1$: subtract each digit of the given quantity from $n - 1$. For example, the 1's complement of binary 11010 is 00101; the 9's complement of decimal 679 is 320. The complement is frequently employed in computers to represent the negative of the given quantity.

complete operation. A calculating operation which includes (1) obtaining all the operands out of memory, (2) making a calculation or editing operation, (3) returning the result to memory, and (4) obtaining the next instruction.

computer. A machine which is able to perform sequences of arithmetic and logical operations upon information.

computer, analog. A computer which calculates by using physical analogs of the variables. A one-to-one correspondence exists between each numerical variable occurring in the problem and a varying physical measurement in the analog computer.

computer, asynchronous. A calculating device in which the performance of any operation starts as a result of a signal that the previous operation has been completed; contrasted with synchronous computer.

computer, automatic. A calculating device which handles long sequences of operations without human intervention.

computer, digital. A calculating device using integers to express all the variables and quantities of a problem.

computer, synchronous. A calculating device in which the performance of all operations is controlled with equally spaced signals from a master clock.

conditional. Subject to the result of a comparison made during computation.

conditional breakpoint instruction. A conditional jump instruction which, if some specified switch is set, will cause the computer to stop, after which either the routine may be continued as coded or a jump to another routine may be directed.

conditional transfer of control. A computer instruction which when reached in the course of a program will cause the computer either to continue with the next instruction in the original sequence or to tranfer control to another stated instruction, depending on a condition which has then been determined.

content. The information stored in any part of the computer memory. The symbol "(...)" is often used to indicate "the content of ..."; for example, (m) indicates the content of the storage location whose address is m.

continuous-run magnetic tape unit. A magnetic tape transport on which the tape moves continuously between characters when reading or writing data. In incremental tape units the tape comes to a stop between characters. (*A*)

control. Those parts of a digital computer which effect the carrying out of instructions in proper sequence, the interpretation of each instruction, and the application of the proper signals to the arithmetic unit and other parts in accordance with this interpretation. The components in any mechanism responsible for interpreting and carrying out manually-initiated directions. Sometimes called manual control. In some business applications of mathematics, a mathematical check.

control, cascade. An automatic control system in which various control units are linked in sequence, each control unit regulating the operation of the next control unit in line.

control sequence. The normal order of selection of instructions for execution. In some computers, one of the addresses in each instruction specifies the control sequence. In most other computers the sequence is consecutive except where a jump occurs.

control, sequential. A manner of operation of a computer such that instructions are fed in a given order to the computer during the solution of a problem.

control unit. That portion of the hardware of an automatic digital computer which directs the sequence of operations, interprets the coded instructions, and initiates the proper commands to the computer circuits to execute the instructions.

control unit, auxiliary. See *centralized control.*

control unit, main. See *centralized control.*

convert. To change numerical information from one number base to another (e.g., decimal to binary) and/or from some form of fixed-point to some form of floating-point representation, or vice versa.

converter. A unit which changes the language of information from one form to another so as to make it available or acceptable to another machine, e.g., a unit which changes information punched on cards to information recorded on magnetic tape, possibly including editing facilities.

copy. To reproduce information in a new location replacing whatever was previously stored there and leaving the source of the information unchanged.

core, magnetic. A magnetic material capable of assuming and remaining at one of two or more conditions of magnetization, thus capable of providing storage, gating, or switching functions, usually of toroidal shape and pulsed or polarized by electric currents carried on wire wound around the material.

counter. A device, register, or storage location for storing integers, permitting these integers to be increased or decreased by unity or by an arbitrary integer, and capable of being reset to zero or to an arbitrary integer.

counter, control. A device which records the storage location of the instruction word which is to be obtained next. The control counter selects storage locations in sequence unless otherwise directed. See also *program counter.*

counter, ring. A loop of interconnected bistable elements such that one and only one is in a specified state at any given time and such that, as input signals are counted, the position of the one specified state moves in an ordered sequence around the loop.

CRT. Cathode ray tube; a device yielding a visual plot of the variation of several parameters by means of a proportionally deflected beam of electrons.

cycle. A set of operations repeated as a unit; a nonarithmetic shift in which the digits dropped off at one end of a word are returned at the other end in circular fashion; cycle right and cycle left. To repeat a set of operations a prescribed number of times including, when required, supplying necessary address changes by arithmetc processes or by means of a hardware device such as a *B-box* or *cycle-counter.*

cycle count. To increase or decrease the cycle index by unity or by a selected integer.

cycle criterion. The total number of times the cycle is to be repeated; the register which stores that number.

cycle index. The number of times a cycle has been executed; or the difference, or the negative of the difference, betwen that number and the number of repetitions desired.

cycle, major. The maximum access time of a recirculating serial storage element; the time for one rotation, e.g., of a magnetic drum or of pulses in an acoustic delay line; a whole number of minor cycles.

cycle, minor. The word time of a serial computer, including the spacing between words.

cycle reset. To return a cycle index to its initial value.

cyclically magnetized condition. A condition of a magnetic material when it has been under the influence of a magnetizing force varying between two specific limits until, for each increasing (or decreasing) value of the magnetizing force, the magnetic flux density has the same value in successive cycles.

D

damping. A characteristic built into electrical circuits and mechanical systems to prevent rapid or excessive corrections which may lead to instability or oscillatory conditions, e.g., connecting a resistor on the terminals of a pulse transformer to remove natural oscillations; placing a moving element in oil or sluggish grease to prevent overshoot.

data. Facts or information taken in, operated on, or put out by a computer or other machine for handling information.

data reduction. Transforming masses of raw test or experimentally obtained data, usually gathered by instrumentation, into useful, ordered, or simplified intelligence.

data link. A communication path that handles binary data messages. (*A*)

data processor. A digital device that processes data. It may be a computer, but in a larger sense it may gather, distribute, digest, analyze, and perform other organization or smoothing operations on data. These operations, then, are not necessarily computational. Data processor is a more inclusive term than computer. (*A*)

data reduction, on-line. The processing of information as rapidly as the information is received by the computing system.

datum. One computer word.

decimal point. In a decimal number, the point that marks the place between positive and negative powers of ten.

decimal-to-binary conversion. Converting a number in the scale of ten into the scale of two.

debug. To isolate and remove malfunctions from a computer or mistakes from a routine.

decade. A group or assembly of ten units; e.g., a decade counter counts to ten in one column; a decade resistor box inserts resistance quantities in multiples of powers of ten.

decentralized control. See *centralized control.*

decode. To ascertain the intended meaning of the individual characters or groups of characters in the pseudo-coded program. (A) To activate a corresponding output line when input lines are activated in accordance with the code for that character.

decode driver. A switching circuit, often with built-in decoding capabilities, used for providing a driving current to core memores. It is used in conjunction with a decode sink circuit. (*A*)

decoder. A logical block which produces an output on one and only one line when one or more input lines are energized; the decoder is used to determine the digit in a given number system to which an indicated code is assigned.

decode sink. A switching circuit that sinks (switches) the drive current of a core memory to ground. It often has built-in decoding capabilities and is used in conjunction with a decode driver. (*A*)

decoupling. A technique for preventing one circuit from reacting on another. It consists of electrical isolation networks applied to the power supply voltages at critical points within a piece of equipment. (*A*)

delay element. An element whose output substantially resembles its input except that there is a time displacement between the two; also *delay-line.*

delay-line, electric. A transmission line of lumped or distributed capacitive and inductive elements in which the velocity of propagation of electromagnetic energy is small compared with the velocity of light. Storage is accomplished by recirculation of wave patterns containing information, usually in binary form.

delay-line, magnetic. A metallic medium along which the velocity of propagation of magnetic energy is small relative to the speed of light. Storage is accomplished by recirculation of wave patterns containing information, usually in binary form.

delay-line, mercury or quartz. A sonic or acoustic delay-line in which mercury or quartz is used as the medium of sound transmission. See *delay-line, sonic or acoustic.*

delay-line, sonic or acoustic. A device capable of transmitting retarded sound pulses, transmission being accomplished by wave patterns of elastic deformation. Storage is accomplished by recirculation of wave patterns containing information, usually in binary form.

delta. See *coincident-current selection.*

demultiplexor. A device that gathers data from several channels and places the data in sequence on a single channel. It is the opposite of a multiplexor. (*A*)

density, packing. The number of units of useful information contained within a given linear dimension, usually expressed in units per inch, e.g., the number of binary digit magnetic pulses stored on tape or drum per linear inch on a single track by a single head.

design, logical. The planning of a computer or data-processing system prior to its detailed engineering design. The synthesizing of a network of logical elements to perform a specified function. The result of both the above, frequently called the logic of the system, machine, or network.

detector. A functional element which produces an output only when inputs corresponding to a sample code or character are present.

diagram. A schematic representation of a sequence of subroutines designed to solve a problem; a coarser and less symbolic representation than a flow chart, frequently including descriptions in English words; a schematic or logical drawing showing the electrical circuit or logical arrangements within a component.

diagram, logical. A diagram representing the logical elements and their interconnections without construction or engineering details.

differential equations. Equations which contain one or more of the derivatives of the dependent variable. (*A*)

differentiator. A device whose output function is in proportion to a derivative of its input function with respect to one or more variables.

digit. One of the n symbols of integral value ranging from 0 to $n - 1$ inclusive in a scale of numbering of base n, e.g., one of the ten decimal digits, 0, 1, 2, 3, 4, 5, 6, 7, 8, 9.

digital. Using integers to represent all the quantities that occur in a problem or calculation.

digital device. Equipment that employs digital techniques in its operation. (*A*)

digital techniques. The method of representing quantities in numeric form and the processing of these numeric quantities. (*See* Chapter 1.) (*A*)

digit, binary. A whole number in the binary scale of notation; this digit may be only 0 (zero) or 1 (one). It may be equivalent to an "on" or "off" condition, a "yes" or a "no," etc.

digit, binary-coded decimal. See *binary-coded decimal.*

digitize. To render an analog measurement into digital form.

digits, check. In a character or word, one or more redundant digits which depends upon the remaining digits in such a fashion that if a digit is corrupted, the malfunction is detectable, e.g., a given digit may be zero if the sum of other digits in the word is odd, and this (check) digit may be one if the sum of other digits in the word is even.

digits, equivalent binary. The number of binary digits required to express a number in another base with the same precision; e.g., approximately $3\frac{1}{3}$ times the number of decimal digits is required to express a decimal number in binary form. For the case of coded decimal notation, the number of binary digits required is 4 times the number of decimal digits.

diode. A circuit element whose resistance depends on the direction of current flow through it. In the forward bias condition it exhibits a low resistance. (*A*)

diode, zenor. A diode element that exhibits a fixed voltage drop over a wide range of current flowing through it. It is employed as a voltage reference. (*A*)

disk file. A data storage device that roughly corresponds to a magnetic drum, except that its storage surface is a flat disk rather than a cylinder. (*A*)

disturb current cycle. The application of 0 current to all freshly written cores in order to reduce the noise current generated on the next readout cycle.

disturbed-one output. See *coincident-current selection.*

disturbed-zero output. See *coincident-current selection.*

domains. An orderly alignment of crystals. Under certain conditions their alignment is visable in thin-film magnetic materials. This alignment can change suddenly with varying magnetic fields applied. (*A*)

downtime. The period during which a computer is malfunctioning or not operating correctly due to machine failures; contrasted with available time, idle time, or standby time.

drive pulse. A pulsed magnetomotive force applied to a magnetic cell from one or more sources.

drum, magnetic storage. A rotating cylinder, made of or coated with magnetizable material, which may store information by the direction of magnetization that exists at fixed referenced sites. Information is entered by passing current of the proper direction through the *drum writing heads;* it is withdrawn without affecting the information storage by examining the voltage appearing at the *drum reading heads.* A single head may be used for both purposes. The portion of the drum which passes beneath a given head is called a *track;* the tracks which are used to store a complete computer word comprise a *channel;* the portion of channel which holds a complete word is called a *sector.* A channel used as a buffer and shared by the input–output unit with the computer is called a *revolver.*

dummy. An artificial address, instruction, or unit of information.

dump. To withdraw all power accidentally or intentionally. To transfer all or part of the contents of one section of computer memory into another section.

dump check. A check which usually consists of adding all the digits during dumping, and verifying the sum when retransferring.

E

Eccles-Jordan trigger. See *multivibrator.*

echo checking. A system of seeking accuracy in data transmission by reflecting the transmitter and comparing the reflected information with that which was transmitted.

edit. The process of removing or inserting information as a record is passed through the computer.

electronic calculating punch. A punch card machine which in each fraction of a second reads a punch card passing through the machine, performs a number of sequential operations, and punches a result on the punch card.

emitter follower. A transistor circuit having a power gain, and generally providing a low-impedance output. The signal polarity is not reversed passing through the circuit. (*A*)

encoder. A logical block which produces outputs on one or more output lines when only one input line is energized. An encoder is used to produce the binary code corresponding to the digit from another number system.

erase. To replace all the binary digits in a storage device by binary zeros. In a binary computer, *erasing* is equivalent to clearing, while in a coded decimal computer where the pulse code for decimal zero may contain binary ones, *clearing* leaves decimal zero while *erasing* leaves all-zero pulse codes.

error. The loss of precision in a quantity; the difference between an accurate quantity and its calculated approximation. *Errors* occur in numerical methods; *mistakes* occur in programming, coding, data transcription, and operating; *malfunctions* occur in computers and are due to physical limitations on the properties of materials. The differential margin by which a controlled unit deviates from its target value.

error, inherited. The error in the initial values; especially the error inherited from the previous steps in the step-by-step integration.

error, rounding. The error resulting from deleting the less significant digits of a quantity and applying some rule of correction to the part retained. A common round-off rule is to take the quantity to the nearest digit. Thus, pi, $3.14159265...$, rounded to four decimals is 3.1416. [*Note:* Alston S. Householder suggests the following terms: "initial errors," "generated errors," "propagated errors" and "residual errors." If x is the true value of the argument, and x^* the quantity used in computation, then, assuming one wishes

$f(x)$, $x - x^*$ is the initial error; $f(x) - f(x^*)$ is the propagated error. If f. is the Taylor, or other, approximation utilized, then $f(x^*) - f.(x^*)$ is the residual error. If f^* is the actual result then $f. - f^*$ is the generated error, and this is what builds up as a result of rounding.

error, truncation. The error resulting from the use of only a finite number of terms of an infinite series, or from the approximation of operations in the infinitesimal calculus by operations in the calculus of finite differences.

exchange. To interchange the contents of two storage devices or locations.

execute. The performance of a complete instruction except for a fetch cycle (which see).

exclusive-OR. A logic element that has an output for input A and B true if: $y = \overline{A}B + A\overline{B}$. (A)

extract. To obtain certain digits from a machine word as may be specified. For example, if the ten-digit number 0000011100 is stored in a machine register, the computer can be instructed to "extract" the eighth digit from the left (in this case a 1) and correspondingly perform a certain action. To replace the contents of specific columns of one machine word by the contents of the corresponding columns of another machine word, depending on the instruction. To remove from a set of items of information all those items that meet some arbitrary condition.

F

factor scale. One or more coefficients used to multiply or divide quantities in a problem in order to convert them so as to have them lie in a given range of magnitude, e.g., plus one to minus one.

fan-in. The number of input lines permissible to a standard gate without impairing system operation to below specification. (A)

fan-out. The number of standard gates that can be driven by a logic element without causing it to operate below specification. (A)

feedback. The returning of a fraction of the output of a machine, system, or process to the input, to which the fraction is added or subtracted. If increase of input is associated with increase of output, subtracting the returned fraction (negative feedback) results in self-correction or control of the process, while adding it (positive feedback) results in a runaway or out-of-control process.

feed, card. A mechanism which moves cards serially into a machine.

ferroelectric. A phenomenon exhibited by materials within which permanent electric dipoles exist and a residual displacement in the D-E plane occurs.

fetch. The portion of a computer cycle during which the location of the forthcoming instruction is determined, the instruction obtained and modified if necessary, and the instruction entered into the control register.

FET-MOS (field effect transistor—metal oxide silicon). A unipolar integrated circuit form having a high density of elemental components. Field effect transistors are employed as active elements. (*A*)

field. A set of one or more characters (not necessarily all lying on the same word) which is treated as a whole; a set of one or more columns on a punched card consistently used to record similar information.

file. A set of items.

fixed-point calculation. Calculation using or assuming a fixed or constant location of the decimal point or the binary point in each number.

fixed-point representation. An arithmetical notation in which all numerical quantities are expressed by the same specified number of digits, with the point implicitly located at the same specified position.

flat-pack. A hermetic sealed package used for integrated circuits. A standard version is about 0.25 inches square and 0.1 inches thick and may have up to 14 leads. Other sizes and different lead numbers are available. (*A*)

flip-flop. See *multivibrator*.

floating-point calculation. Calculation taking into account varying location of the decimal point (if base 10) or binary point (if base 2), and consisting of writing each number by specifying separately its sign, its coefficient, and its exponent affecting the base. For example, in floating-point calculation, the decimal number $-638,020,000$ might be reported as $-6.3802,8$, since it is equal to -6.3802×10^8.

flow chart. A graphical representation of a sequence of programming operations, using symbols to represent operations such as COMPUTE, SUBSTITUTE, COMPARE, JUMP, COPY, READ, WRITE, etc. A flow chart is a more detailed representation than a *diagram*.

flux. Representative lines of magnetic flow. The total number of lines represents the total magnetic strength and the density of lines, the relative field strength. (*A*)

forbidden combination. Combinations in a given code for which no digit corresponds are called *forbidden combinations*, e.g., 1011 in natural binary coded decimal is a *forbidden combination*.

force (verb). To intervene manually in a program and cause the computer to execute a jump instruction.

format, word. The organization of bits within the word. An instruction word is often divided into regions such as: *Operation code, Address,* and *Variant code.* (*A*)

frequency response. A measure of the ability of a device to take into account, follow, or act upon a rapidly varying input condition; for example, in the case of amplifiers, the frequency at which the gain has fallen to one-half of the power factor, or to 0.707 of the voltage gain factor; in the case of a mechanical automatic controller, the maximum rate at which changes in the input condition can be followed and acted upon.

function generator. A device which produces a given function of the independent variable.

function table. (1) A tabulation of the values of a mathematical function for a set of values of the independent variables. (2) A device of hardware or a program or a subroutine which translates from one representation or coding of information to another representation or coding. (3) Logic. A dictionary.

functional unit. A combination of logical elements, simple or compound, and delay elements which performs an elementary computer function; the hardware to do this; e.g., comparator, encoder, pulse generator.

G

gate. A circuit which has the ability to produce an output which is dependent upon a logical function of the input, e.g., an AND gate has an output pulse when there is time coincidence of all inputs. An OR gate—or preferably *mixer*—has an output when any one or any combination of input pulses occurs in time coincidence. Any gate may contain any number of inhibits in which there is no output under any condition of input if there is time coincidence with the inhibit signal.

generate. To produce a subroutine from parameters and sekeletal coding.

generator. A program for a computer which generates the coding of a problem; a mechanical device which produces an electrical output.

generator, pulse train. A functional unit which generates, in response to an input pulse, a fixed number of equally spaced equal amplitude pulses on one line and one post-train pulse on another line a short time thereafter.

H

half adder. A circuit having two output points, S and C, and two input points, A and B, such that the output is related to the input according to the following tables:

INPUT		OUTPUT	
A	B	S	C
0	0	0	0
0	1	1	0
1	0	1	0
1	1	0	1

where A and B are arbitrary input pulses, and S and C are "sum without carry" and "carry," respectively.

hardware. The mechanical, magnetic, electronic, and electrical devices from which a computer is fabricated; the assembly of material forming a computer.

head. A device which reads, records, or erases information in a storage medium, usually a small electromagnet used to read, write, or erase information on a magnetic drum or tape or the set of perforating or reading fingers and block assembly for punching or reading holes in paper tape.

hold. The function of retaining information in one storage device after transferring it to another device; in contrast to *clear*.

hole. A positive charge current carrier in a "P"-material semiconductor. It represents the *lack of an electron*, and behaves as if it were a positive electron. (*A*)

hole site. The place on a punched card or punched paper tape where a hole may or may not appear. This site represents a bit of information. A hole represents a "1" and the absence of a hole (the presence of paper) represents a "0" (sometimes contrariwise).

hunting. A continuous attempt on the part of an automatically controlled system to seek a desired equilibrium condition.

hysteresis loop. For a magnetic material in a *cyclically magnetized condition*, a curve (usually with rectangular coordinates) showing, for each value of the magnetizing force, two values of the magnetic flux density—one when the magnetizing force is increasing, the other when it is decreasing.

I

ignore. A character code indicating that no action whatsoever be taken. (In Teletype or Flexowriter code, all holes punched is an ignore.) An instruction requiring nonperformance of what normally might be executed; not to be executed.

impedance, characteristic. The ratio of voltage to current at every point along a transmission line on which there are no standing waves; the square root of the product of the open and short circuit impedance of the line.

information. Knowledge or intelligence produced, processed, or cognized by the computer.

inhibit pulse. A *pulse* that prevents flux reversal of a magnetic cell by certain specified *drive pulses*.

input. Information received by the computer or its storage device from the outside.

input block. A section of internal storage of a computer generally reserved for the receiving and processing of input information.

input equipment. The equipment used for taking information into a computer.

input/output buffer. An autonomous storage unit which accumulates blocks of information from the I/O unit (from one to several words) for distribution to the computer and consisting of control, storage, and an I/O unit.

input/output equipment. Sometimes *"I/O equipment."* The devices which are used for entering and obtaining information from the computer.

input/output mechanism. The mechanism for transmitting information between an intermediate medium and the computer; includes storage only as suggested by the manufacturer.

input/output unit. The I/O unit consists of three sections—the I/O mechanism, storage to accumulate a convenient amount of information and control logic. The latter supervises the accumulation and distribution of information from the intermediate medium and the computer or awaiting storage devices.

instruction. A set of characters which defines a computer operation, together with one or more addresses (or no addresses) referring to the location of the operands and/or results, and which as a unit causes the computer to operate upon the indicated quantities at the indicated or implied location. [*Note:* the term *instruction* is preferred by many to the term *command* or *order*. *Command* is sometimes reserved for electronic signals; *order* is sometimes reserved to mean sequence, as in "the order of the characters."

instruction, breakpoint. An instruction which, if some specified switch is set, will cause the computer to stop.

instruction, breakpoint, conditional. A conditional jump instruction which, if some specified switch is set, will cause the computer to stop, after which either the routine may be contined as coded or a pump may be forced.

instruction, multiple-address. See *code, multiple-address.*

instruction, one-address. An instruction consisting of an operation and exactly one address. The instruction code of a single-address computer may include both zero- and multi-address instructions as special cases.

instruction, one-plus-one or three-plus-one address. A two- or four-address instruction, respectively, in which one of the addresses always specifies the location of the next instruction to be performed.

instruction, transfer. A computer operation which specifies the location of the next operation to be performed and directs the computer to that operation (or instruction).

instruction, zero-address. An instruction specifying an operation in which the locations of the operands are defined by the computer code, so that on address need be given explicitly.

integrated circuit (IC). A planar device having many circuit elements diffused on the chip and interconnections between elements on the chip is generally by conduction paths on the outside oxide layer. The chip forms a complete logic element. (*A*)

integrator. A device whose output is proportional to the integral with respect to the input variable.

integrator, electronic. An integrating device containing only electronic components. Normally an operational amplifier with capacitance feedback from output to summing point is employed. (*A*)

integrator, electromechanical. An integrating device most usually implemented by a servo employing rate feedback from a tachometer. Like the electronic integrator it derives the time integral of the variable. (*A*)

integrator, Kelvin. A mechanical device that performs the integration of one variable with respect to another variable, not necessarily time. It is the basic device from which mechanical differential analyzers were constructed. (*A*)

interblock space. A portion of the magnetic tape between blocks of information on which nothing is written. This allows time for the tape to be stopped and brought up to reading speed again between blocks.

interlace. To assign successive storage locations to physically separated storage positions, e.g. on a magnetic drum or tape, usually for the express purpose of reducing access time.

internal memory. The total memory or storage which is accessible automatically to the computer. This equipment is part of and directly controlled by the computer.

internal storage. Same as *internal memory*.

interposer. A bar or pin that remains in place when a punch is not to be permitted in a particular column. Movement of the interposer permits a punch of the hole to occur. (*A*)

interpreter. A card-handling device which prints upon a card the information appearing in the card in the form of punched holes. See also *routine, interpretive*.

interpreter code. A code acceptable to an *interpretive routine* which see.

interrupt. A ready or warning signal generated within or external to the computer signifying a condition that needs computer attention. A subroutine normally services an *interrupt*. (*A*)

item. A set of fields containing related information; a unit of information relating to a single person or object; the content of a single message.

intrinsic. A semiconductor material that contains neither donors or acceptors. It is the neutral material before processing to "P"-or "N"-types. (*A*)

intrinsic induction—B_i. In a magnetic material for a given value of the magnetizing force, the excess of the normal flux density over the flux density in vacuum. The equation for *intrinsic induction* is

$$B_i = B - \mu_v H$$

where μ_v is the factor that expressing the ratio of magnetic flux density to magnetizing force in vacuum.

inverter. A logic element that generates the complement of its input. (*A*)

J

jump. An instruction or signal which, conditionally or unconditionally, specifies the location of the next instruction and directs the computer to that instruction. A jump is used to alter the normal sequence control of the computer. Under certain special conditions a jump may be forced by manual intervention; in other words a transfer of control is made to a specified instruction.

jump, conditional. An instruction which will cause the proper one of two (or more) addresses to be used in obtaining the next instruction, depending upon some property of one or more numerical expressions or other conditions.

K

Karnaugh chart (or map). See Veitch diagram. (*A*)

key. A group of characters usually forming a field, utilized in the identification or location of an item; a marked lever manually operated for copying a character, e.g., typewriter, paper tape perforator, card punch manual keyboard, digitizer, or manual word generator.

L

ladder network. A serial attenuation network consisting of sections. Each section, when tied to ground, applies a prescribed attenuation to the signal entered to the networks input. (*A*)

lag. A relative measure of the time delay between two events, states, or mechanisms.

language. The form or means by which information is communicated within or between the computer or within or between the computer's auxiliary devices and in the outside world.

language, human. Information in a form readily understood by an informed native, e.g., English-language typing (in the U.S.A.).

language, intermediate. The language in which information may be stored between the time at which it is obtained from a human source and the time at which it is entered into the computer, e.g., punch cards or magnetic tape codes.

language, machine. The code used by the computer for communication among its related parts or in which the computer performs arithmetic and editing.

latency. In a serial or serial-parallel storage system, the access time less the word time, e.g., the time spent waiting for the desired location to appear under the drum heads or at the end of an acoustic tank.

leap frog test. A program to test the internal operation of a computer which performs a series of arithmetic or logical operations on one section of memory location, then transfers to another section, checks to see that the transfer is correct and then begins the series of operations over again. Eventually the checking program will have occupied every possible position in the memory and begins again. The term *leap frog* comes from the jump seen on a monitoring cathode ray tube during transfer.

LEM. Lunar excursion module—a vehicle of the Apollo program. (*A*)

library. A collection of standard and fully tested programs, routines, and subroutines, by means of which many types of problems and parts of problems can be solved.

line-printing. Printing an entire line of characters across a page as the paper feeds in one direction past a type bar or cylinder bearing all characters on a single element.

line, transmission. Any conductor or system of conductors used to carry electrical energy from its source to a load.

load (unload). To enter (remove) information en masse into (from) the computer from (into) the input (output) unit.

location. A storage position holding one computer word, designated as a specific address or a specific register. The symbol "[X]" is used to indicate "the location at which X is stored."

location hole. A hole punched in paper tape every time a punch magnet is energized or the tape is advanced and by which the tape may be moved mechanically both for punching and reading.

logger. A device which automatically records physical processes and events, usually with respect to time.

logic. The science that deals with the principles and criteria of validity in thought and demonstration; the science of the principles of exact and careful reasoning. The basic principles and applications of truth tables, the relations of propositions, the interconnection of on-off circuit elements, etc., for mathematical computation in a computer. In the phrase *logic of the computer,* same as *logical design,* which see.

logic, mixed. Logic system employing more than one logic type. For instance, AND/OR logic may be combined with NAND or NOR rather than replacing or being replaced by the NAND or NOR logic. (*A*)

logic, propositional. A systematic logic built upon hypotheses of true or false statements. (*A*)

logic, symbolic. The study of the rules governing the composition of propositions using logical elements and symbols, where the symbols represent elementary statements or quantities.

logical comparison. The operation of comparing *A* and *B*; the results is 1 or yes if *A* is the same as *B* and 0 or no if *A* is not the same as *B* (or vice versa).

logical design. That phase of the computer design which combines operational units, functional units, logical elements, and delay elements into an integrated whole supposedly capable, upon realization in hardware, of performing as a computer or computerlike device.

logical element, compound. A function of several variables which uniquely defines the output as either 0 or 1 for all possible combinations of 0 and 1 for each of the inputs; the circuitry to realize the above, e.g., multiple-input AND gate.

logical element, simple, also **logical unit.** A function *c* of two variables *a* and *b* which uniquely defines *c* as either 0 or 1 for all possible combinations of 0 or 1 for each of *a* and *b*; also the circuitry which realizes this performance, e.g., two-input AND gate for $c = a \cdot b$.

logical unit. See *logical element.*

loop. Repetition of a group of instructions in a routine. See *cycle.*

LSB. Least significant bit. (*A*)

LSD. Least significant digit. (*A*)

LSIC (large-scale integrated circuit). A form of integrated circuit which contains a large number of circuit elements. A single LSIC can be a combinational logic subsystem, such as a complete adder. The chip will probably be larger than that for a normal IC. (*A*)

M

machine-available time. Time during which a computer has the power turned on, is not being maintained, and is known or believed to be operating correctly.

machine cycle. The smallest period of time or complete process of action that repeats itself in order. In some computers, "minor cycles" and "major cycles" are distinguished.

machine instruction. The instruction in the form that the machine can interpret without further translation. (*A*)

machine language. See *language, machine.*

malfunction. A failure in the operation of the hardware of a computer.

mask. A pattern applied to diffuse elements on an integrated circuit chip or transistor. (*A*)

matrix. A set of quantities in a specified array, subject to mathematical operations such as addition, multiplication, inversion, etc., according to specified rules. An array of circuit elements, such as diodes, wires, magnetic cores, relays, etc., arranged and designed to perform a specific function, for example, conversion from one numerical system to another.

maxterm. A Boolean quantity consisting of all terms to be used (or complements) ORed together. Any combination of terms and complements is permissible, provided all are included in the term. (*A*)

memorize. The process of setting one or more words into the computer memory.

memory. A device into which information can be introduced and then extracted at a considerably later time.

memory capacity. The amount of information which a memory unit can store. It is often measured in the number of decimal digits or the number of binary digits which the memory unit can store. Other measures of memory capacity have also been defined.

memory, fast-access. In large computers which have two or more sections of memory which differ in access time, the faster (fastest) section.

memory plane. An assemblage of wired magnetic cores, each core represents 2^n bit of a word. The plane is the nth plane. For a memory having m words the plane will contain m cores. (*A*)

memory, plated wire. A random access memory technique which employs magnetic material as a coating on wires. The memory bits are stored as magnetized spots on this wire. The wire itself carries a bit current during the record process, and serves as a sense line during readback. (*A*)

merge. To produce a single sequence of items, ordered according to some rule (i.e., arranged in some orderly sequence), from two or more sequences previously ordered according to the same rule, without changing the items in size, structure, or total number. Merging is a special case of collating.

message. A group of words, fixed or variable in length, transported as a unit.

microsecond. A millionth of a second.

millisecond. A thousandth of a second.

MIL STD 806B. A military standard specifying logic symbology approved by the Department of Defense. (*A*)

minimum-access programming. Programming in such a way that minimum waiting time is required to obtain information out of the memory. Also called *minimum latency programming* or *forced coding.*

minterm. A Boolean quantity consisting of all terms (or complements, or mixed terms and complements) ANDed together. All terms used in the function must appear in either true or complement form. (See *maxterms.*) (*A*)

mistake. A human error which results in an incorrect instruction in a program or in coding, an incorrect element of information, or an incorrect manual operation.

mixed-base notation. A number system in which a single base, such as 10 in the decimal system, is replaced by two number bases, used alternately, such as 2 and 5. See *biquinary notation.*

mnemonic. Assisting, or intending to assist, remembering; a set of letters, usually three or less, used by the programmer or coder to indicate what transpires during a given instruction and usually differing from the machine code for the instruction.

modem. Contraction of *modulator–demodulator.* Used to connect transmitters–receivers and land-line terminal equipment to station-switching equipment, including data-processing units. (*A*)

modifier. A quantity, sometimes the cycle index, used to alter the address of an operand.

modify. (1) To alter in an instruction the address of the operand. (2) To alter a subroutine according to a defined parameter.

modulate. The process of adding the information signal to the carrier. The carrier transmits the information to a distant station. (*A*)

MSB. Most significant bit. (*A*)

MSD. Most significant digit. (*A*)

multiplexor. A device that separates data from a single channel and places it on many channels, either in time sequence or on command. (*A*)

multivibrator. An electronic device which may be found in either of two states. It may be observed by examining the state of either of two output connections. There are three kinds of multivibrators: the *bistable multivibrator,* otherwise called *flip-flop,* has two input leads—a signal on either causes the device to assume the corresponding output state regardless of its previous state; the *monostable multivibrator,* otherwise one shot (used here), has but one (effective) lead which, when energized, causes the device to assume the corresponding output state (say 1) for a fixed length of time (τ) and then return to the 0 state—depending upon the particular circuit, the *one* may or may not be affected by 1 input signals when in the 1 state; the *astable multivibrator* or *free running multivibrator* has no inputs and alternately assumes its 0 and 1 states, remaining in each for a relatively fixed time τ_0 and τ_1, respectively —when the *multivibrator* is said to have a symmetric output. The *toggle* is a *multi* whose inputs are connected together and which operates so that an input signal causes the device to assume the state complementary to the one it has just occupied. (*A*)

multivibrator, free-run. A relaxation circuit of the multivibrator family that oscillates continuously at a frequency that depends on internal R–C components. The output waveform is square. No trigger is needed to start the circuit in operation. (*A*)

multivibrator, one-shot. A relaxation circuit of the multivibrator family that generates a single output square wave only when it is triggered. It does not, therefore, operate continuously. The output square wave has a duration that depends primarily on the values of internal R–C compouents. (*A*)

N

NAND **element.** A logical element that represents "*not* AND." For variable *A*, *B*, and *C* applied to the input the output will be: *ABC*. (*A*)

negative feedback. See *feedback*.

network analyzer. An analog computer using electrical circuit elements which simulates and solves (analyzes) problems of the electrical behavior of a network of power lines and electrical loads, and related problems.

noise margin. The minimum level of noise voltage which will cause faulty operation of logic circuits. (*A*)

NOR **element.** An element with an output only when all inputs are absent.

normalize. To change a floating-point result, such as 63.2×10^8, so that the exponent, in this case 8, and the mantissa, in this case 63.2, lie in the prescribed or standard normal range. For example, in this case, the normal or standard result might be 6.32×10^9 or $.632 \times 10^{10}$ depending on the computer's adopted standard.

notation (in the sense "scale of notation"). A systematic method for stating quantities in which any number is represented by a sum of coefficients times multiples of the successive powers of a chosen base number *n* (sometimes more than one). If a quantity is written in the scale of notation *n*, then the successive positions of the digits report the powers of *n*. Thus 379 in the scale of 10 or decimal notation means 3 hundreds, 7 tens, and 9. The number 379 in the scale of 16 (used in some computers) means 3 times sixteen squared, plus 7 times sixteen, plus 9 (which in decimal notation would be 889). 1101 in the scale of two means 1 eight, 1 four, 0 twos, and 1 one (which in decimal notation would be 13). In writing numbers, the base may be indicated by a subscript (expressed always in decimal notation) when there may be doubt about what base is employed. For example, 11.101_2 means two, plus one, plus one half, plus one eighth, but 11.101_3 means three plus one, plus one third, plus one twenty-seventh. Names of scales of notation which have had some significant consideration are:

Base	Name
2	binary
3	ternary
4	quaternary, tetral
5	quinary
8	octal, octonary
10	decimal
12	duodecimal
16	hexadecimal, sexadecimal
32	duotricenary
2, 5	biquinary

number, pseudo random. A set of digits constructed in such a sequence that each excessive digit is equally likely to be any of n digits where the number is written in the base n.

number system. See *notation*.

O

object program. The program in machine instruction form. (*A*)

octal digit. See *notation*.

odd-even check. Same as *check, parity*.

off-line operation. See *on-line operation*.

one-address code. See *code, multiple-address*.

one output. See *one state*.

one state. A state of magnetic cell wherein the magnetic flux through a specified cross-sectional area has a positive value, when determined from an arbitrarily specified direction of positive normal to that area. A state wherein the magnetic flux has a negative value, when similarly determined, is a *zero state*.
A *one output* is (1) the voltage response obtained from a magnetic cell in a *one state* by a reading or resetting process, or (2) the integrated voltage response obtained from a magnetic cell in a *one state* by a reading or resetting process. A ratio of a *one output* to a *zero output* is a *one-to-zero ratio*.
A *pulse*—for example, a *drive pulse*—is a *write pulse* if it causes information to be introduced into a magnetic cell or cells, or is a *read pulse* if it causes information to be acquired from a magnetic cell or cells.

one-to-partial-select ratio. See *coincident-current selection*.

one-to-zero ratio. See *one state*.

on-line operation. Copying, translating, editing, and pre- and post-processing work which requires the time of the computer. When computer time is not required, this is called *off-line operation.*

operand. Any one of the quantities entering into or arising from an operation.

operation, arithmetic. An operation in which numerical quantities form the elements of the calculation (e.g., addition, subtraction, multiplication, division).

operation, average-calculating. A common or typical calculating operation longer than an addition and shorter than a multiplication; often taken as the mean of nine addition times and one multiplication time.

operation, complete. An operation which includes (a) obtaining all operands from storage, (b) performing the operation, (c) returning result to storage, and (d) obtaining the next instruction.

operation, computer. The electronic action of hardware resulting from an instruction; in general, computer manipulation required to secure computed results.

operation, fixed-cycle. Computer performance whereby a fixed time is allocated to an operation; synchronous or clocked type arrangement within a computer in which events occur at multiples of fixed time intervals.

operation, logical. An operation in which logical (yes-or-no) quantities form the elements being operated on (e.g., comparison, extraction). A usual requirement is that the value appearing in a given column of the result shall not depend on the values appearing in more than one given column of each of the arguments.

operation number. A number indicating the position of an operation or its equivalent subroutine in the sequence forming a program. When a problem is stated in pseudo-code, each step is assigned an operation number.

operation, red-tape. A operation which does not directly contribute to the result; i.e., arithmetical, logical, and transfer operations used in modifying the address section of other instructions in counting cycles, in rearranging data, etc.

operation time. The time allotted to executing an instruction. (*A*)

operation, transfer. An operation which moves information from one storage location or one storage medium to another (e.g., read, record).

operation, variable cycle. Computer action in which any cycle of action or operation may be of different lengths. This kind of action takes place in an asynchronous computer.

operational unit. A combination of functional units and logical and delay elements which performs one computer operation or process. One or more functional units, logical elements, or delay elements may be shared by several operational units; the hardware which realizes the above.

operator. The person who manipulates the computer controls, places information media into the input devices, removes the ouput, presses the start button, and so on; a mathematical symbol which represents a mathematic process to be performed on an associated function.

OR **mixer.** An electrical or mechanical device which yields an output signal whenever there are one or more inputs on a multi-channel input, e.g., an or-mixer is one in which a pulse output occurs whenever one or more inputs are pulsed; forward merging of pulses simultaneously providing reverse isolation.

OR **operator.** A logical operator which has the property such that if P or Q are two statements, then the statement "P or Q" is true or false precisely according to the following table of possible combinations:

P	Q	P *or* Q
false	true	true
true	false	true
true	true	true
false	false	false

order. A defined successive arrangement of elements or events. The word *order* is losing favor as a synonym for instruction, command, or operation, part due to ambiguity.

order, memory reference. An order which includes in its *execute* portion the obtaining of a datum from memory (e.g., add. transfer).

order, reflexive. An order which requires no data processing but rather alters the behavior of the computer (e.g., jump).

output. Information transmitted by the computer or its storage device to the outside.

output block. A segment of the internal storage reserved for receiving data to be transferred out.

output equipment. The equipment used for transferring information out of a computer.

overflow. In a counter or register, the production of a number which is beyond the capacity of the counter. For example, adding two numbers, each within the capacity of the registers holding them, may result in a sum beyond the capacity of the register that is to hold the sum; overflow.

P

pack. To combine several brief fields of information into one machine word. For example, an employee's pay number, weekly pay rate, and tax exemptions may be stored together in one word, each of these fields being assigned a different set of digit columns.

parallel. Handled at the same time in separate equipment; operating on two or more parts of a word of item simultaneously; contrasted with *serial.*

parallel operation. The flow of information through the computer or any part of it using two or more lines or channels simultaneously.

parameter. In a subroutine, a quantity which may be given different values when the subroutine is used in different main routines or in different parts of one main routine, but which usually remains unchanged throughout any one such use; in a generator, a quantity used to specify input-output devices, to designate subroutines to be included, or otherwise to describe the desired routine to be generated.

parameter, preset. A parameter incorporated into a subroutine during input.

parameter, program. A parameter incorporated into a subroutine during computation. A program parameter frequently comprises a word stored relative to either the subroutine or the entry point and dealt with by the subroutine during each reference. It may be altered by the routine and/or may vary from one point of entry to another.

parity. The process of adding, under the defined circumstances, an extra bit to a character or word code. A check of the parity of a character or word will, under defined circumstances, detect a loss-of-a-bit or an addition-of-a-bit type error. (*A*)

partial-read pulse. See *coincident-current selection.*

partial-select output. See *coincident-current selection.*

partial-write pulse. See *coincident-current selection.*

patch. Section of coding inserted into a routine to correct a mistake or alter the routine; explicitly transferring control from a routine to a section of coding and back again.

patchboard. Same as *plugboard,* but not restricted to punch card machines.

patchcord. A short connecting wire cord for plugging or patching between terminals in a plugboard or patchboard.

path length. The length of a magnetic flux line in a core. In a toroidal core with nearly equal inside and outside diameters, the value

$$l_m = \frac{\pi}{2}\,(\text{O.D.} + \text{I.D.})$$

is commonly used.

peak flux density, B_m. The maximum flux density in a magnetic material in a specified *cyclically magnetized condition.*

peak magnetizing force, H_m (or **peak field strength**). The upper or lower limiting value of magnetizing force associated with a *cyclically magnetized condition.*

perforation, rate of. Number of characters, rows, or words punched in a paper tape by a device per unit of time.

peripheral control unit (PCU). A specialized control unit employed to interface peripheral devices to the computer input–output. (*A*)

peripheral device. Any device that is not a part of the main computer, but connected to the computer via the computer's input–output system, often by means of a PCU. Teletype printers, magnetic tape units, disk files, and CRTs are examples. (*A*)

permeability. The property of a magnetic material that permits multiplication of flux lines in air, assuming that the paths are equal in length. It is defined as the ratio:

$$\mu = \frac{\text{flux lines in the magnetic material}}{\text{flux lines in air (if same path)}}$$

The lower the reluctance of a magnetic material the higher its permeability. (*A*)

piezoelectric. Having the property of producing different voltages on different crystal faces when subjected to a stress (compression, tension, twist, and so on) or of producing a stress when subjected to such voltages.

planar process. A technological process fo fabricating transistors, integrated circuits, etc. It consists of several steps that involve etching away a silicon dioxide protective coat, and forming by diffusion techniques "P"- or "N"-regions in the unprotected bulk material on the etched exposed surface. (*A*)

plotter. A visual display in which a dependent variable is graphed by a moving pen or pencil as a function of the independent variable.

plotting board. An output unit which plots the curves of one or more variables as a function of one or more other variables.

plugboard. A removable board holding many hundreds of electric terminals into which short connecting wire cords may be plugged in patterns varying for different programs for the machine. To change the program, one wired-up plugboard is removed and another wired-up plugboard is inserted. A plugboard is equivalent to a program tape which presents all instructions to the machine at one time. It relies on X-punches and other signals in the punch card passing through the machine to cause different selections of instructions in different cases.

plug-in-unit. A subassembly of tubes, resistors, condensers, diodes, and so on, wired together, of a standard type and which as a whole can be plugged in or pulled out easily.

post mortem. A diagnostic routine which either automatically or when called for prints out information concerning the content of all or a specified part of the registers of the computer, after a problem tape has "died" on the computer. The purpose of a post mortem tape is to assist in the location of an error in coding the problem or in machine function.

potentiometer (pot). A variable precision resistor. Less precise pots that dissipate power are termed *rheostats.* Pots are analog computing elements, in which the voltage appearing at the wiper terminal is proportional to the wiper's position for linear versions. (*A*)

precision. The degree of exactness with which a quantity is stated; a relative term often based on the number of significant digits in a measurement. See also *accuracy.*

precision, double. Retention of twice as many digits of a quantity as the computer normally handles, e.g., a computer whose basic word consists of 10 decimal digits is called upon to handle 20-decimal-digit quantities by keeping track of the 10-place fragments.

prestore. To set an initial value for the address of an operand or a cycle index; to store a quantity in an available or convenient location before it is required in a routine.

preventive maintenance. Maintenance of any system which aims to prevent failures ahead of time rather than eliminate failures which have occurred.

printer. An output mechanism which prints or typewrites characters.

priority. Establishment, in a program, of a system of ordered preference or rank. (*A*)

priority interrupt. An interrupt system for which the individual interrupts have rank. Higher level interrupts will be serviced before lower level interrupts on the basis of rank. (*A*)

process control. Automatic control over industrial processes for manufacturing continuous material or energy, such as refining oil, generating electricity, or making paper.

program. A plan for the solution of a problem. A complete program includes plans for the transcription of data, coding for the computer, and plans for the absorption of the results into the system. The list of coded instructions is called a *routine;* the act of planning a computation or process from the asking of a question to the delivery of the results, including the integration of the operation into an existing system. This programming consists of planning and coding, including numerical analysis, systems analysis, specification of printing formats, and any other functions necessary to the integration of a computer in a system.

programmer. A person who prepares instruction sequences without necessarily converting them into the detailed codes.

programming, automatic. Any technique in which the computer is used to help plan as well as to help code a problem; e.g., compiling routines, interpretive routines.

programming, optimum. See *minimum-access programming*.

programming, random-access. Programming without regard for the time required for access to the storage positions called for in the program; contrast with minimum-access programming.

program register. The register in the control unit of the computer which stores the current instruction of the program and thereby completely controls the operation of the computer during the cycle of execution of that instruction. Same as *control register*. Also called *program counter*.

program-sensitive malfunction. A malfunction which occurs only when some unusual combination of program steps occurs.

program tape. The tape which contains the sequence of instructions to the computer for solving a problem.

program time. The time allotted to decoding the instruction counter contents, fetching the operand instruction, and decoding the instruction fetched. (*A*)

pseudo-code. An arbitrary code, independent of the hardware of a computer, which must be translated into computer code.

pulse. A change in intensity or level over a relatively short period of time, e.g., a shift in electric potential; i.e., if the voltage level of a point shifts with respect to ground for two microseconds, one says that the point received a two-microsecond pulse.

punch, calculating, electronic. A card-handling machine which reads a punched card, performs a number of sequential operations, and punches the result on a card.

punch, card. A device which perforates or places holes in cards in specific locations designated by a program.

punch, summary. A card-handling machine which may be electrically connected to another machine—e.g., tabulator—and which will punch out on a card the information produced, calculated, or summarized by the other machine.

punched tape. Paper tape punched in a pattern of holes so as to convey information.

punching, rate of. Number per unit time of cards, characters, blocks, fields, or words of information placed in the form of holes on cards, or tape.

punch position. The location of the row in a columniated card; e.g., in an 80-column card the rows or "punch positions" may be 0 to 9 or "X" and "Y" corresponding to positions 11 and 12.

Q

quantity. An *integer* or multiple thereof. *Quantity* is preferred to *number* in referring to numerical data.

quantizer. A device which converts an analog quantity into a digital number.

R

radix. The base of the number system. For binary it is 2, for octal 8, for decimal 10, etc. (*A*)

range. All the values which a function may have.

ratio, operating. The ratio obtained by dividing the number of hours of correct machine operation by the total hours of scheduled operation, e.g., on a 168-hour week scheduled operation, if 12 hours of preventive maintenance is required and 4.8 hours of unscheduled downtime occurs, then the operating ratio is $(168 - 16.8)/168$, which is equivalent to a 90 per cent operating ratio.

read. To copy, usually from one form of storage to another, particularly from external or secondary storage to internal storage; to sense information on a recording medium.

read-around ratio. In electrostatic storage tubes, the number of times a specific spot (digit or location) may be consulted before "spill over" will cause a loss of information stored in surrounding spots, immediately prior to which the surrounding information must be restored; read-around number.

read pulse. See *one state.*

reader, card. A mechanism that permits the sensing of information punched on cards by means of wire brushes or metal feelers.

reader, tape, magnetic. A device capable of converting to a train or sequence of electrical pulses, information recorded on a magnetic tape in the form of a series of magnetized spots.

reader, tape, paper. A device capable of converting to a train or sequence of electrical pulses, information punched on a paper tape in the form of a series of holes.

reading, rate of. Number of characters, words, fields, blocks, or cards sensed by an input sensing device per unit of time.

readout, destructive. If the reading of information in a storage medium destroys the information, this is called *destructive readout:* otherwise it is *nondestructive readout.*

readout, nondestructive. A readout of the memory word in which there is no need to provide a write cycle to restore the contents. The memory word is not subject to destruction during the readout process as with DRO. (*A*)

real time operation. Solving problems in real time. More precisely, processing data in time with a physical process so that the results of the data-processing are useful in guiding the physical operation.

recirculation. To shift the contents of a shift register or delay line out one end and then back in the other. (*A*)

recomplement. To complement data or a bit that is already a complement. (*A*)

record. All the information regarding one individual or item pertinent to a given problem or set of problems, usually located on one physical document or consecutive locations on the intermediate medium or in the computer memory. The document upon which the results of the computer appear in human language is sometimes called the *output record.*

reel. A spool of tape, generally magnetic.

reference record. An output of a compiler that lists the operations and their position in the final specific routine, and contains information describing the segmentation and storage allocation of the routine.

reference time, T_0. An instant near the beginning of switching chosen as an origin for time measurements. It is variously taken as the first instant at which the instantaneous value of the *drive pulse,* the voltage response of the magnetic cell, or the integrated voltage response reaches a specified fraction of its peak pulse amplitude.

regenerate. In the operation of electrostatic storage, to restore information currently held in a cell on the cathode ray tube screen in order to counteract fading and disturbances.

register. The hardware for storing one computer word. Registers are usually zero-access storage devices.

register, addressable. A register to which there corresponds an address which may be used as the location of the operand in the instruction word.

register, circulating (or memory). A register (or memory) consisting of a means for delaying information and a means for regenerating and reinserting the information into the delaying means.

register, control. The accumulator, register, or storage unit which stores the current instruction governing the computer operation; an instruction register.

register, index. A register loaded under computer control and used for the purpose of modifying instruction. Its contents is usually added wholly or in part to an instruction that has been called for execution. (For example, in this manner the effective address may be changed.) (*A*)

register, recirculating. A register whose contents are recirculated under normal operating conditions. (*A*)

register, program. A register in the control unit which stores the current instruction of the program and controls computer operation during the execution of the instruction; control register; program counter.

register, shift. A register within which information may be reoriented by a circular permutation.

remanence, B_d. The magnetic flux density which remains in a magnetic circuit after the removal of an applied magnetomotive force. [*Note:* This should not be confused with *residual flux density*. If the magnetic circuit has an air gap, the *remanence* will be less than the *residual flux density*.]

relay. An electromechanical switching device having an energizing coil and one or more contactors to carry the switched current or voltage. (*A*)

relay, reed. A special relay in which the contactor is opened or closed by the superimposition of a magnetic field on the contactor itself—the contactor being magnetic. (*A*)

remember. To obtain information from the computer internal memory without removing the impression of the information from the memory; *remembering* for a destructive read-out memory requires both reading and writing.

repetition rate of pulse. The number of electric pulses per unit of time experienced by a point in a computer, usually the maximum, normal, or standard rate of pulses.

repertory (or **repertoire).** Total list of instructions that the computer can execute. (*A*)

representative circulating time. A method of evaluating the speed performance of a computer. One method is to use one-tenth of the time required to perform nine complete additions and one complete multiplication. A complete addition or a complete multiplication time includes the time required to procure two operands from high-speed storage, perform the operation, and store the result, and the time required to select and execute the required number of instructions to do this.

reproducer. A punch card machine that punches cards to agree as may be specified with other cards.

rerun. To run a program or a portion of it over again on the computer.

rerun point. One of a set of planned-for points in a program such that if an error is detected in between two such points, to rerun the problem it is only necessary to go back to the last rerun point, instead of returning to the start of the problem. Rerun points are often three to five minutes apart so that very little computer time is required for a rerun. All information pertinent to a rerun is available in standby registers during the whole time from one rerun point to the next.

reset. To return a register or device to zero or to a specified initial condition.

reset pulse. A *drive pulse* which tends to reset a magnetic cell.

residual flux density, B_r. The magnetic flux density at which the magnetizing force is zero when the material is in a *symmetrically cyclically magnetized condition.*

resolver. A device which separates or breaks up a quantity, particularly a vector, into constituent parts or elements, e.g., to form the three mutually perpendicular components of a space vector.

response. A reply strobe to a command strobe, generally in a direction peripheral to the computer. (*A*)

restore. To return a cycle index, a variable address, or other computer word to its initial or preselected value; periodic regeneration of charge, especially in volatile, condenser-action storage systems.

retentivity, B_{rs}. The property of a material which is measured by the *residual flux density* corresponding to the *saturation induction* for the material.

return. To go back to a specific, planned point in a program, usually when an error is detected, for the purpose of rerunning the program.

revolver. See *drum, magnetic storage.*

rewind. To return a film or tape to its beginning.

RFI (radiofrequency interference). Generally refers to unintentional and uncontrolled radiation from electrical and electronic equipment. This radiation requires the use of suppressive measures to curb its effects. (*A*)

ring counter. A counter having an individual counter element for each counting state. (*A*)

robot. A machine containing sensing instruments, acting mechanisms, and guidance circuits, where the circuits receive signals from the sensing instruments, perform reasonable calculations on those signals, and deliver appropriate signals to the acting mechanisms. A machine that runs by itself; an automaton. A thermostatically controlled automatic oil furnace in an ordinary home is a robot according to both the first and second definitions; a spring-wound clock is a robot by the second definition but not by the first.

roll back. See *rerun.*

roll out. To read out of a register or counter by the following process: add to one digit in each column simultaneously; do this 10 times (for decimal numbers); when the result in each column changes from 9 to 0, issue a signal.

round off. To change a more precise quantity to a less precise one, usually choosing the nearest precise one; *see precision.*

rounding error. The error resulting from dropping certain less significant digits of a quantity, and applying some adjustment to the more significant digits retained. Also called *round-off error.* A common round-off rule is to take the quantity to the nearest digit. Thus pi, 3.14159265..., rounded to four decimals is 3.1416. [*Note:* Alston S. Householder suggests the following terms: *initial errors, generated errors, propagated errors,* and *residual errors.* If x is the true value of the argument, and x^* the quantity used in computation, then, assuming one wishes $f(x)$, $x - x^*$ is the initial error and $f(x) - f(x^*)$ the propagated error. If f_a is the Taylor, or other, approximation utilized, then $f(x^*) - f_a(x^*)$ is the residual error. If f^* is the actual result then $f_a - f^*$ is the generated error, and this is what builds up as a result of rounding.]

routine. A sequence of operations for a digital computer to perform. The sequence of instructions determining these operations. A set of coded instructions arranged in proper sequence to direct the computer to perform a desired series of operations. See also *subroutine* and *program.*

routine, compiling. An executive routine which, *before* the desired computation is started, translates a program expressed in pseudo-code into machine code (or into another pseudo-code for further translation by an interpreter). In accomplishing the translation, the compiler is required to decode, convert, select, generate, allocate, adapt, orient, incorporate, or record.

routine, diagnostic. A specific routine designed to locate either a malfunction in the computer or a mistake in coding.

routine, executive. A set of coded instructions designed to process and control other sets of coded instructions; a set of coded instructions used in realizing "automatic coding"; a master set of coded instructions.

routine, floating point. A set of coded instructions arranged in proper sequence to direct the computer to perform a specific set of operations which will permit floating-point operation, e.g., enable the use of a fixed-point machine to handle information on a floating-point basis from an external point of view. Floating-point routines are used in computers which do not have built-in floating-point circuitry.

routine, general. A routine expressed in computer coding designed to solve a class of problems, specializing to a specific problem when appropriate parametric values are supplied.

routine, interpretive. An executive routine which, as the computation progresses, translates a stored program expressed in some machine-like pseudo-code into machine code and performs the indicated operations, by means of subroutines as they are translated. An interpretive routine is essentially a closed subroutine which operates successively on an indefinitely long sequence of program parameters (the pseudo-instructions and operands). It may usually be entered as a closed subroutine and excited by a pseudo-code exit instruction.

routine, minimal latency. Especially in reference to serial storage systems, a routine so coded by judicious arrangement of data and instructions in storage, that the actual latency is appreciably less than the expected random-access latency. Also called *minimum-access routine.*

routine, rerun. A routine designed to be used in the wake of a computer malfunction or a coding or operating mistake to reconstitute a routine from the last previous rerun point; roll-back routine.

routine, sequence checking. A routine which checks every instruction executed, printing certain data, e.g., printing out the coded instruction with addresses, and the content of each of several registers; or it may be designed to print out only selected data, such as transfer instructions and the quantity actually transferred.

routine, service. A routine designed to assist in the actual operation of the computer. Tape comparison block location, certain post mortems, and correction routines fall in this class.

routine, specific. A routine expressed in computer coding designed to solve a particular mathematical, logical, or data-handling problem in which each address refers to explicitly stated registers and locations.

routine, test. A routine designed to show whether or not a computer is functioning properly.

routine, trace. See *routine, sequence checking.*

run. One performance of a program on a computer; performance of one routine, or several routines automatically linked so that they form an operating unit, during which manual manipulations are not required of the computer operator.

S

sample-hold. An analog circuit which stores an analog voltage or current level for a period of time. In other words, it captures an analog sample and holds it until the next sampling interval. (*A*)

saturation flux density. See *saturation induction.*

saturation induction, B_s. The maximum *intrinsic induction* possible in a material (see *intrinsic induction*). *Saturation induction* is sometimes loosely referred to as *saturation flux density.*

scale. To alter the units in which all variables are expressed so as to bring all magnitudes within the capacity of the computer or routine at hand.

scale factor. One or more factors used to multiply or divide quantities occurring in a problem and convert them into a desired range, such as the range from plus one to minus one.

scanner. An instrument which automatically samples or interrogates the state of various processes, conditions, or physical states and initiates action in accordance with the information obtained.

scientific programming. An operation that permits a computer to process scientific problems or calculations. This operation is typically one of much detailed calculation and a relatively small amount of input or output. (*A*)

sector. See *drum, magnetic storage.*

segment. To divide a routine in parts, each consisting of an integral number of subroutines, each part capable of being completely stored in the internal storage and containing the necessary instructions to jump to other segments; in a routine too long to fit into internal storage, a part short enough to be stored entirely in the internal storage and containing the coding necessary to call in and jump automatically to other segments. Routines which exceed internal storage capacity may be automatically divided into segments by a compiler.

select. To take the alternative *A* if the report on a condition is of one state, and alternative *B* if the report on the condition is of another state; to choose a needed subroutine from a file of subroutines.

selection ratio. See *coincident-current selection.*

selector. A device which interrogates a condition and initiates a particular operation according to the interrogation report.

semiconductor. A material that is midrange between a conductor and insulator in its electrical properties. Devices in the transistor family are frequently referred to as *semiconductors.* (*A*)

sense. To examine, particularly relative to a criterion; to determine the present arrangement of some element of hardware, especially a manually set switch; to read holes punched in paper.

sequence. To select *A* if *A* is greater than or equal to *B*, and select *B* if *A* is less than *B*, or some variation of this operation.

sequence control tape. Program tape (obsolescent term).

serial. Handled one after the other in a single piece of equipment.

serial bit stream. A continuing succession of binary "1's" and "0's" on a single wire—i.e., a serial binary transmission. (*A*)

serial operation. The flow of information through the computer or in any part of it using only one line or channel at a time. Contrasted with *parallel operation.*

serial storage. Storage in which time is one of the coordinates used to locate any given bit, character, or (especially) word. Storage in which words, within given groups of several words, appear one after the other in time sequence, and in which access time therefore includes a variable latency or waiting time of zero to many word-times, is said to be serial by word. Storage in which the individual bits comprising a word appear in time sequence is serial by bit. Storage for coded-decimal or other nonbinary numbers in which the characters appear in time sequence is serial by character; for example, magnetic drums are usually serial by word but may be serial by bit, or parallel by bit, or serial by character and parallel by bit, and so forth.

serial transfer. A system of data transfer in which the characters of an element of information are transferred in sequence over a single path in consecutive time positions.

servo. See *servomechanism.* (*A*)

servomechanism. A closed loop system in which the error or deviation from a desired or preset norm is reduced to zero, and one in which mechanical position is usually the controlled variable; e.g., a synchronized drum storage system requires a servomechanism to insure synchronism between a crystal-controlled electronic oscillator and a rotating cylinder; an anti-aircraft fire control gun-positioning system requires a servo to insure that deviations are corrected.

set pulse. A *drive pulse* which tends to set a magnetic cell.

shaper. A differentiating or clipping circuit which produces a single pulse when a bistable device changes fom one state to another. (*A*)

shift. To move the characters of a unit of information column-wise right or left. For a number, this is equivalent to multiplying or dividing by a power of the base of notation.

shift, arithmetic. To multiply or divide a quantity by a power of the number base, e.g., binary 1011 represents decimal 11, therefore two arithmetic shifts to the left is binary 101100, which represents decimal 44.

shift, cyclic. A shift in which the digits dropped off at one end of a word are returned at the other in a circular fashion; logical, non-arithmetical, or circular shift.

shift, end around. See *shift, cyclic.*

shift, long. An order which permutes circularly the characters in several registers.

shift out. To cause information to move within a register toward one end, in such a way that as information passes out this end, 0's are entered into the other end.

shift pulse. A *drive pulse* which initiates shifting of characters in a register.

sign control logic. The combinational logic required to restore the proper sign to the number resulting from an arithmetic calculation (also called *sign control network*). (*A*)

sign digit. A digit, usually 1 or 0, used to designate the algebraic sign of a quantity (plus or minus).

signal conditioning. Circuits which normalize an analog level to within a specified sampling range. These circuits may also act as demodulators and impedance-level changers. (*A*)

significant digits. Digits appearing in the coefficient of a number when the number is written as a coefficient between 1.000. . . and 9.999. . . times a power of 10 (called scientific normal form); and similarly for any base of notation other than 10. Examples: .000376, which is equal to 3.76 times 10^{-4}, has three significant digits; 12 million, equal to 1.2 times 10^7, has two significant digits; 300,600, equal to 3.006 times 10^5, has four significant digits; in the statement, "J. B. Smith's book had exactly 1000 pages," "1000" has four significant digits, although ordinarily 1000 would have only one significant digit.

simulation. The representation of physical systems and phenomena by computers, models, or other equipment.

simulator. A computer or model which represents a system or phenomenon and which mirrors or maps the effects of various changes in the original, enabling the original to be studied, analyzed, and understood by means of the behavior of the model.

single-address. See *code, multiple-address.*

skip. An instruction to proceed to the next instruction; a "blank" instruction.

slow memory. Sections of the memory from which information may be obtained automatically but not at the fastest rate of the several sections.

software. All the design and development associated with the generation of programs comes under the classification of *software design.* The development and delivery of subroutines, diagnostic programs, compilers, assemblers, etc., as part of the system, are all items of software. (*A*)

solver, equation. An analog calculating device which solves systems of linear simultaneous non-differential equations or determines the roots of polynomials or both.

source program. The program to be applied as written in the source language, usually in assembler, compiler, or generator form. (*A*)

sort. To arrange items of information by a key contained in the items according to a rule.

sorter. A machine which sorts punched cards.

specific coding. Coding in which all addresses refer to specific registers and locations.

squareness ratio. (1) B_r/B_m. For a material in a *symmetrically cyclically magnetized condition,* the ratio of the flux at zero magnetizing force to the maximum flux density. (2) R_s. For a material in a *symmetrically cyclically magnetized condition,* the ratio of the flux density when the magnetizing force has changed halfway from zero toward its negative limiting value, to the maximum flux density. [*Note:* Both of these ratios are functions of the maximum magnetizing force.]

stacker, card. A mechanism that accumulates cards in a bin after they have passed through a machine operation; a hopper.

standardize. To adjust the exponent and mantissa of a floating-point result so that the mantissa lies in the prescribed normal range; normalize; see *floating-point calculation.*

star-wheel. A hole-sensing device which pivots an attached contactor to the open or closed position, depending on whether the points of the star fall into a punched hole, or not. (*A*)

step. An indication of the ordinal sequence in which the instructions are stored within the computer memory; to each step there can correspond one and only one instruction—an instruction may be used on none, one, or many steps.

storage. Any device into which information can be copied, which will hold this information and from which the information can be obtained at a later time; the erasable storage in any given computer.

storage, circulating. A device using a delay line, or unit which stores information in a train or pattern of pulses, where the pattern of pulses issuing at the final end is sensed, amplified, reshaped and reinserted in the delay line at the beginning end.

storage, dynamic. Storage such that information at a certain position is moving in time and so is not always available instantly; e.g., acoustic delay line, magnetic drum; circulating or recirculating of information in a medium.

storage, electrostatic. A device possessing the capability of storing changeable information in the form of charged or uncharged areas on the screen of a cathode ray tube.

storage, erasable. Media which may hold information that can be changed; i.e., the media can be reused; e.g., magnetic tape, drum, or core.

storage, external. Storage facilities divorced from the computer itself but holding information in the form prescribed for the computer; e.g., magnetic tapes, punched cards, and so forth.

storage, magnetic. Any storage system which utilizes the magnetic properties of materials to store information.

storage, mercury. Columns of a liquid mercury medium used as a storage element by the delaying action or time of travel of sonic pulses which are circulated by having electrical amplifier, shaper, and timer circuits complete the loop.

storage, nonerasable. Media used for containing information which cannot be erased and reused, such as punched paper tapes and punched cards.

storage, nonvolatile. Storage media which retain information in the absence of power and which may be made available upon restoration of power; e.g., magnetic tapes, drums, or cores.

storage, parallel. Storage in which all bits, or characters, or (especially) words are essentially equally available in space, without time being one of the co-ordinates. Parallel storage contrasts with serial storage. When words are in parallel, the storage is said to be *parallel by words.* When characters within words (or binary digits within words or characters) are dealt with simultaneously, not one after the other, the storage is *parallel by characters* (or *parallel by bit* respectively).

storage, secondary. Storage facilities not an integral part of the computer but directly connected to and controlled by the computer; e.g., magnetic drum, disk file, magnetic tapes, and so forth.

storage, serial. Storage in which time is one of the coordinates used to locate any given bit, character, or (especially) word. Storage in which words, within given groups of several words, appear one after the other in time sequence, and in which access time therefore includes a variable latency or waiting time of zero to many word-times, is said to be *serial by word.* Storage in which the individual bits comprising a word appear in time sequence is *serial by bit.* Storage for coded-decimal or other non-binary numbers in which the characters appear in time sequence is *serial by character;* e.g., magnetic drums are usually serial by word but may be serial by bit, or parallel by bit, or serial by character and parallel by bit, and so forth.

storage, static. Storage such that information is fixed in space and available at any time; e.g., flip-flop, electrostatic, or coincident-current magnetic-core storage.

storage, temporary. Internal storage locations reserved for intermediate and partial results.

storage, volatile. Storage media such that if the applied power is cut off, the stored information is lost; e.g., acoustic delay lines, electrostatic tubes.

storage, working. A portion of the internal storage reserved for the data upon which operations are being performed.

storage, zero-access. Storage for which the latency (waiting time) is negligible at all times.

store. To transfer an element of information to a device from which the un-altered information can be obtained at a later time.

strobe. A pulse employed to signal a specified condition such as "move data now." (*A*)

subroutine. The set of instructions necessary to direct the computer to carry out a well-defined mathematical or logical operation; a subunit of a routine.

A subroutine is often written in relative or symbolic coding even when the routine to which it belongs is not.

subroutine, closed. A subroutine not stored in its proper place in the linear operational sequence, but stored away from the routine which refers to it. Such a subroutine is entered by a jump, and provision is made to return, i.e., to jump back to the proper point in the main routine at the end of the subroutine.

subroutine, dynamic. A subroutine which involves parameters, such as decimal point position or item size, from which a relatively coded subroutine is derived. The computer itself is expected to adjust or generate the subroutine according to the parametric values chosen.

subroutine, open. A subroutine inserted directly into the linear operational sequence, not entered by a jump. Such a subroutine must be recopied at each point at which it is needed in a routine.

subroutine, static. A subroutine which involves no parameters other than the addresses of the operands.

substep. Each step of a computer's task in the computer with centralized control is often divided into substeps—a portion of a step.

substitute. To replace an element of information by some other element of information.

substrate. A ceramic surface normally containing finely deposited conductors for interconnecting paths and mounting pads. Can be used to mount several IC chips in a single package. (*A*)

summing network. An analog network permitting the summation of several voltages or currents that represent variables. (*A*)

switch, function. A circuit having a fixed number of inputs and outputs designed such that the output information is a function of the input information, each expressed in a certain code or signal configuration or pattern.

switching time. (1) T_s, the time interval between the *reference time* and the last instant at which the instantaneous voltage response of a magnetic cell reaches a stated fraction of its peak value. (2) T_x, the time interval between the *reference time* and the first instant at which the instantaneous integrated voltage response reaches a stated fraction of its peak value.

symbol, logical. A symbol used to represent a logical element graphically.

symmetrically cyclically magnetized condition. A condition of a magnetic material when it is in a *cyclically magnetized condition* and the limits of the applied magnetizing forces are equal and of opposite sign, so that the limits of flux density are equal and of opposite sign.

synchronous. See *computer, synchronous.*

system, data processing. The assembly of equipment including a computer (if used) and associated processing equipment, the purpose of which is to solve a problem or set of problems. The system often includes the procedural details and computer coding called the *program.*

T

tabulator. A machine which reads information from one medium, e.g., cards, paper tape, magnetic tape, and produces lists, tables, and totals on separate forms or continuous paper.

tag. A unit of information, whose composition differs from that of other members of the set so that it can be used as a marker or label; a sentinel.

tally. To add 1 to or subtract 1 from a quantity, usually to the content of a register; tally *up* is used to indicate addition of a unit, while tally *down* indicates subtraction of a unit.

tank. A unit of acoustic delay line storage, containing a set of channels each forming a separate recirculation path; a circuit consisting of inductance and capacitance used for the purpose of sustaining electrical oscillations.

tape, magnetic. A tape or ribbon with a magnetic surface on which information may be placed as magnetically polarized spots.

tape, program. A tape which contains the sequence of instructions required for solving a problem and which may be read by the computer.

tape reservoir. That part of a magnetic tape recording and/or reproducing system which is used to isolate the inertia of the tape from the drive system.

telemeter. To transmit measurements and observations over a distance, as for example by radio transmission from a guided missile to a receiving magnetic tape recorder on the ground.

teletype. An alpha-numeric communication system that employs teletype data equipment. It employs either Baudot or ASC II code at rates of from 10 to 15 characters per second. (*A*)

ternary. Pertaining to the system of notation utilizing the base of 3, employing the characters 0, 1, and 2.

test, crippled leap frog. A variation of the leap frog test, modified so that it repeats its tests from a single set of storage locations rather than a changing set of locations.

test, leap frog. A program designed to discover computer malfunction, which performs a series of arithmetical, or logical operations on one group of storage locations, transfers itself to another group of storage locations, checks the correctness of the transfer, then begins the series of operations over again. Eventually, all storage positions will have been occupied and the test will be repeated.

thermistor. The thermistor is a solid-state, semiconducting device made by sintering mixtures of the oxide powders of various metals. It is made in many shapes, such as beads, disks, flakes, washers, and rods, to which contact wires are attached. As its temperature is changed, the electrical resistance of the thermistor varies. The associated temperature coefficient of resistance is extremely high, nonlinear, and negative.

thermocouple. A device made of two bi-metal joints (forming a closed loop) so that if the two junctions are at different temperatures, a difference of potential exists between the two junctions.

thin-film technology. A technology for depositing extremely thin layers of material in the order of a few angstroms of thickness. (*A*)

three-address. See *code, multiple-address.*

threshold field, H_0. The least magnetizing force in a direction which tends to decrease the *remanence,* which, when applied either as a steady field of long duration or as a pulsed field appearing many times, will cause a stated fractional change of *remanence.*

thyratron. A hot-cathode, gas-discharge tube in which one or more electrodes are used to control electrostatically the starting of a unidirectional flow of current.

time, code checking. All time spent checking out a problem on the machine making sure that the problem is set up correctly, and that the code is correct.

time, engineering, or servicing. All machine downtime necessary for routine testing, for machine servicing due to breakdowns, or for preventive servicing measures, e.g., block tube changes. Includes all test time following breakdown and subsequent repair or preventive servicing.

time, idle. Time in which machine is believed to be in good operating condition and attended by service engineers but not in use on problems.

time, no charge machine-fault. Unproductive time due to a computer fault such as the following: (1) nonduplication; (2) transcribing error; (3) input/output malfunction; (4) machine malfunction resulting in an incomplete run.

time, no charge non-machine-fault. Unproductive time due to no fault of the computer such as the following: (1) good duplication; (2) error in preparation of input data; (3) error in arranging the program deck; (4) error in operating instructions or misinterpretation of instructions; (5) unscheduled good testing time, run during normal production period when machine malfunction is suspected but is demonstrated not to exist.

time, production. Good computing time, including occasional duplication of one case for a check or rerunning of the test run. Also, duplication requested by the sponsor; any reruns caused by misinformation or bad data supplied by sponsor. Error studies using different intervals, convergence criteria, and so forth.

time, pulse. In a cycle of computer processing, the instant at which information scanned for detection.

time pulse distributor. Control section logic which is responsible for the generation of individual timing pulses and their initial distribution. (*A*)

time, standby unattended. Time in which the machine is in an unknown condition and not being used to solve problems. Includes time in which machine is known to be defective and work is not being done to restore it to operating condition. Includes breakdowns which render it unavailable due to outside conditions such as power outages.

time, system improvement. All machine downtime needed for the installation and testing of new components, large or small, and machine downtime necessary for modification of existing components. Includes all programmed tests following the above actions to prove machine is operating properly.

time-varying. Varies as a function of time. (*A*)

toggle. See *multivibrator*.

track. See *drum magnetic storage*.

transcribe. To copy, with or without translating, from one external storage medium to another.

transducer. A device which converts energy from one form to another; e.g., a quartz crystal imbedded in mercury can change electrical energy to sound energy as is done in sonic delay lines in computer storage systems.

transfer. To copy, exchange, read, record, store, transmit, transport, or write data; to change control; to jump to another location. See *jump*.

transfer check. Verification of transmitted information by temporary storing, retransmitting, and comparing.

transfer, parallel. A system of data transfer in which the characters of an element of information are transferred simultaneously over a set of paths.

transfer, serial. A system of data transfer in which the characters of an element of information are transferred in sequence over a single path in consecutive time positions.

transform. To change information in structure or composition without altering the meaning or value; to normalize, edit, or substitute.

transient. A phenomenon experiencing a change as a function of time; something which is temporary; a build-up or breakdown in the intensity of a phenomenon until a steady state condition is reached; an aperiodic phenomenon; the time rate of change of energy is finite and some form of energy storage is usually involved.

transistor. A semiconductor device used for signal amplification, normally having three connections—an emitter, a base, and a collector. It can also be used as a switch, and exhibits considerable power gain under most circumstances. It is represented as a four-terminal active network. (*A*)

translate. To change information (e.g., problem statements in pseudo-code, data, or coding) from one language to another without affecting the meaning.

transmit. To reproduce information in a new location replacing whatever was previously stored and clearing or erasing the source of the information.

transport. To convey as a whole from one storage device to another.

trigger. See *multivibrator*. (Sometimes employed as verb to mean *pulse* or *strobe*.) (*A*)

trouble-location problem. A test problem whose incorrect solution supplies information on the location of faulty equipment; used after a check problem has shown that a fault exists.

trouble-shoot. To search for a coding mistake or the cause of a computer malfunction in order to remove same.

truncate. To drop digits of a number or terms of a series thus lessening precision. See *precision*. For example, the number pi, 3.14159265..., is *truncated* to three figures in 3-14.

truncation error. The error resulting from the use of only a finite number of terms of an infinite series, or from the approximation of operations in the infinitesimal calculus by operations in the calculus of finite differences.

trunk. A path over which information is transferred; a bus.

truth table. A list in tabular form of the output of a logical function or element for all combinations of inputs.

tube, Williams. A cathode ray tube used as an electrostatic storage device of the type designed by F. C. Williams, University of Manchester, England.

two-address code. See *code, multiple-address*.

typewriter. An I/O device used to receive information directly or indirectly from the computer in computer or human language by means of a modified conventional electric typewriter. The computer typewriter is often used to convert language for direct communication with the computer; in combination with a paper tape punch it converts human to intermediate language.

U

ultrasonics. The field of science devoted to frequencies of sound above the human audio range, i.e., above 20 kilocycles per second.

unconditional. Not subject to conditions external to the specific instruction.

undisturbed-one output. See *coincident-current selection*.

undisturbed-zero output. *See coincident-current selection.*

uni. See *multivibrator.*

unload. See *load.*

unpack. To decompose packed information into a sequence of separate words or elements.

unwind. To code explicitly, at length, and in full all the operations of a cycle thus eliminating all red-tape operations in the final problem coding. Unwinding may be performed automatically by the computer during assembly, generation, or compilation.

V

validity. Correctness; especially the degree of closeness by which iterated results approach the correct result.

variable. A quantity that is to be included in a calculation and is not considered to be a constant. In algebraic exercises it often takes the form of x or y. It may take on a range of values. The *independent variable* is assigned values within the range. The corresponding *dependent variable* will take on values depending on the equation involved. Use of more than two variables is not uncommon. (*A*)

variant code. The instruction processing of a computer may be modified on the basis of the coding of one or more bits occurring within the instruction format. Normal addressing, use of index registers, indirect addressing, etc., may be specified by variant codes. (*A*)

vectoring. Direction of a vehicle to a prescribed location as specified by x–y or other coordinate systems. When applied to a CRT display the term refers to the generation of lines on the scope rather than alpha-numeric characters. (*A*)

Veitch diagram. A chart which permits maxterms and minterms to be plotted. Reduction of Boolean functions can be obtained from the plotted patterns. Its usage and general appearance is similar to a *Karnaugh chart* (or *map*). (*A*)

Venn diagram. A diagram on which the relationships of propositional logic may be plotted and demonstrated. The AND and OR condition of up to three variables is easily demonstrated. Generally the Veitch diagram or Karnaugh map is easier and more convenient to use when plotting methods are necessary. (*A*)

verifier. (1) A punch card machine operated manually which reports by signals whether punched holes have been inserted in the wrong places in a punch card or have not been inserted at all. (2) An auxiliary device on which a previous manual transcription of data can be verified by comparing a current manual transcription character-by-character during the current process.

volatile. See *storage, volatile.*

W

winding. A conductive path, usually of wire, inductively coupled to a magnetic core or cell. When several windings are employed, they may be designated by the functions performed. Examples are: sense, bias, and drive windings. Drive windings include read, write, inhibit, set, reset, input, shift, and advance windings.

wire, magnetic. Wire made of a magnetic material along small incremental lengths of which magnetic dipoles are placed in accordance with binary information.

word. A set of characters which occupies one storage location and is treated by the computer circuits as a unit and transported as such. Ordinarily a word is treated by the control unit as an instruction, and by the arithmetic unit as a quantity. Word lengths are fixed or variable depending on the particular computer.

word time. The time required to transport one word from one storage device to another. See also *access time.*

wrap. See *tape-wound core.*

write. To record or copy information in reusable form for future reference.

write pulse. See *one state.*

X

X_S3. See *code, excess-three.*

Z

zero. The computer's conception of zero. [*Note:* the computer may provide for two zeros. Positive binary zero is represented by the absence of digits or pulses in a word. Negative binary zero in a computer operating with 1's complements may be represented by a pulse in every pulse position in a word. In a coded decimal computer, decimal zero and binary zero may not have the same representation. In most computers, there exist distinct and valid representations both for positive and for negative zero.]

zero-access storage. Storage for which the latency or waiting time is negligible.

zero-address instuction. See *code, multiple-address.*

zero output. See *one state.*

zero state. See *one state.*

zero suppression. The elimination of non-significant zeros to the left of the integral part of a quantity before printing is begun. One of the operations in editing is to suppress these zeros.

zone. Any of the three top positions 12, 11, and 0 in an 80-column punch card; in these zone positions a second punch can be inserted, so that with punches in the remaining positions 1 to 9, enough two-punch combinations are obtained to represent alphabetic characters. A portion of internal storage allocated for a particular purpose.

INDEX